FELTHAM MADE ME

by Paolo Sedazzari

Foreword by Mark Savage

Published by Zani Media

For information contact:
paolo99@icloud.com

Cover design by Gavin Sanctis
Based on the photography of George Plemper

Dog, Wolf, Bear Illustration on page 353 by Emma Broughton

Visit us at www.zani.co.uk

Foreword

For anyone who was born in the 60's, went to school in the 70's, partied hard in the 80's & 90's or you just want to know more about these times, then Feltham made me is THE book to read!

I literally, could not put this book down. I can relate to it all and it brought back many memories that time dusts over.

Paolo Sedazzari writes from the characters first person narrative, which allows us to see that history is actually his-story,the perspective of the individual and sometimes slightly different from the other protagonists who shared the same experience.

We meet the three protagonists at the institution that shapes our lives and from my experience, is a microcosm of life, school. State school, comprehensive school. The place where an adolescent has to navigate through social and peer pressure and sometimes, create a character in order to cope and survive. From the explosion of punk in the late 70's, where working class kids were empowered to take control of our lives, through the 80's and the entrepreneurial culture of making money, the acid house scene and MDMA. From growing from an early teenager through the angst of late teens, morphing into adolescents into our twenties and waking up to the reality of our broken or unfulfilled dreams of our youth in our thirties.

Feltham Made Me is about the friendships we forge that can shape who we are, who we become and how we relate to each other and the world, the tragedies of life and the successes and how we can change.

Mark Savage

FELTHAM MADE ME   4

FELTHAM MADE ME

An oral history, compiled and edited by Paolo Sedazzari

The poet Richard F. Burton likened the truth to a large mirror, shattered into millions upon millions of pieces. Each of us owns a piece of that mirror, believing our one piece to be the whole truth. But you only get to see the whole truth when we put all the pieces together.

This is the concept behind **Feltham Made Me**. It is the story of three lads growing up together in the suburbs of London, put together from the transcripts of many hours of interviews. Most of the material has come directly from the three men – Dermott Collins, Peter Wyatt and Jerry Zmuda. But I have also included interviews with their teachers, parents, friends, enemies, work-mates and chance acquaintances.

As each character in **Feltham Made Me** takes over the narrative baton with their own individual spin, we hear differing, often conflicting, accounts of the same incident. Who is telling the truth? Neither? Or both? Often our own distortions and exaggerations reveal another truth about ourselves.

So why choose these particular three men and put their lives under the microscope? The honest answer is - I don't know. I just felt compelled to do so. I first met these lads when their band played a rather eventful gig at my college – the Polytechnic of Central London (PCL) aka PC Hell, back in the eighties. Standing around in the cupboard-stroke-dressing room next to the stage, I witnessed a very agitated but highly amusing row kicking off between the three.

I next set eyes on these boys a couple of years later as the smoke cleared on the dance floor at Queens, a Sunday afternoon club for the then nascent acid house scene. I was delighted to discover that the boys had sunk their differences and were now promoting clubs together. A few years later I decided I was going to chronicle their lives in **Feltham Made Me**. There was something about their coolness and idiocy that to me embodied the spirit of Britain's ever evolving music and fashion scene. They are participators, protagonists – they don't always succeed – but they have a go. I love that spirit.

Dermott, Jerry and Peter are not celebrities - they are everyday people with modest incomes like you and I. But what I have done here is examine their lives in the same way the media would to a celebrity. Just ordinary boys living ordinary lives – and yet when you look closer they are fascinating.

And in telling their stories we are given a history of British cultural life from the seventies to the present day. I am sure many people born in Britain at around the same time while see a good many parallels with their own lives.

But the cultural reference points in **Feltham Made Me**, be they Planet of the Apes, Subbuteo, Man About the House, Punk, John Peel, The Jam, 2-Tone, The Young Ones, The Smiths, Acid House are merely shifting scenery to the real story. A story about male friendship and the strains put upon it over the years.

The transition from boyhood to manhood is never easy. In **Feltham Made Me** we chart every painful and significant step along the way – from screaming kids in a playground right through to bickering men in a boozer.

The biggest job for me was deciding what to leave out, and how much to put in, and in doing so, try and identify the narrative thread. It's in this way only that I claim authorship of this book.

But it will become immediately clear to anybody reading **Feltham Made Me** what this book is all about. On the very first page Jerry's mother expresses her strong disapproval of his new friend. The crux of the story in **Feltham Made Me** is here.

Wherever I can, I have let the people speak for themselves in their own words. But you will understand I have had to do some considerable editing, to avoid repetition and when their words have veered away from the point. I did attempt to "correct" the grammar, and try and bring a level of uniformity to the use of past and present tense. A very frustrating exercise, because my interviewees, like most of us when we recount an anecdote, will switch between past tense and present tense at will. In trying to "correct" the grammar I often found myself violating the spirit of what was being said. So I reverted back to allowing the boys to speak in their own choice of words – with all their occasional glorious grammatical inconsistencies and eccentric speech patterns. It reads better that way. But also gives a truer picture - and the truth this is what we are looking for in **Feltham Made Me**.

The book has a very broad appeal, but I suspect the people who will enjoy this book the most are those who have lived their lives similar to our heroes. For anyone who bunked off school to go and see their favourite band play a sound check, for anyone who were inspired to form a band with their friends, for anyone whose lives were changed in a sweaty basement after taking a pill, and for anyone who hit 30, looked at themselves in the mirror and thought "What the fuck do I do now?"

So that's it from me – from here on in I'll let the boys and their supporting characters tell the story for themselves.

> You see a place that's bleak,
> But this is home to me,
> And I'm here to say -
> Feltham Made Me,
> What I am today.

© Lyrics courtesy of Jerry Zmuda
Feltham Made Me is dedicated to Carl Young and Peter Wyatt.
Paolo Sedazzari, May 2017, London

FELTHAM MADE ME   8

Chapter 1
Primary School – It's Monkey Time

HERE WE GO WITH DERMOTT & JERRY

JERRY ZMUDA

Ever since I can remember I've been obsessed with talking animals. That's why I loved cartoons. I would try and teach Ruben, the family Labrador, to talk. I'd say to him - "Come on Ruben - if you learn to talk we can go and have adventures like Scooby Doo."
But Ruben just stared back, panting. Never said a word.

DERMOTT COLLINS

Basil Brush was ace. Morning, noon and night there's me trying to make my laugh sound exactly like him, 'coz I wanted to be Basil Brush.

PETER WYATT

I was never one for staying in and watching cartoons. I was an outdoor kid. Football. I was always playing football. Until I cracked my wrist practising my overhead kicks. But once it mended I was straight outside again, playing football.

JERRY ZMUDA

I was eight when I noticed Dermott for the first time. We were in Mrs. Dalrymple's art class and a kid had opened a cupboard door. An avalanche of Janet and John books slid out. The books were called *Here We Go*, and on the cover was a picture of Janet and John sitting on an inflatable horse waving.
Quick as a flash, Dermott says –
"They're falling out saying Here We Go." And he mimicked the wave. For some reason I found this achingly funny, and Mrs. Dalrymple could not stop me from laughing. From then onwards I just knew I had to hang around this kid Dermott.

DERMOTT COLLINS

Jerry laughed at all my jokes. All of them. Even the shit ones. So it was - "Yeah OK, you can be my friend."

PETER WYATT

I never knew Dermott and Jerry in them days, they were in cosy old Sunbury on Thames and I was on the other side of the big smoke in Rayleigh, Essex.

It amazes me how Dermott and Jerry can go on about their primary school days in so much detail. I hardly remember anything, it was such a horrible time. But something always sticks out - Dad taking me to Upton Park to see West Ham, and Dad pretending he personally knew all the players as they ran past. I mean, I may have been eight but I wasn't fucking stupid. I remember him telling me how one day we were going to live in a big mansion, with servants and a Rolls Royce. "We are going to be joining the jet set!" I wanted to believe him, and I really did for a while.

MR. HEYWARD (primary school teacher)

The joy of seeing children discover the world, to see their faces light up with wonder - it's one of life's great marvels. The learning curve is much quicker, much steeper in their younger years. They start off the term barely able to read, and within months they're reading fluently - understanding new words. That's why I became a primary school teacher. I soon wish I hadn't.

DERMOTT COLLINS

Fucking loved primary school. Totally fucking loved it. Up to that school gate, strutting past Mr. Trent with his megaphone giving me the eye 'cos he knows I'm trouble. Seeing all them kids running around in the playground. Would think to myself - It's Show Time! - and off I went.

JERRY ZMUDA

Springfield School was in London's leafy suburbia, a place called Sunbury on Thames - a pleasant place to be given your introduction to the world. I was the sort of kid who liked to sit next to the window, day-dreaming. I would stare over at the rail-track at the end of the field, then up at the planes in the sky. I remember thinking to myself - this is my starting point in life - I can go anywhere I want in the world - but this will always be home.

DERMOTT COLLINS

When I was a kid me head was crammed full of stuff like outer space, Basil Brush and explosions. Teachers would try and steer me into thinking about boring things. Guess that's what education is supposed to be about. But I was having none of it.

JERRY ZMUDA

My only worry was that hole forming in the elbow of my school jumper, getting bigger each day. And the more I played with it, the worse it got. It was only a matter of time before my Mother would notice. That was my world. But that was all about to change.

NATALIE ZMUDA (Jerry's Mother)

It was soon after Jerry started talking about his new friend Dermott that his accent started worsening. Jerry used to speak so nicely, but now he was sounding quite common.

IT'S MONKEY TIME

JERRY ZMUDA

"It's Monkey Time!" that was Dermott's cue to go crazy. He'd throw his head back and make a loud hooting laugh, then dance like a demented monkey. I was compelled to join in.

With Dermott around, life instantly stepped up a gear. Sleepy Sunbury on Thames went into amazing Technicolor. If Dermott wasn't playing a joke on someone, he was hatching some crazy plan. My favourite was to hide inside Hambleys toy store just before closing time. Then come out when everyone's gone, so we'd have the whole store and the toys to ourselves - and all night to play with them. What a brilliant plan - count me in.

DERMOTT COLLINS

I was well into me crank phone calls. Oh! Yus My Dear! The golden days before 1471. Remember going round Jerry's - his old dear doing the weeding in the garden. Got hold of the telephone directory - searching for my next victim.

JERRY ZMUDA

He was flicking through the book, until his finger rested on one name. He was trembling with excitement as he showed me it. Norman Ladyman. He began dialling as my Mother continued weeding in the garden. Dermott puts on his serious adult voice - "Hullo Can I speak to Norman Ladyman please?"

The man came to the phone. "Ha! He's called Ladyman. He's a lady and a man." And he hung up - I was creased with laughter. That's when Mother came in.

NATALIE ZMUDA

Making abusive phone calls is one thing, but to use my phone to do it was quite another. I said to this Dermott - boy - "What would your father say if he knew what you are doing?" He replied - "He'd say - well done son, good one." He was remorseless.

JERRY ZMUDA

So with Dermott we created our own little world of silly voices and catchphrases. We had the Rudies Department, enforced by Wolfdog Willy who came down like a tonne of bricks on anybody swearing or doing anything rude. But his punishments were always far ruder than the initial offence. But my favourite was the cartoons we drew of Ruben the Rubbish Dog. He'd try to save a man down a mine-shaft, like Lassie, but he'd mess it up and cause an almighty avalanche that wiped out an entire village.

DERMOTT-TITUS

MR. HEYWARD

I was on break duty one morning when little Tommy Higgins dashes up to me from the playing field. "Sir! Sir! Come quickly! Jerry Zmuda's been attacked by giant insects." I immediately knew this had to be a wind up, but I looked at this kid and he was genuinely terrified. So I sprinted up there and, sure enough Dermott Collins had tricked him with some rubber toy insects. I laughed it off, but it was a sign of things to come. The Chinese have the water torture - we've got Dermott Collins.

DERMOTT COLLINS

Always liked Mr. Heyward. A real good bleeding sport. When we heard he was going to be our form teacher we were well pleased.

MR. HEYWARD

Towards the end of term, Mrs Dalrymple collared me in the staff room with a big grin. "You're going to have your work cut out for you next term - you've got Dermott Collins in your form." I was saying "Dermott may be a horror - but he's still nothing but a kid." I thought I could handle him.

JERRY ZMUDA

I was walking past the staff room one morning when I overheard Mrs. Dalrymple say to Mr. Heyward - "Have you got a Dermatitis crisis already?"
I told Dermott about the teachers calling him Dermatitis, and he was thrilled. Thrilled to be nicknamed after an especially irritating skin disease.

DERMOTT COLLINS

Kushti! From then on my nickname was 'Titus. I get under yer skin.

SARAH BAXTER

JERRY ZMUDA

Mr. Heyward kept on accusing me of being distracted by Dermott, but in my last year at Springfield my centre of attention had shifted. A vision of wonder named Sarah Baxter - luscious lips, full ruddy cheeks that weighed down to reveal her chipmunk buckteeth. BUT SHE'S A GIRL. I was terrified to even make eye contact, and I barely ever said a word to her. Did she ever notice me?

SARAH BAXTER

Those two were pathetic, completely childish. I mean I know we were all kids but they were beneath childish. There was us, trying to fucking learn and that Dermott and his laughing hyena sidekick always trying to be funny. It got so boring.

DERMOTT COLLINS

At primary school my favourite word was Minge. Minge this and Minge that. Minge, all day along. It was a word I picked up off me brother. Didn't know what a Minge was, let alone what one looked like, but that didn't stop me from Mingeing it all the time.

SARAH BAXTER

There's Dermott thinking he's clever because he's discovered this new word – Minge. Why couldn't my parents have sent me to St. Ignatius? That was an all-girls school.

A TALE OF TWO HOME-LIVES

PETER WYATT (over in Rayleigh)

I was always wanting to play outside. There was something indoors that didn't feel right. Mum and Dad didn't row a lot - but I could sense that Mum was drifting away from Dad. Dad would try and cheer her up with some daft gag he'd lifted off the Two Ronnies or Benny Hill, and Mum would just look away.

JERRY ZMUDA

Silence reigned in the Zmuda household, most of the time myself, Magdalena my sister, Mum and Dad would sit in the dark just watching TV. I'd never known anything else, so I didn't think much of it. Ruben the dog got all the attention, and the only demonstrations of warmth and affection in the house were directed at him.

FRANK COLLINS (Dermott's Father)

Any friend of Dermott's was welcome round our house - and Jerry seemed a nice lad.

JERRY ZMUDA

Dermott's home life was the polar opposite of mine - a 24 hour teeming hive of activity. He lived with his Dad, Frank, and his two older brothers. There was a procession of Aunties doing the washing, preparing meals and his brothers were real faces about town, so all their mates would come over and just hang out. Then they'd be the various girlfriends.

I would sit in the living room and just watch the world come in and out - it was better than television. But someone was conspicuous by her absence - there was no Mother in the house. Naturally I asked Dermott about this, but he just changed the subject.

DERMOTT COLLINS

I'd often go to Jerry – "let's get round yours. I need some bleedin' peace and quiet."

PETER WYATT

At our home in Rayleigh, pride of place over the fireplace was a faded yellow cutting from the local paper in a golden frame. It had a picture of my old man with an ear to ear grin holding up a row of banknotes. The headline was 'ALL WYATT FOR A FEW QUID.'
He bet fifty quid that Hursty would score a hattrick against the Krauts in '66, and he earned himself two and a half grand, which I'm told in them days was a fair amount of lucre. But that taste of smalltime celebrity for Dad was his undoing. He thought he had the Midas touch, and Mum tells me his gambling got much worse from that moment on.

JERRY ZMUDA

Eventually I asked Dermott face on where his mother was, this time demanding an answer, and he said she'd gone away. I felt really sorry for him. I know that his grandmother and aunt were round a lot to look after him. But it's not the same as having a full-time mother doting over you.

DERMOTT COLLINS

The good thing about having two older brothers is that they'd tell you all the jokes, so at school you're one step ahead of all the other kids. The flip side is that they were always clipping you and telling you to shut it. That's why I liked school so much - so I could get away from those fuckers.

POLSKA! POLSKA!

JERRY ZMUDA

They used to call me The Commie. Based on the fact that I had a Polish name. I tried to explain to them that my Polish grandfather was a pilot, fought the war with the RAF, and stayed in Britain and raised his family here, precisely to get away from the Communists. But kids don't listen.

DERMOTT COLLINS

I tried to help Jerry out. He hated his nickname The Commie. So I had a go at calling him Zoom from his surname being Zmuda. Never caught on. Still they called him the Commie Bastard.

JERRY ZMUDA

I was leaving school one afternoon and this kid I hardly knew jabbed his finger at me and says "You Poles are going to get thrashed tonight!" I panicked - what was he talking about? When I got home and watched the TV it clicked. He meant the World Cup qualifier between England and Poland at Wembley.

PETER WYATT

I remember sitting down with me old man to watch England's World Cup qualifier against Poland. We had to beat them to qualify. We attacked, and attacked and attacked and we only came away with a draw. I was in tears, but my Dad he was even worse - the silly sod had put on the best part of a grand on Martin Chivers getting a hat trick. Someone should have told him that saying about lighting never strikes in the same place twice.

DERMOTT COLLINS

Me Dad's Irish, he had the accent, the silly jokes, the whole bit. My brothers were all born here in England, spoke with same English accent I did, but they all called themselves Irish. When we were watching England play Poland in '73 they were all celebrating when England didn't win. I was thinking - get a fucking life will you? This is our country now.

JERRY ZMUDA

I watched the game with a sense of defeat, as Brian Clough was going on about what a bunch of amateurs and clowns the Poles were. Then the game started, and guess what? We were playing rather well. Our star was the goalkeeper Jan Tomaszewski, they should build a statue for that man, if they haven't already.

I'll never forget my sense of outrage when our forward, the nippy Grzegorz Lato, was running clear on goal and Roy McFarland pulled him back. The commentator said something like - "He had to do that or he would have scored." I thought - talk about double standards, if a foreigner had done that, the English commentator would have been baying for his blood.

When Domarski scored for Poland, me and Grandad were leaping around. The foreigners were beating the English, it was so INSPIRING. Poland eventually held England to a draw and so knocked them out of the World Cup, it gave me a sense of pride. I went to school the next day with my chest puffed out, ready for whatever beating they were going to dish out.

DERMOTT COLLINS

Jerkski Zmuda what a bleeding turncoat. Poland knocks England out of the World Cup and now he's fucking Mr. Polska. Do admire him for this though - we walked into the playground and Big Gary Abbott goes to him - "We won't give you a kicking if you don't mention the game." Jerry nodded his head, went quiet for a bit and then he starts jumping and shouting "POLSKA! POLSKA!" Gary and the boys didn't hold back from their pummelling but RESPECT!

JERRY ZMUDA

I asked my Dad to teach me Polish, but he waved me away and said - "Ah! What do you want to learn that for?" I went to My Grandad - who gave me a few words but that was it.

DERMOTT COLLINS

Sometimes kids at school would call me Paddy and say stuff about the IRA. I would just give 'em a whack and leave it at that. Didn't want to get involved in all that Ian Paisley and the IRA stuff. Knew nothing about it and didn't want to.

But I didn't mind being The Paddie. The big family event every week was the Dave Allen show. All the brothers would sit around and laugh all the way through. I thought he was ace an' 'all, though being a kiddy wink I didn't always get the joke. Raise a glass to Dave Allen makes, yer proud to be a Mick.

THE GOSPEL ACCORDING TO CAINE FROM KUNG FU

JERRY ZMUDA
> The weekly school assembly - did you have them at your school? Each
> class would take turns to put on a little play with some moral to it or
> some story out of the bible. Our turn came. I get to go on stage and
> perform, my young heart was racing - I could be discovered and
> become a star.

DERMOTT COLLINS
> Saw this clip from that film *Jesus Christ Superstar* where Jesus walks
> into a temple and goes mental and smashes it up - and he's singing
> while he's doing it. I thought let's do that for our assembly - but give
> it a Kung Fu twist.

JERRY ZMUDA
> It was from the Gospel according to John. Jesus visits the temple and
> is incensed when he sees that the temple is being used as a market
> place. In his anger he tears the market down.

MR. HEYWARD
> I was tricked. I watched the rehearsal for approval and it was so
> boring I have to say I didn't notice anything wrong, but on the actual
> performance in front of the whole school - Dermott goes into his
> Bruce Lee bit, kicking down the stall.

JERRY ZMUDA
> So Dermott was dressed as Jesus, wearing a false beard and robe, and
> he was Kung Fu kicking down this market stall. I was supposed to be
> playing a taken aback market trader, but I was in stitches.

DERMOTT COLLINS
> As I was on that stage, kicking down the stall I looked out into the
> audiences. Some kids were laughing, others goldfish-mouthed, some
> girls were even screaming. I loved being on stage. A lot of people used
> to say about me - "Yeah Titus he gives it all the north and south but
> he never delivers". But I was A FACE after that performance. But
> Mr. Heyward was not happy.

MR. HEYWARD

I got summonsed by the headmaster Mr. Petty, and he lays into me. Blaming me for not controlling my class. I was so angry. I said to him the only way to stop Dermott doing stuff like this is to ban him altogether from any school performances.

PLANET OF THE APES, PLANET OF THE APES, PLANET OF THE APES

PETER WYATT

You couldn't be a lad in Britain growing up in the mid seventies without getting into *Kung Fu*. There was nothing better on a Saturday afternoon, after your weekly bath, than to watch *Kung Fu* on TV in your dressing gown. Then practice all the moves - in slow motion of course.

DENNIS MCBRIDE (Dermott and Jerry's classmate)

The biggest mistake of my young life was inviting Dermott and Jerry round for tea to watch *Kung Fu*. My Mum's from Aberdeen - so it stands to reason she'll speak with a Scottish accent. Do you think those tossers would ever stop going on about it?

JERRY ZMUDA

We were about to swap my *Thunderbirds* annual with Dennis McBride's *Kung Fu* annual. As we were at the front door, Dennis's mum comes rushing out and kills the deal with the immortal line – *(Scottish accent)* "Yer noh swawping that Kung Foo ahnewal."
And so a legend was born.

DERMOTT COLLINS

"Yer noh swawping that Kung Foo ahnewal." Every time we saw Dennis we started on that. He wanted to kill us.

JERRY ZMUDA

But the influence of *Kung Fu* was waning, another planet had come into our orbit and everything was to revolve around that. I'm talking about the *Planet of the Apes*.
During the summer holidays Dermott's eldest brother had taken us to see *Battle for the Planet of the Apes* which was amazing - easily the

best film ever made. When the *Planet of the Apes* TV series started I was in heaven. I couldn't think about anything else apart from *Planet of the Apes*, *Planet of the Apes*, *Planet of the Apes*.

DERMOTT COLLINS

Me and Jerry decided *Kung Fu* was for ponces. But some kids were still bang into it. There was trouble brewing at our school.

JERRY ZMUDA

Then one day at assembly this kid sneaks over and says – "You like Planet of the Apes? We prefer Kung Fu and we want to discuss it in the playground at break time." I knew he meant a fight, so I told Dermott. Thankfully he was into *Planet of the Apes* too so I wasn't going to face this battering alone.

When break time came along there were four of them, rough kids off the estate, waving their arms around Kung Fu style. They had us surrounded. I was wetting myself. Then the moment I will never forget - Dermott yells at the top of his lungs - "NOW FIGHT LIKE APES!"

I felt my first ever adrenalin rush - my fear evaporated and I rushed one of the kids. He was doing a showy Kung Fu kick and I knocked him off balance and he hit the concrete, I kicked him a few times, he wasn't getting up for a while. This other kid was doing some more Kung Fu moves, I dodged a few of those and punched him straight in the nose, he went flying. I looked over to see how Dermott was doing. He was in a bundle on the ground with two other kids.

By this time, Mr. Heyward had come over and broke it up. It was over in a few seconds, but those moments were enough to turn this frightened chimpanzee into a hardened gorilla warrior.

DERMOTT COLLINS

If Jerry ever tells you how well he fought against the Kung Fu kids, don't believe a word. I was there - he was crapping himself.

JERRY ZMUDA

We had our own idea for a film and TV series. On my toy farm I had five toy donkeys so I came up with *Donkey Planet*.

It was about a donkey who after being mistreated by the farmer decides to take over the planet. He raises an army of donkeys and they have a big battle with the army. As we got older, Dermott added the storyline that the donkey was originally a human who lost his penis in a farming accident. He decides to have a donkey penis grafted on, so he can be hung like a donkey, and then bit -by bit he turns into a donkey, BUT HE CAN STILL TALK AND THINK LIKE A HUMAN. I've seen films made out of worse ideas than that.

MR. HEYWARD'S KARMA MASTER-CLASS

MR. HEYWARD

I clearly remember standing in front of that class and Dermott's eyes burning into me. I started to think there was something evil about that boy, and it soon became clear that anything that happened that was amiss - Dermott was behind it. Like the day Sammy Rogers was in my class feeling ill, white as a sheet, I was taking him to the school nurse. Halfway down the corridor - I hear Dermott shout - "It's Monkey Time" and laugh maniacally. I ran back and he's sat at his desk - trying to look all angelic. But I knew this was his doing. I grilled Sammy - what happened? Eventually he spilt the beans.

DERMOTT COLLINS

Sammy Rogers lost a bet. I said I want twenty nicker - but he didn't have the money. So I gave him some raw sausages that my old man had thrown out. I said – "Eat those then." I didn't expect him to - but he did.

MR. HEYWARD

So this evil child had made poor Sammy Rogers eat raw sausages. Knowing it would make him feel ill, knowing it would disrupt my class.

DERMOTT COLLINS

The bet was over the word Minge. He didn't believe that it was the place between a lady's legs. He thought it was the lumps in their jersey. So I won the bet.

MR. HEYWARD

I'm not a humourless bloke. I can live with Dermott hiding in the cupboard for register and jumping out when his name is called. I can live with him blackmailing some kid into writing "Mr. Heyward is a

FELTHAM MADE ME   21

Chutney Ferett" on the blackboard before class. But the relentless nature of it was wearing me down. Sometimes I felt like crying before facing another day at school.

I talked to my wife about it, and she told me that I should seriously talk to him - try and make him see the errors of his ways. She was right - I wasn't going to let this kid and his snivelling side-kick beat me. I was going to work on those boys and change them for the better.

JERRY ZMUDA

I got a nasty shock when Mr. Heyward included myself with Dermott for a break time detention. Was I one of the naughty boys now?

MR. HEYWARD

I let the boys think they were going to spend the whole break doing lines. But then I said "OK - no lines for you lads. I've got something to say. But let me get myself a coffee first, I'll be right back."

As I reach the door Dermott says - "White - two sugars." I felt anger well up in me, and I thought no - no – you're not going to beat me.

JERRY ZMUDA

So instead of giving us lines, Mr. Heyward told us about Karma. Everything we do has an effect - and we must be responsible enough to make sure that what we do affects people in a good way - and we don't harm anybody. I really respected that.

MR. HEYWARD

I cited the example of how they made little Tommy Higgins believe that Jerry had been attacked by giant insects. This may seem harmless fun to them, but I plainly recalled the look of horror on poor Tommy's face - he was nothing short of traumatized because Tommy is a sensitive nervous lad. Then Dermott says - "That's why we chose him Sir - because he's so easily taken in."

DERMOTT COLLINS

Mr. Heyward gives us a load of north and south about the Karma Sutra and stuff - and how we should be nice to people in the Cosmos. I said - "Alright - I don't disagree with that, but you've got to have a bit of fun as well."

MR. HEYWARD

They listened. I give them that - they listened. But would they put it into practice? Think of others before they did what they did? That remained to be seen.

MEANWHILE OVER IN RAYLEIGH, ESSEX

PETER WYATT

It was a Sunday morning and Dad was AWOL. Mum was cooking for me and telling me 'good riddance to bad rubbish' about Dad.

These two men turned up on the doorstep, one was fat, the other was really tall. Mum opened the door and they barged in, asking where Dad was. The fat one had my mother's face caught in his hand, squeezing it like a vice and he was saying "I Know you know where he is, so tell us."

This is a sight no boy should ever see. I tried to stop him but the tall one just squatted me away. Dad should have been here to deal with this. The fat man kept on saying, - "Where's Mr. Wyatt?" and slapping my Mum. Harder each time. I can still hear the cracking sound. Then I realised, with Dad gone, I was now Mr. Wyatt.

LET'S WRECK THE NATIVITY PLAY

PETER WYATT

After the debt collectors came round, Mum decided to move out of the area a bit sharpish, so I had to change schools. My old man had gone into hiding - he'd rung Mum after the visit and said he was going to sort it and everything will be back to normal soon. Mum said - "Don't bother, I'm leaving you." I was gutted because I was given the part of Joseph in the Christmas Play - and what with us moving away, I couldn't play the part.

We stayed round our aunties for a while which was fun, but then Mum got a job at Heathrow airport so we had to leave Essex and go to the other side of London. This place called Feltham. I didn't like it, with the planes going past all the time and a noisy dual carriageway nearby. It wasn't all cosy and homey like Rayleigh - all me aunties and uncles were far far away. It was horrible.

JERRY ZMUDA

When the posters went up for the auditions for the Christmas play, I thought - this is my big chance. So I auditioned for the part of Joseph and I was crushed when I didn't get it. I was holding back tears of bitterness. Had that Kung Fu Jerusalem assembly counted against me?

DERMOTT COLLINS

Poor Jerry had set his heart on being in that play. They gave his part to some fucking stiff head-boy type. They always do. So I says to him - "Let's give those monkeys a nativity play to remember."

JERRY ZMUDA

So we had a strategy meeting round my house, locked doors, hush hush. Dermott was coming out with all sorts of ideas to wreck the nativity play, like sawing the legs off the wooden donkey so Janice Adams who was playing Mary would fall off. Then he wanted to handcuff Dennis McBride, who was playing Herod, to a pole so he would miss his cue.

DENNIS MCBRIDE

There were six other kids up for the part of Herod and I landed it. Mr. Keddy told me I had a good voice and projected well. I was very proud. I spent every day rehearsing my lines.

JERRY ZMUDA

After several hours of elaborate planning to wreck the School Nativity play, we had ended up with nothing better than this - we were going to heckle King Herod.

DENNIS MCBRIDE

Picture the scene. I am ten; I have never performed in public before. I am King Herod in the school nativity play - a big part, with lots of lines to remember. I had spent every day for four weeks, FOUR WEEKS, learning my lines and rehearsing. The big day comes, me Mum and Dad are out there.

DERMOTT COLLINS

It was class, all the parents were sat in the chairs and the kids were sat on the floor down the side. We were whispering just loud enough for Dennis to hear us, but most of the audience couldn't. Then we started pulling faces at him and whispering "Yer noh swawping that Kung Foo ahnewal."

DENNIS MCBRIDE
I do my speech and then next to me, on my right, are two horrible kids going "Minge" and "You're not swapping that Kung Fu annual" all the way through it, pulling faces at me. I couldn't concentrate, I dried up, then I shouted at them. "FUCKING SHUT UP."

DERMOTT COLLINS
When Dennis cracked, screaming at us, the audience thought he'd gone nutty.

MR. HEYWARD
When I saw Dermott and Jerry in the audience pulling faces. I saw red and jumped in. It disrupted the school nativity play. In the grand Karma scheme of things, those boys are going straight to hell.

MULE TRAIN

NATALIE ZMUDA (Jerry's mother)
You can imagine my horror to receive a letter at Christmas from the headmaster of Springfield school, wanting to see me about my son's behaviour at the school nativity play. I discovered that Dermott's father Frank had also been summonsed.
When I met Frank Collins that day outside the headmaster's office, he was laughing the whole thing off, saying something like "boys will be boys." I told him that wrecking the school Nativity play was not everyday boisterous behaviour. We are the only parents who have been called down the school, no one else. His reply was - "Well they have to pick on the Irish kid and the Pawlak kid." Err Excuse me - Jerry's grandfather may be Polish but JERRY IS NOT A PAWLAK.

FRANK COLLINS
I met Jerry's mum. Very nice lady. Very upset about the whole affair. I did my best to put it all in its place. It's just boys playing.

DERMOTT COLLINS

Dad's the friendliest geezer in the world, talks to everyone and anyone. Never looks down on anyone - except to pick them up. I know he didn't make a good impression on Jerry's parents when they met the first time. But his big mistake was to invite them to his traditional New Years Day open house knees up. By the time they had turned up in the afternoon, Dad was already pretty well leathered. It was all going off a bit "mine's a pint of Courage Best. Gertcha." Which obviously ain't Mister and Missus Zmuda's scene at all.

Dad thought he'd impress them with his party piece, singing *Mule Train* while banging a tea tray against his head. It always made us laugh like monkeys, but I look over at Mr. & Mrs. Zmuda - staring down into their glasses of wine, faces dripping with embarrassment.

PETER WYATT

I wasn't at that party. Remember I hadn't met Dermott and Jerry yet, but I've since seen Dermott's Dad doing *Mule Train* and banging his head with the tea-tray, and it's a sight to see. Hilarious! Put that man on the telly!

STINKY WINNIE THE POOH

PETER WYATT

I've been at my new school in Feltham about a month when Mum says - "Do you want to invite some of your new friends over for tea?" So I invited about four kids I played football with.

We were all sat up in my bedroom playing Subbuteo, when one kid looks up and sees Georgie, this stuffed chubby orange bear. I didn't really play with him any more, but he was my oldest toy. The kids start chanting STINKY WINNIE THE POOH, STINKY WINNIE THE POOH. I wasn't having it - these horrible 'oiks from Feltham making fun of my favourite toy, so I stood up and booted this kid snack on the nose - blood spurted everywhere. It all kicked off - several Subbuttueo players got crushed. Mum had to dive in and break us up. Nobody takes the piss out of Georgie - nobody.

So you could say I was having trouble fitting in at my new school.

JERRY DISOBEYS

NATALIE ZMUDA

It was clear that Jerry had fallen victim to a bad influence. I sympathized with Dermott - it can't be easy going through life without a mother. But I couldn't allow him to drag Jerry down.

JERRY ZMUDA

Right after the New Year's Day *Mule train* episode Mum and Dad wanted to talk to me. I knew it was serious because they had the TV off. Mum looked me straight in the eye and said, - "We don't want you to see that boy Dermott any longer. He's a bad influence and he's from a bad family."

Naturally I protested. Then father came in with - "He's going to end up in prison, and you'll end up there with him if you're not careful." There was no question of me ending my friendship with Dermott. If prison was where we were heading, then so be it. They made me promise that I would stop seeing him, but I had my fingers crossed behind my back.

NATALIE ZMUDA

I then took steps to ensure that Jerry went to a different secondary school from Dermott. After he left primary school - Jerry would never see Dermott again.

THE WALKING TREE INCIDENT

JERRY ZMUDA

Of course I carried on going around with Dermott. But I told Mum I had found a new friend, Jonathan Bagg - who didn't really exist. It was our little joke - Johnny Bagg. Get it?

MR. HEYWARD

To Mr. Petty the Headmaster I represented the permissive society, rock'n'roll, strikes and the general demise of all that he values. He was aching for a chance to get at me. It was only a matter of time before he found something else to hang on me.

DERMOTT COLLINS

Mrs. Clack had tree trunk lungs. Nobody could deny it. One day at afternoon break, I clocked her hobbling out the school gate, and I shouts over "LOOK OVER THERE IT'S A WALKING TREE." Me and Jerry got pulled up in front of Mr. Petty the headmaster and we denied it at first. After several hours, they wore a confession out of us. Just to swerve it away from us I said that Mr. Heyward had told us that Mrs. Clack had tree trunk legs, and we hadn't noticed them before. Pettycoat bought it and it took the heat off us and onto Mr. Heyward. I felt bad. Mr. Heyward may have been a hippy - but he was still a good bloke.

JERRY ZMUDA

Mr. Heyward talked to us in a way no other teacher did. He told us about his favourite music, the Beatles and Cream, about his interest in eastern religions. He showed us the books he was reading. I especially remember *Dreams, Memories and Reflections* by Carl Gustav Jung. While other teachers just wanted to shout at you and tell you what to do, Mr. Heyward seem to actually stand for something - he had beliefs. I felt guilty that we got him into trouble.

DERMOTT COLLINS

Mr. Heyward got into even more hot water when I let slip that he told us about the Karma Sutra when he had us in detention.

DERMOTT IS TOLD A CRUEL TRUTH

DERMOTT COLLINS

All my memories of Primary school days were all happy. Apart from one. One day at home when I was about eight I was having a scrap with Ryan my youngest brother. He were about 12 at the time, so it weren't exactly fair. It got heated, and then he says to me - "You're a bad seed you are! Mum died giving birth to you. That's how bad you are." I was shocked I didn't say anything, I just blotted it out. I just wanted to forget about it and just be funny all the time.

PETER WYATT

I hate self pity and I tried not to feel sorry for myself with all the trouble I had at home. It's rough as a kid when your Dad isn't around.

But it must have been even rougher for Dermott with no Mum. He says life was a great for him in primary school, but I think he's not being fully honest with himself.

THE LAST DAY OF PRIMARY SCHOOL

JERRY ZMUDA

The last day of primary school, and I was saying goodbye to the setting of my early childhood. Worst of all, Mother told me that I would be going to Feltham School next term, and Dermott was going to a different school. I was distraught because I was going to be spending the rest of my life without my best friend. I felt my world ending. My eyes were welling up, but I didn't want anyone to see me cry.

DERMOTT COLLINS

On the last ever day at Springfield they had a Sports day, all the teachers were on a high security alert. They thought me and Jerkski had some big plan to ruin it, and they kept their eyes on us. There was big pileup in the sack race, and the teachers came dashing over to where we were sitting, as if we'd made it happen.

SARAH BAXTER

How can you not cry on your last day of primary school? You'd have to have a heart of stone. I'd really got attached to some of the kids at Springfield, but then there were others I hoped I would never see again.

PETER WYATT

On the last day of primary school, everyone was crying. But not me. I was glad to get it over with. Looking forward to going to a massive school where everyone was the new kid, not just me.

DERMOTT COLLINS

Our class sang The Carnival Is Over at the last assembly on the last day. And by the first chorus - nearly everyone was blubbing like pathetic monkeys. I thought the toilet pipe had burst. Jerry especially - I'll never, never, never let him forget that. What a soppy git. Me - my eyes were dry as a bone. I ain't the sentimental type.

JERRY ZMUDA

I went up to Mr. Heyward to say goodbye and he just glared back at me. I guess he wasn't planning on forgiving Dermott and I any time soon.

MR. HEYWARD

There they were on sports day - the last day of term. I saw them laughing, laughing, laughing at it all. Sending it all up. I hated those two kids. I still do. They ruined my career as a teacher and worse still, destroyed my faith in human nature. My belief that everyone is basically good, if you only give them a chance. Well, they decimated that. On that last day of primary school I swore to myself that I would get even with those fuckers. That karma would catch up with them one day.

Chapter 2
Feltham School
- Welcome to the Bowels of Hell

THE FIRST DAY AT FELTHAM SCHOOL

SARAH BAXTER

Dad told me Feltham School was this massive school with all the latest state-of-the-art facilities. So I was expecting some space age high tech building. What a pack of fucking lies.

JERRY ZMUDA

On my first day at Feltham School I was stupidly early, by something like an hour and a half. So I was the first child there. I had nothing else to do but stand and stare at this ugly grey slab of concrete that was to be my school for the next five years. Then a gang of kids strolled in, all big boots and long lank greasy hair. They were looking over and laughing at me in my pristine all-new school uniform. I went up to the teacher to ask where the toilet was. I didn't want to go, I just needed something to do. I opened the toilet door with trepidation. The graffiti - CFC BOYS KICK TO KILL, AGGRO, PAKIS OUT, NF. Grotesque marker pen pictures of genitalia and graphic illustrations of violence. I was in the bowels of hell.

DERMOTT COLLINS

All set to go to Kennington Manor, then what do you fucking know? Dad gets a letter from the Principal - me place's been withdrawn. The old man gets miffed and gets down the school, and they tell him off the record they didn't want me there because of my seriously bad references from primary school. And I don't think the reputation of me brothers helped much neither.

FRANK COLLINS (Dermott's Dad)

It was prejudice pure and simple. Just because of the bother Ryan had. He had been provoked. It was the seventies and Irish people were constantly getting flack for the troubles - and teachers could say what the feck they liked in them days. Nowadays you got the race relations board but in them days we just had to put up with it.

FELTHAM MADE ME   31

DERMOTT COLLINS

So the only school nearby that would take me was - drum roll - Feltham School. They'd take anybody. I knew way back in August I was going to be joining my dear old buddy Jerkski. But didn't tell him, thought I'd spring the big surprise on the playground on the first day.

JERRY ZMUDA

Feltham School was a world away from Springfield Primary School. To begin with, it was ten times the size, and that was only the lower school. But the big difference was the kids, full of menace and rage. Staring at you - searching for a reason to hate you. Wrong football scarf, wrong shoes, wrong skin colour. I was told by my sister's friends that Feltham was horrible - but I wasn't expecting it to be quite this horrible. I got given some advice - if a bunch of kids came up to you asking if I've had my DL yet - WALK AWAY.

PETER WYATT

I had this plan - if any kid came up to me, trying to reckon it, I was going to do them. I was going to show them that you don't take Peter Wyatt for a mug.

So I get past the school gate and these older kids come up, looking serious.

"Are you a first year?"

"Yeah."

"Have you had your DL yet?"

"DL? What's a DL?"

The main kid had an air of authority and he goes - "You'd better come this way." They showed me round this wall and then all of sudden they have me surrounded and they shout - "DEAD LEG!" They kicked me to the ground. Very painful - and really embarrassing. The ringleader I later knew to be Terry South.

JERRY ZMUDA

The teacher on the megaphone barked instructions to congregate on the main playground and they would sort us out into our classes. I looked around, hoping to get a nicer selection from this ramshackle bunch of kids. THAT'S WHEN I SAW HIM. Looking in my direction with a coy smile. I was so overjoyed I nearly hugged him - thank God

I stopped myself in time. The Feltham kids would have ripped me apart for being a 'mo. We were split into different classes, but at least I had a friend at Feltham School.

A few minutes later I saw the radiant Sarah Baxter, she did not seem that excited at seeing me.

SARAH BAXTER

I saw that drip Jerry was going to be in my class. Then I saw that tosser Dermott, thank God he wasn't. Now at least I might learn something.

PETER WYATT

I stood around hobbling on the playground tarmac, nursing my bruised legs as the teacher with a megaphone is calling our names out. I was doing my best to look hard and fearless, so no one would start on me again, but I melted when I saw this beautiful vision join our crowd. The megaphone announced her as Sarah Baxter.

DERMOTT COLLINS

Was Feltham School violent? Put this way - in all that time I only got into two rucks. But each fight lasted about two and a half years.

MR. DUNNE (Feltham School Teacher)

I had this reputation for being able to handle the hard nuts. It worked against me, because then I got assigned as the form teacher for all the roughest kids at Feltham. My strategy was a simple one - put the mouthy ones in a head-lock on the first day. This was tried and tested. Thank fuck I retired before all this PC Bollocks came in. I do remember that first day with 1 F. I'd put six of 'em in a headlock before break-time. Dermott naturally included.

DERMOTT COLLINS

Mr. Dunne was our form teacher, he did metal-work. He was more like a club bouncer than a teacher. He talked like a sea-lion - you know rasping. Oi. Oi. Give us some fish.

JERRY ZMUDA

So I've been at Feltham about a week. Trying to stay out of trouble. I'm standing around the playground, and there's this almighty kerfuffle.

About twenty of the roughest kids are around this poor wretch. Turns out it's his birthday - and they are giving him the bumps. He's getting tossed up in the air to be met by a stack of DMs on the way down. Mercifully he was only 12. After the 12th bump - they give him one for luck and hurl him high into the air. When he hits the ground he's met by a hale of more swinging DMs - the poor lad had to curl himself into a tight foetal position. My birthday wasn't until April but I was taking that bit of information to the grave.

MR. DUNNE

Of course being called Mr. Dunne some of the kids called me Mr. Dung - very predictable. But with this year's lot I become aware that the kids in my form - especially Dermott - were constantly making loads of Seal and Sea-Lion noises. Dermott asking me if I like fish and then the next day he's asking me if I can balance a ball on my nose, and the kids are smirking. So eventually I come straight out and ask him - "What's all this about seals?"

And Dermott says - "It's alright Sir - it's got nothing to do with you sounding like a sea-lion." It was headlock time.

THE MAN ABOUT THE HOUSE AFFAIR

JERRY ZMUDA

It wasn't long before Dermott was holding court in a corner of the playground telling all the jokes he'd heard from his older brothers. He started off with your bog standard kid's jokes, but within a couple of weeks he was coming up with some real smutty material - jokes about VD and vaginas - which I barely ever understood. I laughed along anyway.

DERMOTT COLLINS

The way I saw it was this - at Springfield I'd been playing gigs at the Fulham Greyhound. With Feltham School I was playing to bigger crowds at the Hammersmith Odeon. In my mind, my act was going down a storm.

PETER WYATT

Every morning I'd see Dermott in his patch outside the metalwork shop, making this handful of kids laugh. I'd stand near just so I could

overhear. The one that made me crack up was Dermott saying –
"Excretion….. Me Dad puts that in his hair. Excretion 2000." Then he
tells this long joke, but all I could hear properly was the punch-line -
"my arse is still sore." And everyone explodes with laughter. I was
trying to work out the rest of the joke - it was driving me mad.

JERRY ZMUDA

After a while I started feeling the pressure. I was Dermott's side-kick
but I hadn't told a joke yet. I was in danger of sliding into anonymity.
On the bus to school Dermott offered to help me out and gave me
what he described as "a top quality joke."

DERMOTT COLLINS

The joke was - a geezer goes up to a Doctor and he's starkers except
for a nappy made of clingfilm, and the Doctor goes "I can clearly see
your nuts." Simple right?

JERRY ZMUDA

At the playground as I began telling the joke, all these kids staring at
me, eyes burrowing into me, it made me nervous and I ended saying
instead - "I can clearly see your testicles." Which of course
completely misses the point of the gag.

DERMOTT COLLINS

Went all quiet - only sound were the wind and a tumbleweed blowing
across the playground.

JERRY ZMUDA

Worse humiliation was to come with the Man About House affair. In
the playground we'd talk about our favourite comedy programmes,
but in the Zmuda household, my parents frowned on ITV, so one of
the programmes I never go to see was *Man About The House*. I made
the mistake of confiding with Dermott.

DERMOTT COLLINS

So we're talking about *Man About the House*, laughing away and so is
Jerry. I pull him up in front of everyone - "what was your favourite bit
then?" Knowing full well he hadn't seen it.
Jerry's struggling - "I don't know - all of it."

"Yeah, but which bit did you think was the funniest?"

"I don't know."

"What about the bit where he goes 'Ain't your Mum got no gherkins?"

"Yes that was very funny."

"Ah! Caught ya!"

Bit of a bastard I know, especially to my best friend, but I can't stand fakes.

JERRY ZMUDA

> The joke that caused me the most embarrassment was - 'Why can't women count past 70? Because when they get to 69 they find it a bit of a mouthful.' I didn't get this one either and Dermott says to me - "Ask your mother". So I did, over dinner - and she went all quiet.

PETER WYATT

> It was driving me bonkers - how can you make a joke with 'my arse is still sore' as a punch-line? I was actually lying awake at night trying to work it out. Something to do with sitting down? I desperately wanted to ask Dermott, but I hadn't spoken to him yet, so I couldn't just go up to him.

JERRY ZMUDA

> While Dermott was a hit with a dozen or so kids in the corner by the metalwork shop, I was worried for him. Dermott is a mouthy so-and-so, and at primary school he could get away with that relatively unchallenged. But Feltham was another world. I could see a horde of mean looking second years scowling at Dermott when he was showing off.

MISTER FROGSPAWN

JERRY ZMUDA

> I had been forewarned about Mr. Hobsbawn - the Lower School Head. His assemblies were legendary, where he laid down his blue print for a better humanity - a monotonous preachy drone.

SARAH BAXTER

> Mr. Hobsbawn taught Technical Drawing. He was always wearing these high starched collars that made his neck sore. Always wore

brogues and checked trousers and saying stuff like - "You're for the high jump," or "I'll have your guts for garters." Which I always thought was a bit of a weird Hannibal Lecter thing to say. Mr. Hobsbawn just came across as a man out of his time - he belonged in the thirties - the 1830s.

JERRY ZMUDA
Frogspawn always had a watery eyed intense look.

DERMOTT COLLINS
Frospawn looked like he was desperate for a shit. Like he'd just had a massive dump, but then realized he hadn't properly cleared out, and he badly needed to go again. Top wind up material. I remember going into his class and saying - "Ah! I've got VD"
"TD - You've got Technical Drawing boy!"
"No - I've got VD Sir - I'm seeing the Doctor about it."
"I would be very surprised if you did have it."
"Why's that Sir?"
"Because it's something that happens to people when they're much older."
"You'd be surprised what I get up to."
"No doubt."
"Have you ever had it Sir?"
"I'm not having this absurd conversation."
"Too late Sir - you just did."

SARAH BAXTER
The whole atmosphere at Feltham was tension - a clash between the stiff and awkward Hobsbawn and the violence of the kids.
But that all changed when we took Art - my favourite class. There I felt relaxed and creative. Miss Ferguson was an enthusiastic teacher and she encouraged me to paint what I wanted. I used to draw these women in long colourful gowns and she'd bring me up to show them to the rest of class. I blushed red like a cherry but I was very proud. It was through Miss Ferguson that I realized I had artistic talent.

JERRY ZMUDA
The first few weeks of term was in September, and the girls were still wearing their summer dresses. In the art class the sunlight used go

straight through Miss Ferguson's dress - then if I looked left I could see the outline of Sarah Baxter's breast. I pierced a hole into my school trouser pocket and just watched them as I played with myself under the desk. Once Miss Ferguson looked over at me and asked - "Everything alright Jerry?" I nearly exploded then and there.

PETER WYATT

I could see all the boys in art-class looking at Sarah Baxter with their tongues hanging out. I felt like whacking them - saying "hands off - she's mine."

CRISIS? WHAT CRISIS?

PETER WYATT

Mum was still very down a lot of the time, sighing deeply and bursting into tears, and this was wrecking me head. I was sitting in classroom one wet break-time thinking about it all - when this kid Colin Greene came in. He'd just got the new album from Supertramp from the school library. He was so bloody cheerful about it, and it was getting me even more down. Then Dermott and Jerry showed up.

JERRY ZMUDA

Colin was showing off his Supertramp album. The cover had a picture of a man sun-bathing surrounded by a town decimated by a nuclear bomb. The album was called *Crisis? What Crisis?* It gave off this air of smugness that was bound to annoy Dermott.

DERMOTT COLLINS

It was doing my head in. So I takes the record out of the sleeve. Colin's ain't smiling no more. I said –
"The way they make these records these days - they're shatter proof. Let me show you."
And WHACK! I smash the record over Jerry's head.

PETER WYATT

I was stunned, just sat there gawping as the record shattered over Jerry's head and then I cracked up. I totally forgot about Mum and our troubles. I was laughing about it for the rest of the day. But Colin Greene didn't see the funny side, which of course made it funnier.

DERMOTT COLLINS

>After the record smashed into dozens of pieces, I said - "That record's a dud - you should take that back."

JERRY ZMUDA

>After the *Crisis What Crisis?* incident I was hurled into Frogspawn's office. I thought I was in trouble as Dermott's collaborator, but instead he was asking me if I wanted to report Dermott for bullying. "Bullying who?" I asked.
>"Bullying you - Jerry Zmuda."

DERMOTT COLLINS

>I'd trained Jerry well - don't ever open your mouth and don't grass on your mates.

JERRY ZMUDA

>Frogspawn was like a bulldog on a blood soaked burglar, he just wouldn't let go. His watery eyes sizzled as he was saying –
>"Some people think it's clever to go around putting other people down, hurting people. Don't let these people win. I can help you beat your tormentor. But I can't unless you make an official complaint."
>I was trying to explain that Dermott was my friend. "What kind of a friend smashes a record over your head?" Good question. That got me thinking.

PETER WYATT

>Until then I thought Dermott was just another mouthy show-off - every class in every school in every town has one.
>But after that *Crisis What Crisis?* record-breaking thing I saw Dermott differently. He really was mental - and he really didn't give a fuck.

DERMOTT COLLINS

>So Frogspawn orders me to replace the record. I explained the sit to me old man, and he rolls his eyes, tuts and gives me the dosh to buy the album. But I've got me pride. I can't go into a shop and buy a Supertramp album. The girl behind the counter will think I actually like them. So I nicked it from Record Scene. So it were that what got me into shop-lifting.

JERRY ZMUDA

Within a few months, Dermott had become notorious at Feltham.
But he was getting the backs up of a quite a few of the hard-nuts. I
knew Dermott had really gone too far when he was tripping girls over
saying - "Girls are falling at my feet." He did this to Yvonne Waters -
and Terry South, the toughest kid in the lower school, fancied her.

DERMOTT COLLINS

At Feltham School I just carried on from where I left off at Springfield.
But I could tell that some people weren't getting into the Wonderful
World of Titus and his Monkey Time.

RUMBLE AT THE SCHOOL DISCO

JERRY ZMUDA

Everyone was really excited when the posters went up for the Lower
School disco. We thought it would be fun, little did we know what
was in store for us.

PETER WYATT

I had to go to the school disco. I'd never been to one before, but I
knew the score. At some point in the night the DJs whacks on a slow
soppy record that birds like - *I'm not In Love* or something like that -
and you ask the girl for a dance. That's how you get in there. My
strategy was simple - be the first to ask Sarah Baxter.

TERRY SOUTH

We got more than our fair share of cunts at Feltham. And it's the
first rule of nature - if you behave like a cunt - you get slapped like a
cunt. And if anybody on this planet deserved a slap it was that
Dermott Collins and his snivelling side kick Jerry.

MR. DUNNE

Guess who they roped in to do the security at the school disco?

SARAH BAXTER

The disco was held in the annex block over in the Upper School. They
didn't want us to smoke or get up to anything, so all the time these
vile glaring strip lights were on. One was strobing gently which at least

gave some kind of disco effect. We were all just standing around, too self-conscious to dance under that horrible bright light.

PETER WYATT

The DJ had a small fuzz-light on top of the speaker - which he turned on for *BlockBuster*. This would have been around March 1976 and being 12 and all that, I had no idea that punk was starting up somewhere.

DERMOTT COLLINS

I didn't suspect a thing. The DJ was playing *Funky Week-end* - I was singing over it – "Spunky Week-end." No-one laughing - just eye-balling me. Should have twigged then and there.

JERRY ZMUDA

Then Terry South came up to us and said he wanted to see us both outside. I knew it meant only one thing.

PETER WYATT

Terry South had about a dozen of his cronies all about to jump Dermott and Jerry. I was thinking - this ain't cricket - and I liked them two kids, even though I hadn't properly spoken to either of them yet.

DERMOTT COLLINS

So we went outside and we turned to face them. Must have been about forty of them, the roughest, toughest kids in mean old Feltham. We were brown bread.

JERRY ZMUDA

I was looking behind me to see if there was anywhere to run, we were surrounded. The DJ inside was now playing *I Love To Love* by Tina Charles. So this was going to be the sound-track to our kicking of death. Then it occurred to me, it was Dermott they wanted. I was just the accomplice. I was about to plea for mercy - saying kill him not me - when the US Cavalry appeared.

DERMOTT COLLINS

This large fair-haired kid from Jerry's class pushed his way to the front, and he said to them all - "two against twelve is not on. You want to start something you all go through me first - one by one."

TERRY SOUTH

It fucking was not twelve against two. It's just so many people hated them - that they all wanted to see them both get a good kicking.

MR. DUNNE

I thought all the boys at the disco had got bored and gone home. But then I looked outside and I see a group of kids about to lay into Dermott. I have to be honest, I did think about turning a blind eye...

JERRY ZMUDA

Terry and Peter were squaring up to each other - when all of a sudden it kicked off. Somebody booted Peter - Peter punched Terry - some kids jumped Peter. Dermott and I pulled them off - then the three of us just pushed our way past and ran. Thankfully Mr. Dunne, the metalwork teacher, caught hold of Terry while the others chased us up the road, but eventually gave up.

DERMOTT COLLINS

The three us managed to see a chink of daylight and we ran out of there faster than Speedy Gonzales on Sulphate. What the fuck happened? I'd love to see a slo-mo. But somehow we survived and we owed it all to Peter. Laughing with relief we piled down the chippy.

JERRY ZMUDA

I was looking at Peter - this saint of a kid. He risked his life to save us.

DERMOTT COLLINS

I swear he had this glow around him. Like the ready-break kid.

PETER WYATT

I have to say, it felt good being a hero to them two. I played it down - as if I did this sort of thing all the time. As we stood outside the chippy wolfing down our hot chips - we talked about music - Electric Light Orchestra and The Who.

DERMOTT COLLINS

Jerry showed himself up. He said his Mum had said that the Electric Light Orchestra shouldn't be allowed to call themselves an orchestra, because people might buy their records thinking it was classical.

PETER WYATT

After saving their sorry arses I thought this earned me the right to off load on them. To really say out loud what I was going through. I had never got the chance to do that with anybody.

DERMOTT COLLINS

Turns out our knight in shining armour is a life story merchant.

JERRY ZMUDA

Over chips Peter opened up, he told us all about his Dad with his gambling debts and going into hiding, how his Mum had to move to a new area to find a job. I thought to myself - he's had it really hard. My life is a breeze in comparison.

PETER WYATT

I even told them how much I liked Sarah Baxter - and then I thought fuck - now somebody else is feeling her up to 10CC. Then I remembered something else - the 'My arse is still sore' joke. Dermott you have to tell me the rest of that joke. Now!

DERMOTT COLLINS

A teenage boy comes in late one evening, and his Dad flies into a rage. "What time do you call this?"
"Sorry Dad," the weary son replies "I've just had my first ever sexual experience," and he sprawls out on the couch.
The dad is filled with pride. "That's different son - tell your old man all about it." "Not right now Dad I'm too tired."
The next day the Dad goes into work still glowing after what his son has told him. He's telling everyone at the canteen - "chip off the old bloke." After work he goes down the pub, buying everyone drinks, still bragging about his son.

FELTHAM MADE ME   43

He gets home and finds his son – still sprawled out on the couch. "Aren't you going out tonight then son?" Asks the father - "start as you mean to go on - practice makes perfect." "Uh! I couldn't," replies the son.

PETER WYATT

"My arse is still sore!"

JERRY ZMUDA

And so a friendship was formed - and every break-time, going home time, we'd be with Peter. It wasn't just that we felt safer having him around, it just seemed so right, so perfect.

DERMOTT COLLINS

The dynamic duo had become a terrific trio.

THE SEPTIMUS GRUNDY CAPER

PETER WYATT

Our music teacher Mr. Dorrit caught us hanging around the school corridors playing penny-up-the-wall, and started calling us the Unholy Trinity, which made us giggle. One of the places the Unholy Trinity used to hang out after school was the Septimus Grundy graveyard. It was well spooky.

JERRY ZMUDA

After school we would go to this magnificent antiquated church, reading the gravestones holding our hot bag of chips. The sun going down, magic hour they call it, and everything was bathed in this eerie sepia glow. It felt as though we are passing into the world of spirits. This was where we found the gravestone with the name Septimus Grundy 1888-1952. What a wonderful name!

DERMOTT COLLINS

We blagged the vicar into thinking the church was haunted by the spirit of Septimus Grundy. We did this writing in chalk 'release my soul - Septimus.' Then we went there at night. The vicar was alone in his office and I shouts through the door - 'I am Septimus - your mother sucks cocks in hell' you know like the girl in the Exorcist. None of us had seen the film but me brother told us about it.

PETER WYATT

Dermott got so into playing tricks onto this poor sod of a vicar, eventually the vicar cracked - he grabbed some books and did this big exorcism. When the C of E found out, they kicked him out the church.

DERMOTT COLLINS

The vicar shouted at us from behind the door —"Go home and stop bothering me, you stupid child!" I replied in my Exorcist girl voice — "I am not a stupid child - I am Septimus Grundy!"

JERRY ZMUDA

Dermott tells the story that we convinced the vicar into thinking his graveyard was haunted, and the Vicar performed an exorcism, and as a result the Church of England had him defrocked. It's a wonderful yarn - but sadly totally untrue.

PETER WYATT

So I'm getting to know my new pals, the Odd Couple. Over school dinner I ask Dermott about his mother - because I'd never heard him mention her once. He looked down at the table and saw this one baked bean and goes - "Who's bean here?" - and started laughing. Wouldn't talk about her.

ALL ABOUT ANGELA

PETER WYATT

Angela Knowles was the first punk I ever saw. I couldn't understand it. She wasn't a bad-looking girl, why would she want to look like some twisted clown?

JORDI KNOWLES (FELTHAM SCHOOLKID)

Yes I am the famous Angela Knowles's younger brother. I say famous because she was fairly notorious in the Feltham, Hounslow, Isleworth area from about 1976 onwards.

The first music Angela got into was David Bowie. When she was 12 she used to stay in her bedroom and play *Life On Mars* over and over again. I guess a lot of girls of her generation went through that phase. But she never read the magazines that normal girls her age read - you know *Jackie* and *Look-in*, she used to read the *NME* and that's where she found out about the Sex Pistols, and the trouble caused at one of their gigs. It all started from there.

DERMOTT COLLINS

It was me brother Ryan who took Angela Knowles to see the Sex Pistols at the Nashville in April 1976. From then on she became a punk and poor Ryan couldn't handle it. He brought Angela to the house a coupla times, we were still sharing a bed-room. There she was, sat on my bed - flicking through my brother's records, couldn't stop gawping.

SANJEEV SRIDHARAN (FELTHAM SCHOOL-KID)

Angela was in my form at Feltham School and so I had the privilege of being able to observe her from close-hand. She was a wonderful knot of contradictions – she was angry, but she was also very funny, she was aggressive, but could also be very gentle, she was intelligent but would do things that were amazingly stupid. It never got boring with her around. She was the very first punk in the area.

JORDI KNOWLES

There was a time when me and my sister were really close, but I was so ashamed when they started sending Angela to see the visiting school shrink. Does that mean she's officially insane? Does it run in the family? All the time, people would ask me – "What's going on with her? Why's is she like this? What is she trying to pull?" I really didn't know my sister any more.

DERMOTT COLLINS

The school counsellor weren't based in Feltham. She only came to Feltham once a fortnight, because she had to do the rounds of all the other schools in the area. So all the problem kids at Feltham got seen on Wednesday afternoon - every fortnight. Which at least got me out of freezing me nuts off in games. So I turn up and I spy through the key-hole and I see Angela's in the hot-seat. I listen in and she's laughing

- her face all lit up, but I couldn't make out what she's saying. At the end of the session, when she flew out the door she smiled at me - a proper nice smile. The smile was as if to say - you're alright you're one of the problem kids seeing the shrink like me.

THE BUZZER QUIZ

DERMOTT COLLINS

The buzzer quiz was supposed to be a bit of end of term fun. End of term fun Mr. Frogspawn style. The fifth year boffins would get together with Froggie and set up this eletronic buzzer thing. The questions were stuff like - guess the teacher talking in a stupid voice, guess the record played backwards. They call it fun Jim, but not as we know it. But poor Jerry was well into it.

JERRY ZMUDA

As my first year at Feltham was coming to an end, one thing was dominating my thoughts. The school inter-divisional buzzer quiz. Each house - blue, green, red and yellow, had a representative from one year, and I was determined to be first year rep for the Green Team. Only three kids entered the qualifying round, and I was thrilled to win the place.

DERMOTT COLLINS

Why do you want to bother doing some noncey Buzzer Quiz? If you want to get on stage and have loads of people staring at you, there's better ways of doing it.

SANJEEV SRIDHARAN

I was on the third year of the Green Team and that's how I got talking to Jerry. He starts pumping me with all these naive questions - like "What's it like to be Asian?" He was equating my experience with his, having Polish parents. I told him it was very different for him. Being white meant he could blend into the background, but my colour was there for every bonehead and NF supporter to see at all times. Down Feltham High Street, Hounslow Bus Garage, everywhere.
But I wasn't offended by Jerry, I could tell his heart was in the right place. But I gave him some serious advice - stay away from that Dermott Collins, that boy is trouble.

DERMOTT COLLINS
　　So Jerry made his reputation by doing the Buzzer Quiz.

JERRY ZMUDA
　　So the quiz is off and running. Frogspawn is the quiz master, and the rules are simple - whoever buzzes first, gets to answer the question. He asks a question and I press my buzzer and I thought – strange, I thought I buzzed first. Then it happened again. And I thought – hell! My buzzer's not working. Then Mr. Hobsbawn asks - "What was the city of Leningrad previously called?" I buzzed immediately and nothing happened, now I know for certain it's not working. I couldn't bear the shame of being seen not to be able answer a question about Eastern Europe - so I jumped out of my seat, past the desk and ran into the middle of the stage - yelling - "It's St. Petersburg! It's ST. PETERSBURG!"

DERMOTT COLLINS
　　Yup! Jerry really got himself a reputation after that buzzer quiz. A reputation for being a prize cock. And he had the costume to go with it. All I can say is thank God for school uniform, because the clobber his old dear would give him to wear outside school was a proper gilt-edged invitation to take the piss - Delamare jeans, round collared shirts - stripey tank-tops. People would say to me - "How can you go around with that pratt?" I was stumped for an answer.

FROGSPAWN'S ANTI-PUNK ASSEMBLY

PETER WYATT
　　What was the historic event of Christmas 1976? The Sex Pistols swearing on live TV of course - "you filthy bastard - what a fucking rotter." I heard it made some lorry driver kick in his television. Brilliant! Now I understood where Angela Knowles is coming from.

JERRY ZMUDA
　　I missed it. As we know, my parents, turned their nose up at commercial television, so we were watching Richard Stilgoe on the other side.

DERMOTT COLLINS

By January 1977 everybody in Britain was talking about punk. So with his finger on the pulse, Mr. Frogspawn decides to do an assembly on the evils of punk rock. We should have all started gobbing at him.

JERRY ZMUDA

His assembly was hilarious and hideously embarrassing in equal measures. The premiss was this - why should people listen to music that advocates hate, when they could listen to music with a positive message? He chose one of his favourite songs as an example. That's when it got really embarrassing.

PETER WYATT

He started going on about little ants pushing down rubber tree plants. Then he played us the song. Then he made us sing it. I was cringeing so much, I didn't know where too look.

JERRY ZMUDA

After that experience we all felt dirty, violated, I asked Mr. Dunne if I could go home and have a shower.

DERMOTT COLLINS

Few days later I'm with a bunch of lads and we're hanging around the staff car park and Mr. Frogspawn is getting into his car. I shout across to him "Whoops there's goes another rubber tree plant - yer Cunt!" Frogspawn's face goes all purple and blows a stack. He dashes across to where we were. I scarpered, and hid round the side of the wall.

PETER WYATT

Frogspawn was bellowing - "I know it was Dermott. I know it was Dermott. I recognize his voice." But nobody grassed him up, even the kids who hated Dermott. Because Dermott was speaking for every kid in the school.

DERMOTT COLLINS

I was the Don after that. The fucking Don d'yer hear me? Best of all Angela Knowles came up to me after assembly and shook my hand. When I felt her hand squeeze mine, my heart went all wobbly.

JERRY ZMUDA

Nationwide on the BBC did an item on Punk with Derek Nimmo, I think it was, and to me it just appeared plain horrible and disgusting. Then on a freezing cold morning I'm standing around in the playground, and Graham Kirby is saying that very soon they'll be more punks going around than there were Bay City Roller fans. I had visions of us all being up to our necks in vomit and bitten off ear lobes. I thought the apocalypse was about to begin - I was terrified.

DERMOTT COLLINS

Jerry had tears in his eyes and he was saying - "They're taking over - the Punks are taking over." Fucking classic!

JERRY ZMUDA

Graham Kirby then told me about this Vibrators concert where during the show the band threw vibrators into the audience. At the end of the night most of them had been used. I didn't know what a vibrator was, how you used one or anything, but it still sounded shocking.

JORDI KNOWLES

Nowadays people colour and spike their hair and no-one bats an eye-lid. And the way Angela looked then wouldn't look outrageous now. But in 1977 there was very real hatred and hostility. My sister Angela got it constantly. Shops would refuse to serve her, people would shout out at her in the street, laugh and jeer at her, threaten her. I tried to talk to her about it. "Why are you bringing all this on yourself?"

SANJEEV SRIDHARAN

Angela turns up to school all punked out - and our form teacher Mrs. Pennington flies into a rage and sends her home. The look of triumph on Angela's face, I watched her dancing along the empty playground and out the school gate.

SCHOOL DINNERS IS FOR MUGS

DERMOTT COLLINS

I thought it was about time I started seriously thinking about my future. Was I going to follow me old man into the building game? I didn't fancy it - too much like hard graft, and them building site portaloos stink to high heaven. So that's why I decided to start thieving. The big difference between the seventies and today? It was much easier to shop-lift. There was no CCTV and hardly any security, just the occasional bozo store detective. The only anti-theft devices were them crappy circular mirrors like something out of Play School.

JERRY ZMUDA

I only became Dermott's shoplifting accomplice by virtue of being with him in Woolworths when he'd steal things. When he stuffed as much as he could under his Harrington, he'd ram a kettle under my coat.

DERMOTT COLLINS

My thieving career began with porno mags. Grab a stash of them - Mayfair, Knave, Whitehouse and take them down the 40 acre waste ground and sell them for a juicy bit of profit. So you could say that at the age of 13 I was running a very successful porn empire.

JERRY ZMUDA

The 40 acre waste ground was like the wild west - with no teachers around it was lawless. It was there that Dermott would sell the porno mags we'd stolen. Then we'd head down the Wimpy and spend our profits on a slap up meal.

DERMOTT COLLINS

Best feeling in the world for a kid - a wedge in yer sky-rocket and you're down the Wimpy ordering the most expensive stuff on the menu. I told Jerry – "school dinners is for mugs."

JERRY ZMUDA

Dermott was lording it up, splashing out on an extra large cheese burger with extra chips, and it seemed as though he had discovered his true calling - shop-lifting.

FELTHAM MADE ME   51

PETER WYATT

> I knew Dermott and Jerry were nicking stuff. I thought they were stupid, I tried telling them to use their energies for something useful. But what can you do? I wasn't their old man.

DERMOTT COLLINS

> As my operation was getting bigger, I needed a place to stash my loot. I couldn't do it at home, what with sharing a bedroom with Ryan. So I said to Jerry - "I'll have to stash the pornos round yours."

JERRY ZMUDA

> I was naturally not keen on this at all, but I got rail-roaded. We had to choose a time when Mother wasn't around. Mother still didn't know that Dermott had gone to Feltham and I was still associating with him. She still thought I was friends with the fictional Jonathan Bagg. So we chose one Saturday afternoon when Mother had gone shopping.

DERMOTT COLLINS

> So we're in Jerry's bedroom with a massive pile of freshly nicked porno mags - Mayfair, Knave, Fiesta, Whitehouse. There's nothing like that plastic coated smell of freshly nicked porno mags. Jerry says there's a box under the bed where he keeps his old toys. Inside there's a whole stack of Rupert Bear annuals.

JERRY ZMUDA

> What's so wrong with that? Besides I don't get them anymore.

DERMOTT COLLINS

> Except there was the Rupert Bear annual for 1977. The big secret was out - Jerry still gets a Rupert Bear annual.

JERRY ZMUDA

> I was still only twelve, OK thirteen - what's wrong with your parents buying you a Rupert Bear annual for Christmas? Anyway we were arguing about Rupert Bear, when we heard the front door slam.

Dermott instantly stuffs the porno mags into the box and slides it under the bed. Then we heard the thud-thud-thud as Mum walks up the stairs.

DERMOTT COLLINS

I said to Jerry – "Just take it easy. I'm your friend Jonathan Bagg, she hasn't laid eyes on me for at least two years, she won't recognize me as Dermott."
"You sure? You sure?" Jerry was getting all jittery.
"Trust me," I said. The door swings open.
"Who's This?"
"Good Morning Mrs. Zmuda," I said playing it ultra-smooth, "I'm Jerry's friend - Jonathan Bagg."

NATALIE ZMUDA

Did he think I was born yesterday? I'd recognize that evil smirk anywhere. I was still smarting over him using my phone - MY PHONE - to make crank phone calls.
So this meant that whenever Jerry was telling me he was with Jonathan - he was actually with Dermott. This was beyond betrayal.

JERRY ZMUDA

But worse was to come. After Dermott had gone, there was me getting ready for my night alone with this collection of stolen porno mags. I grabbed a copy of Mayfair because I liked the pouting brunette on the cover. My hands shook with tremulous expectancy as I opened up the centre pages, to reveal her in all her full-length leggy naked glory. That's when Mum barged in. From that she went on a top to bottom search of my room and so found the very large stash of porno mags sharing space with Rupert and his chums. Mayfair was bad enough, but The Whitehouse which was real hard core was extremely shocking for Mother. I was grounded for a month.
It got me thinking about what Sanjeev was saying. There was me trying to get on - reading books, doing the Inter-Divisional quiz, possibly representing the school, and there was Dermott shop-lifting and getting me deep into trouble.

DERMOTT COLLINS

So Jerry's Mum turfed all my hard-stolen merchandise in the dustbin. I sneaked round the dustbins at midnight to try and find them - but she'd burnt them all - every last one. Now with Jerry grounded, I was going nicking on me Jack. Then going down to the 40 acre to sell them off. That's where I got turned over by some fourth years. They just came up to me, punched me on the hooter and swiped all me mags, then they went through all me pockets and took all me money.

And I thought nicking was going to be easy money. Graham Kirby told me that selling stolen gear down the 40 acre was small time - I should go and see Cobra. He could be my fence, and give me protection, but only if I nicked propah gear.

PETER WYATT

Around this time the Unholy Trinity boys were starting to split - we were just into different things. Dermott was thieving, Jerry was grounded and reading his books, and I was still pining for Sarah Baxter. So why didn't I just ask her out? Because I had to do something to grab her attention, I had to win her heart. I couldn't just ask her out straight out the blue can I? Something had to happen. But I had to make it happen.

SARAH BAXTER

When punk happened I just ignored it. People now on the telly always go on about 1977 being the year of punk, but they forget about all the great disco and soul music that was around at the time. That's what most decent people were into. The film of the year was *Saturday Night Fever* and the record of the summer was Donna Summer's *I Feel Love*. Punk was just for the nutters.

PETER WYATT

I like all music - well OK not all, but most of it. I loved the energy of punk and related to the anger, but I loved the romance of soul music. I mean you can hardly get a girl in the mood by playing her *Bodies* by the Sex Pistols can you?

DERMOTT COLLINS

Ryan was a bastard of a brother to me. The only good thing he did for me was introduce me to the Ramones - and lend me his guitar. Oh - and bring Angela Knowles into my bedroom.

JERRY ZMUDA

So what turned me from being a nervous kid, scared of punk, to someone who, not only embraced it, but lived for it? Well they're not regarded as a cool band now - but it was The Stranglers that did it for me. I saw them do *No More Heroes* on Top of The Tops - coming out of a blast of smoke. They were ace, and I was gripped. No videos in those days, the only way I could relive the excitement was to talk about it. So I phoned up Dermott straight afterwards and he shared my enthusiasm. I felt closer to him again.

PETER WYATT

It was the music scene that brought the Unholy Trinity back together.

JOHN PEEL & GOOD TIMES

PETER WYATT

I went with this girl to see *Saturday Night Fever* at Staines cinema. After the film I took her round the back of the building - it was there where I lost my virginity. It was hardly romantic - but it was a start. I did my best to make sure Sarah didn't find out - but you know how girls talk.

SARAH BAXTER

This may sound really big-headed, but I knew Peter fancied me. Those soppy sheep-dog eyes that always lingered on me whenever I said anything in class. He seemed very nice, but a bit too shy. Girls don't like that - at least I don't. Then I'd heard he'd taken Kim Fricker to the pictures to see *Saturday Night Fever*. I'd seen it three times already, but why didn't he ask me?

PETER WYATT

Looking back on it now, I can't blame her at all. But when Mum started seeing men, it really wound me up. It made me want to hit people. We had moved out of Bedfont to some pokey flat in Egmont Court, Walton on Thames, and there was me left all alone. So that's when I started inviting Dermott and Jerry over. We'd have our late night chatting sessions - listening to John Peel. We used to tape the show and when it finished at midnight, we'd play it back again. Good Times.

JERRY ZMUDA

It's the simplest things that give the most pleasure. What I wouldn't give today, to be back round Peter's flat in Egmont Court - orange terrylene curtains, hollow imitation wood doors, sweating plastic coated armchairs that made embarrassing noises whenever you moved. But it was sat right there where I was at my happiest - chatting endlessly and listening to John Peel. No drinking or smoking - just music and conversation.

DERMOTT COLLINS

Thought John Peel was boring, but Jerry and Peter worshipped him. I kept saying - "Stop playing all this shit - play The Ramones!"

PETER WYATT

But our favourite band was The Jam - the announcement of a new single or album - was a major event for us. We'd dash down Record Scene, the day it came out and get Grant to play it for us over and over again.

JERRY'S LIFE ON A KNIFE EDGE

JERRY ZMUDA

Before I knew where I was, I found myself back shoplifting with Dermott. But I was terrified of getting caught, so I took a little pen knife with me, one of those ones where you had to stick your thumb nail in to open it. Just in case a shop owner caught us, and I could fight my way out.

DERMOTT COLLINS

With Jerry back nicking with me, I thought I'd start him off on the easy stuff, like the Asian shop-keeper down by the Mount. It's all way too shakey and the geezer tugs us with a sports bag full of Peak Freans and Abbey Crunch. He's slapping us around the mush. CRACK! saying - "I call the police!" CRACK! The wife squealing in the back ground.

JERRY ZMUDA

When the shop-keeper mentioned the police it set my internal alarm bell off. I reached towards the pen knife in my back pocket. I was getting ready to pull it out, as he kept slapping both of us hard round the face.

DERMOTT COLLINS

As the shop-keeper was slapping us, I saw Jerry reaching into his back pocket and trying to get his blade out. I thought - don't do it. You'll wind us up in Borstal.

JERRY ZMUDA

My life was literally on a knife edge. A few seconds later I would have opened out the blade and the headlines would have been - WHATEVER NEXT? 14 YEAR OLD PULLS KNIFE ON ASIAN SHOP-KEEPER. I would have ended up well truly on the road to sodomy and crime. But thankfully the man softened and said - "Never come to this shop again." He opened the door and we gratefully slipped out.

SANJEEV SRIDHARAN

Dad had a nightmare running his shop. Being near the school he got all the school kids trying to thieve. And the abuse he got - some of the kids when they got caught would act as if it was their right to steal from him because they were British-born and he wasn't. It was hell.

JERRY ZMUDA

When I found out that the man I nearly pulled a knife on was Sanjeev's Dad - I felt sick. What do I do? In desperate need for redemption I told Sanjeev everything - he laughed it off, but he was never the same with me afterwards.

COBRA - THE LOCAL FAGIN

JERRY ZMUDA

I was about to go to Frogspawn's TD class when Dermott grabs hold of me and says - "Come on let's go see Cobra." So he takes me to this neglected semi-detached over in Hanworth, there's piles of stuff stacked up everywhere, presumably stolen, and there's Cobra out in the yard playing with his cross-bow. It's immediately clear why he's called Cobra, when you see the large snake tattoo on his neck. He's got a suedehead haircut - dressed in Fred Perry and bleached jeans. The tattoo on his fore-arm said Borstal Boy. He's the sort of lad I would cross the road to avoid, and here I was in his garden with him holding a cross-bow.

DERMOTT COLLINS

Used to go round and see Cob when I was bunking school. Cobra was the real thing. Been to borstal - the one that made Feltham famous. Mad and fearless - I wanted to be like him. He had this cross-bow which he kept shooting out in his garden. Swears he was Robin Hood in a previous life.

PETER WYATT

Rumour has it that Cobra had wanked off his dog. I mean it could all be lies - but just being the sort of bloke who had those sort of rumours about him was a signal to steer clear. I mean you never heard any rumours about me wanking off a dog? Have you?

JERRY ZMUDA

Cobra is playing William Tell in the back yard. Placing the apple on the head of a large yellow teddy bear. Right away I could sense his antipathy towards me. He takes the apple off the head of the bear and with a fire blazing in his eye gives it to me.
"There you are - put that on your head."
"No way."
"Come yer poof!"
I looked at the bear and his head is covered in punctures and holes.
"I did them on purpose, he was pissing me off - staring at me all the time."
I said – "That doesn't exactly inspire me with confidence."
Cobra turns to Dermott, mimicking me. "Your friend talks like a ponse! And he looks like a ponse - SO HE MUST BE A PONSE! Get him out of here."
Frogspawn's stuffy TD class was a joy compared to this, I couldn't get out of there quickly enough.

DERMOTT COLLINS

Cob was just winding Jerry up, and Jerry being the highly strung stiff type took it all the wrong way. Cobra's a sweet and funny guy. Heart of Gold when you're one of his mates - or "shaking with the snake" as he says. Cobra calls me over one day, he said he wanted a catch-phrase something that people would always connect with him. We spent hours knocking ideas around until eventually we nailed it - YOU CUNT! DO YOU WANT A SLAPPING?

JERRY ZMUDA

So Cobra became Dermott's fence, the local Fagin, buying up the stuff he stole from the shops. But I stayed well away, I told Peter about my concerns, that I was scared we were losing Dermott to the criminal classes.

PETER WYATT

I agreed with Jerry. Dermott was going too far with his shop-lifting. Neither of us wanted him to end up like Cobra - a full-time criminal and a dodgy character, with rumours about him wanking off dogs. So we sat him down round mine and had words.

DERMOTT COLLINS

When Peter sat me down - with Jerry, and Peter's wearing this 'I'm-a-parent-and-I'm-concerned-face' my first reaction was - get the fuck out, don't tell me how to live my life. But then I realized Peter really cares. I was quite taken by that. In the end I told them I would cut down my shop-lifting - keep it to essentials, and not do anything too risky.

JERRY ZMUDA

Dermott lied to us, plain and simple. We sat him down round Peter's, he promised us he wouldn't go around with Cobra again, and he would stop stealing.

PETER WYATT

One serious chat was never going to solve this. We had to keep an eye on him and make our feelings known.

AT HOME WITH ANGELA KNOWLES

DERMOTT COLLINS

Hate to admit it, but I was starting to get into them fortnightly shrink sessions. The lady was actually listening. But every time she cracked on at me to talk about me Mum, I would make a joke or change the subject. But she did start me thinking about what I was doing to other people. Anyway, I leave the session one afternoon, and I get a right turn when I see punky Angela Knowles waiting outside for me.

JORDI KNOWLES

Angela was seldom coming home these days, just to change her clothes, raid the fridge before Father came home. I had virtually disowned her at this point. I just didn't want to talk to her.

DERMOTT COLLINS

She said - "I know you've been listening in on my sessions - so I thought I'd listen in on yours." We were walking down the lane, talking about our shrink experience and she says to me - "Let me take you to the house."

JORDI KNOWLES

Angela had found this abandoned house, on one of the lanes off by the industrial estate. It was all boarded up but she had broken her way in. She took me there once and told me that she was going to make her home there. It freaked me out.

DERMOTT COLLINS

Angela was talking about how, because she's a punk, everybody thinks she spits. But she was saying - "Spitting's disgusting - I've never spat in my life." This girl was super-funny, taking the piss out the way people dressed, taking the piss out of herself. She talked about leaving Feltham School in a blaze of glory.

We came to this house at the end of this real spooky road, no-one about. It's all boarded up, she takes me round the back and lifts up one of the pieces of wood and we go inside. The place was bare, no furniture, no running water, no electricity. But what really mattered was that we had the whole place to ourselves.

Then we started talking. I mean REALLY talking. For the last four months the shrink had been trying to get me to open up about not having a mother. But with Angela it all came gushing out. I told her how horrible it felt to be sharing a room with an older brother who still blames me for losing his Mum. And I felt guilty. I always, always, always felt guilty for being alive instead of the Mother I never met. I even told her how horrible a strain it was trying to be funny all the time. She listened and then she told me that I had met my Mother - when I was in her womb - and that connection lasts forever - and that my mother doesn't blame me for anything. She hugged me. I just melted in her soft warm arms, me and her alone in that empty house. Our house.

Chapter 3
More Feltham School
Let's Go Botley Down Record Scene

LET'S GO BOTLEY DOWN RECORD SCENE

PETER WYATT

In Sunbury precinct there was this shop called RECORD SCENE and to us it was a temple. A temple to the music we loved - all that was good and exciting in life. Next to the counter was a mural display of colourful seven inch picture sleeves - The Jam, The Clash, The Sex Pistols, Blondie, The Buzzcocks, Generation X. I got a buzz just by hanging out there flicking through the records, watching the people passing in and out, the staff playing all the new releases.

JERRY ZMUDA

You walked past the dreary old Building Society, a grimy looking Sandwich Bar and there it was – a dirty luminous sign that read RECORD SCENE in a cheesy seventies typeface. It didn't look much from the outside, but inside it was an Aladdin's Cave. Music was always playing, usually Punk or New Wave, and on the wall was all the singles on display. But it was flicking through the album racks where I learnt about David Bowie, Iggy Pop and Lou Reed, pouring over every detail of the artwork, memorizing the track listings. I learnt more hanging out in Record Scene after school than I ever did in class.

GRANT WILLIAMS (Record Scene manager)

These three snotty nosed kids used come in all the time, just looking at the records, always asking me to put this or that album on. Hardly ever bought anything. I suspected the mouthy one was thieving.

JERRY ZMUDA

That's where we spoke to Carl Young for the first time. Of course we all knew him by his nickname Botley, which is a reference to the local lunatic asylum Botley Park. He had this really severe pudding bowl haircut that resembled a German helmet, so Dermott greeted him with an Achtung! and a Nazi salute, and Carl actually seemed flattered and pleased.

DERMOTT COLLINS

He came bounding up to us, and he showed us this record he'd just bought *No More Heroes* by The Stranglers.

"Mum thinks I've bought Mike Oldfield," he says.

"You're secret's safe with us."

Then he goes - "I'd like to get that Blondie next," and I said -

"Don't we all?" Sweet guy, but a bit simple.

PETER WYATT

Was Botley, I mean Carl simple or retarded? No, when you got talking to him he was quite together - amazing at remembering facts. He just came over as a bit odd. He used to stand around in the playground on his todd, in his clarkes commandos wearing a Puffin Book-club badge and reading a ladybird book on Ancient Egypt. Of course at Feltham School that was a red rag for a piss-taking.

JERRY ZMUDA

Botley had taken a shine to us. Whenever we saw him at school, he would dash over to us and talk about some new band he'd read about in Sounds or heard on John Peel.

DERMOTT COLLINS

I'd ask him – "Why do they call you Botley?"

"Because I'm Botley." Was his answer. And he'd pull his Botley face. We were talking about girls and I was arguing with Peter that Ice-blond Angela Knowles was easily in the same class as Sarah Baxter. Then Botley cuts in - "No they're not in the same class. Sarah Baxter is in third year, class 3D, and Sharon Knowles is a fifth year class 5E." We pissed ourselves.

JERRY ZMUDA

We got very protective over our friend Botley - enjoying our animated discussions on whether The Jam were better than Sham 69 - or whether Debbie Harry was more attractive than the girl who presented Blue Peter. We took him under our wing and Peter made sure that no-one ever picked on Botley when he was around.

WHEN ANGELA ATTACKED THE TEACHERS

PETER WYATT

Our parents would say – "where were you when JFK was assassinated?" At Feltham School it was – "where were you when you heard about Angela Knowles attacking two teachers?" It set tongues wagging faster than rattlesnake tails. She had really gone over the edge this time.

SANJEEV SRIDHARAN

I was there, I was actually there, and I still can't quite believe it. Angela was always a volcano waiting to blow, and when she finally did it was like the finale of *Taxi Driver* – but with laughs.

Mrs. Pennington was standing over her – accusing her, Angela stood up and just casually tipped her glasses off, then Angela slapped her across the face. It was pretty mild really. But Mrs. Pennington was yelping "STOP THAT! STOP IT!" Then Pennigton scrambled out of the class with her glasses still on the floor. Moments later in walked Mr. Dunne the metal work teacher – he's well over six foot - about 15 stone. As he opens the door, Angela leaps over and slams the door on him – so he's wedged in the door yelping in pain.

MR. DUNNE

I don't turn up to work to have my nuts jammed in a door. After that Angela Knowles incident I went straight to the Head, demanding danger money.

SANJEEV SRIDHARAN

Mr. Dunne eventually manages to push the door open, then Angela hurls a chair at him and she climbs out the window and jumps. Thankfully for Angela it was just one floor up. And so ended Angela's education at Feltham School. The rest of the class just looked on, we didn't laugh, didn't intervene, just stared with our mouths hanging open. It wasn't until about fifteen minutes later that it sunk in what we'd seen – and then we couldn't stop laughing.

DERMOTT COLLINS

Soon as I heard about it, I dashed over to the derelict house, and there she was. She knew she was going to get expelled and she was real upset - but only because of upsetting her Mum. It was now her time to open up to me. She told me that she hated her father but he had backed off the last few years because she had been blackmailing him - over what I don't know. I was holding her in my arms. I thought - this is my chance to kiss her.

JORDI KNOWLES
The headmaster came round with a police officer demanding to know where Angela was. I feel like a bastard now but I told them about the house. I was 13 - I thought the authorities knew best, and maybe they would take her away for a bit, give her some treatment and when she came back, I'd have my normal funny sister back.

DERMOTT COLLINS
I went home to get a sleeping bag, so we could sleep in the house together. So we're snuggled up together when we hear this cracking sound outside. It's a police car radio. Me and Angela scramble up into the attic and hide in the blackness as the old bill look round. After they'd gone I say – "This is no good - let's go stay at mine."

FRANK COLLINS (Dermott's Dad)
I was more than happy to find a room for Angela at the inn. Met her before when Ryan had brought her home, nice girl, though a strange taste in make-up. It was Ryan that over-reacted.

DERMOTT COLLINS
Angela was having a bath when Ryan came back - pissed from the pub as usual. I was talking to her through the door, Ryan recognized her voice and went spastic with rage. He started trying to punch the door through - and then punching me - accusing me of moving in on his bird. Thankfully Dad and Connor - me eldest - stepped in.

FRANK COLLINS
Angela got dressed and said she'd leave, and apologized for the trouble she caused. I said – "Not a bit of it - you need somewhere to stay - you could stay right here and Ryan can go and fuck himself." And Ryan did, he went off into the night - God knows where.

DERMOTT COLLINS

So she slept in the bed opposite me - where Ryan usually slept. It were strange, I woke up in the middle of the night and looked over at her - she seemed all peaceful. But when I next woke up in the morning - she'd gone. On the bed was a piece of note paper and written in pencil, it said –

To Dermott

You and your father have both been so wonderfully kind to me, I really appreciate it. You are very good friend. Luv Angela

I've kept that scrap of paper to this day.

JERRY ZMUDA

So Angela got expelled. A landmark for Feltham School - because Feltham School never expelled anybody, it took in the kids who got expelled from other schools.

Her mother apparently was trying to get her accepted into another school, so she could at least sit her exams. But nobody would take her. I expect they thought, if she's too bad for Feltham School - she must be really bad.

DERMOTT COLLINS

I bunked off school and met her down the house. We talked about all sorts of crazy stuff. We were going to set up home here, I'd steal food and stuff, and bit by bit we'd build ourselves a new home. I was well excited.

FRANK COLLINS

Ryan came back the next day - I thought he would have sobered up and seen some sense but no, we was still intent on causing mayhem. I got my mate to see him off.

DERMOTT COLLINS

The following morning I get to the house, climb in through the back but something's not right - there's paint over the walls, and Evostick tubes on the deck, and in the main room there's these greasy herberts, boot boys sprawled out all over the place, obviously sleeping off a glue binge. "Angela," I call out - but she's not there.

I then went to her parent's house - not there. I was out of my mind with worry. So later that day I went back to the old house and got an even bigger shock. The house is now a blacked out charred ruin. Those fucking Glue-Sniffers, I thought. But where the fuck was Angela?

PETER WYATT

Dermott had jumped to the conclusion that those boot boys had burnt the house down. But the kids' story was that they had seen Angela set fire to the house. Apparently she had returned to the house, found them all in her space sparked out, so she got some lighter fuel and set fire to the curtains. One of the kids would have died if it hadn't of been for the Fire Brigade. This was serious.
The finger was pointing at Angela - and she had gone on the run.

JORDI KNOWLES

Before the house burnt down, the police just wanted to tell Angela off for assault - striking two teachers. Now she was wanted for arson and attempted murder. She had really done it this time.

DERMOTT COLLINS

I wanted to believe she was innocent, I wanted to believe she was going to get in touch. I couldn't talk to Jerry about all this - what does he know about girls? Peter tried to be comforting but there wasn't a lot he could do. Angela was gone and I was in pieces.

SMIKE AND IN THE CROWD

JERRY ZMUDA

Smike, real name - God I can't remember - was the first kid I knew who smoked pot. He had long hair and was a bit of a hippy, but that didn't bother me at all. I remember going round his house and playing *In the Crowd* off *All Mod Cons* over and over again. He really liked the bit where it went psychedelic at the end.

DERMOTT COLLINS

I loved Smike - long hair - round face – always, always smiling.
It was round Smike's that I ate puff for the first time. A big lump it was. It was intense, I don't know why people don't eat puff more often. He was playing that record *In The Crowd* for the thousandth time, and I could see the music - actually see it - in a cartoon over my

head, the bass swirling round and drum clipping just above it. Smike's house was a great hang-out - while it lasted.

PETER WYATT

My only problem with Smike was that he was always trying to get us into Genesis. He'd put the album on, and rave about their drummer, a guy called Phil Collins, who was going to be a big influence on Smike in later life.

JERRY ZMUDA

I was round Smike's listening to records - stoned. Then I got seized by this paranoia. I jumped up and shouted "I'm supposed to be revising." Everyone started laughing and eventually so did I. It was another St. Petersburg moment.

PETER WYATT

Smike had very liberal parents, they would let him have all his friends round, smoking and hanging about all hours of the day, thinking it's better to have them stay in the house and do it where they're safe, rather than do it in the 40 acre or Hounslow Bus Garage. But the parents soon gave that policy a complete U-turn after a month or two of Dermott and Jerry coming round.

DERMOTT COLLINS

Smike's Dad was into all sorts of music, which he tried to open us up to. "Consider this to be a musical Education," he used to say to us, as he put another boring album on. He played us an album of folk music from Persia and he started having a smoke. He goes to the toilet and I thought fuck this - so I turn the record from 33 rpm to 45 rpm. He comes back and the record's whizzing around like Pinky and Perky. He says - "Listen to that playing! There's more energy there, than a hundred of your new wave bands."

PETER WYATT

I think the last straw was when Dermott put fertilizer in his finest Moroccan.

DERMOTT COLLINS

No sense of humour that geezer.

NEW TERM STARTS HERE

NATALIE ZMUDA (Jerry's mother)
> With Jerry starting his fifth year at Feltham, I told him – "This is your last chance." I urged him to knuckle down and do the best he could at his 'O' levels, and to stay on and do his 'A' levels. It was time now to seriously think about his future, stop wasting time. **And to stay away from Dermott.**

JERRY ZMUDA
> Feltham School was not a high-achieving school academically. If you left school with one 'O' level you get nicknamed 'the professor'. But Mum was right, I figured I may as well do the best I could at school.

NATALIE ZMUDA
> His sister Magdalena set a good example. She was just starting her degree in English at Kings College. I told her to talk to Jerry and show him what life could be like if he furthered his education.

SARAH BAXTER
> As I started my fifth year at Feltham I looked around. I lived in a suburban semi-detached, Dad imported fruit and veg and worked down Covent Garden - a simple life. I decided to improve my surroundings. To me, that is what disco, soul jazz-funk call what you like, was all about, adding a bit of colour and life to the world. And that's what I was going to do with my life. What was I good at? What did I want to get into? Clothes making. Textile design.

GRANT WILLIAMS
> One of the snotty-nosed kids came to see me, asking me if I had any jobs going at Record Scene for when he left school. He was trying to be all charming and self-effacing saying – "I hang out here all the time I might as well get paid doing it." I said I'd make a note of his name and keep it on file. Yeah right - file it in the bin.

PETER WYATT

Now of course I know that when people say they are keeping your name on file, they really mean - fuck off, we're never going to call you. But at Record Scene I went away thinking I really had a chance.

BUNKING OFF SCHOOL TO SEE THE JAM

JERRY ZMUDA

I picked up the NME and yelped with excitement - the Jam were bringing out a new LP in November and it was called *Setting Sons*. I was reading those track listings over and over again - in my feverish anticipation I was making up my own songs and lyrics based on the titles – 'there's a Girl on the Phone - there's a Girl on the Phone - give the dog a bone - there's a girl on the phone.'

DERMOTT COLLINS

Friday 23rd. November 1979. A date tattooed on my brain for all time.

PETER WYATT

I was pissed off with Mum hardly ever being at home, pissed off with West Ham struggling in the league and really frustrated that Sarah Baxter was still not taking any notice of me. So I'm watching Top of the Tops on me todd and The Jam came on with *Eton Rifles*. They'd somehow managed to get in the Top 3 for the first time ever. But Weller didn't seem too happy about it, so pissed off and angry - just how I felt. I remembered reading they were playing in Southampton the next day.

JERRY ZMUDA

So I turn up to school this wet and drizzly morning, and outside Peter is waiting for us. In his hand was last week's NME - he showed me it. The Jam are playing the Southampton Gaumont today. School is off.

PETER WYATT

No fucking debate, we were going down to Southampton that day to see The Jam.

JERRY ZMUDA

But I didn't have any money - and besides how are we going to get there? Peter said -

PETER WYATT

Fuck money! Where there's a will - there's a way.

DERMOTT COLLINS

It was much easier to bunk the trains in them days. But where the fuck is Southampton?

JERRY ZMUDA

I was still recovering from the newsagent/pen knife let off, I gave my word to God that I'll never do anything bad ever again, and here I was bunking the train all the way to Southampton.
But Dermott and Peter weren't being discreet. They were all excited, singing Jam songs at the top of their lungs - shouting at suited commuters on the platforms. Calling school girls over - "School's off! Come with us to see The Jam." The train journey seemed to go on forever. I thought to myself "We are going to get caught. We are not going to see the Jam. We are going to get arrested and spend the night in a police cell."

PETER WYATT

We were so fucking excited to be going to see The Jam. After bunking the train journey all the way - it didn't occur to us we wouldn't get in to see our favourite band today. We jumped over the barrier at Southampton and went up to the nearest geezer – "Excuse mate - where's the Gaumont?"

DERMOTT COLLINS

Mid-afternoon, we get directed towards this large building. Like a massive bingo hall. I could hear this noise from the outside - it was *Thick As Theives*. We walked round the side, and the door was open - so we whizzed in saying hullo to the roadie. To our amazement he said hullo back.

FELTHAM MADE ME   71

JERRY ZMUDA

We walked into the auditorium it was empty, AND THERE THEY WERE ON STAGE. All three of them - playing a song. After seeing them on Top of the Tops and looking at their pictures in the papers it was a real thrill seeing them in real life. They seemed so short.

DERMOTT COLLINS

I always preferred the Ramones, but it was ace to see them on stage, going through their set. But where was everyone else? I thought the Jam were popular.

PETER WYATT

"It's a sound-check you mong," I explained to Dermott. They're making sure everything sounds OK before everyone turns up.

JERRY ZMUDA

I was expecting any moment someone to come up to us and say 'go on - get out'. I would have taken the sound-check - that was exciting enough. If we couldn't get into the actual concert I still would have gone home happy.

PETER WYATT

We sat and watched the band by the mixing desk – gob-smacked. We felt real privileged to be there. A Friday afternoon spent watching The Jam doing a sound-check beats Frogspawn's dreary TD class hands down.
There were some other kids hanging about, wearing parkas and covered in badges, we said hallo. After Paul, Bruce and Rick finished, they walked off stage - but wait for this - RICK BUCKLER GAVE US A WAVE.

DERMOTT COLLINS

Then this big long-haired geezer in a Rockpile Tour T-shirt came up to us. I was about to start taking the piss when he said "You got tickets for tonight?" We acted all cagey - he said "It's sold out - but if you hide in the toilets until doors open - you can stay to see the band." Cheers for the tip.

JERRY ZMUDA

So this saint of a roadie let us go outside and get ourselves some chips, and then he let us back in, so the three of us could hide in the toilet and wait for the doors to open. But Dermott would not - could not - shut up. Nightmare!

PETER WYATT

Dermott started shouting out the window, I pulled him back and told him to shut up! Then we got joined in the toilet by this young geezer in a flying jacket. He was also on the bunk like us, he didn't crack a smile once.

JERRY ZMUDA

First thing he says to us is "How many times - have you seen them?" I say - that soundcheck was our first time. "Twenty three times," he says puffing his chest out. I was mightily impressed.

PETER WYATT

Dermott said – "You must think they're quite good then," but he just carried on talking. Telling us that The Jam peaked last year and all the kiddy winks getting into them was ruining it - overlooking that he was talking to three fifteen year olds bunking off school.

DERMOTT COLLINS

He was called Lionel. LIONEL! From Bracknell. If my name was Lionel and I came from Bracknell I wouldn't give it the big 'un.

JERRY ZMUDA

It eventually got dark, and this young guy walks in - young like us. "Excuse mate - have they opened the doors yet?" The kid nodded. We had done it!

DERMOTT COLLINS

I always got a thrill from thieving - but this was the best one yet - it was like the Great Escape, and I couldn't stop myself from singing.

PETER WYATT

As the place filled up, we went straight past the bar and rushed up to the front. Who wants to drink when you're about to see The Jam?

We watched The Vapors, dodgy haircuts but they were pretty good, but when they finished you could feel the expectancy fill the air. My ticker was doing a jig.

JERRY ZMUDA

We were getting squashed at the front, my rib-cage felt like it was going to burst. But there was no chance I was going to move. The Jam are going to be on stage any minute!

DERMOTT COLLINS

Then this old geezer with a teddy boy quiff came on stage. I thought he was going to tell some jokes - you know warm the crowd up. Then he howls into mic –
"Put your hands together - for the best fucking band in the world - The Jam."
Then everything went Mental.

JERRY ZMUDA

Yes the soundcheck was amazing - but this was something else. With thousands of other fans. The first earth-shattering chord was hit and all of a sudden you're caught up in wave of people bobbing up and down. I was wearing these cheap slip-on shoes - halfway through the set they slipped off.

DERMOTT COLLINS

It all got too much for Jerry. It was like a mad spirit got hold of him. I mean, I'm supposed to be the crazy one.
He fell over trying to out-pogo everyone else. He accidentally got hit in the face, his nose was bleeding - he didn't care. But then he got blood over this kid's mohair suit. It would have got nasty if Peter hadn't stepped in.

JERRY ZMUDA

They played pretty much most of the new album, thankfully I knew most of the words by then. But they also played a lot off *All Mod Cons*. *Tube Station* was absolutely stunning.

PETER WYATT

Our adventures didn't end with the gig. Outside we had to run the gauntlet of NF boneheads hanging around, ready to clump anybody who dressed a bit like a Mod. What's wrong with these fucking people?

JERRY ZMUDA

I lost my shoes but I was grateful to be scruffy when we got outside and it all kicked off. In amongst all the broken glass, blood and melee we somehow managed to find the station in a strange town.

PETER WYATT

We were waiting for the train home, tired and drained. We lay on the bench but we couldn't sleep - playing over and over in our heads what we had just witnessed. Then this gang of skinheads walk onto the next platform.

JERRY ZMUDA

They were Eastleigh Skinheads. I assumed they were Eastleigh because they were chanting EASTLEIGH SKINS. Then they started the Sieg Heiling. These were the kids that attacked our fellow Jam fans. I felt a snap of anger and I shout across at them – "Shut Up!" As I felt the words leave my lips I had the instant wish to call them back. Too late! Their heads all bolted round to face us.

DERMOTT COLLINS

A steam roller of a dozen bald heads and two dozen DMs are coming straight at us.

PETER WYATT

There was nothing else for it. We ran like bastards - crossing the tracks - I shouted to the others – "Don't step on the live rail!" We crossed another platform, then another track, then we ran onto a stationary train.

JERRY ZMUDA

This was difficult for me running in my socks. Thank god they were thick towling ones. But that was cast far from my mind as I just sprinted as fast as I could. The skinheads are baying for our blood, running after us over the tracks. As we got onto the train, my thoughts were - this is a bad move, we'll be ambushed. But Peter was leading the way.

PETER WYATT

Inside the train, we hid inside the guard's cabin, crushed up really small in the dark.

JERRY ZMUDA

I heard the skinheads get in the train shouting as they got nearer, a truly ugly sound. Getting louder, getting nearer.

DERMOTT COLLINS

Don't mind telling you. Even with Saint Peter to protect us I was fucking bricking it.

JERRY ZMUDA

To our relief the skinheads howls faded in the distance. Eventually the train lights came on and Peter poked his head outside. Where had the skinheads gone?

PETER WYATT

The train was getting ready to move. The skinheads meanwhile were running up the platform looking for us in all the windows. I shout to the others "Hide in the toilets!" We did it just in the nick.

JERRY ZMUDA

As the train engine spluttered into the life, I heave a huge sigh of relief, but it's not over yet. I could hear the heart-wrenching sound of the skinheads yelling, still searching for us. They will see us as we pass them on the train.

PETER WYATT

The train starts moving, the skinheads are on the platform. The train picks up speed. I open the train door. I splatter one of the skinheads with it as the train goes past. "Sieg Heil on that - you cunt!"

JERRY ZMUDA

Another sickening sound – this time the crunch as the skinhead collided against the open door.

DERMOTT COLLINS

The skinhead's sparked out on the deck. Dead we hope. The other skinheads chase after us, we are about to start laughing as the train leaves the platform.

JERRY ZMUDA

But then the train brakes suddenly. The guard must have pulled the emergency stop. The skinheads are now back on the train.

PETER WYATT

So we abandon the train and we run up the track, panting furiously.

JERRY ZMUDA

I had no shoes, my feet were stinging with pain but still I ran along the railway track and into the darkness of the night. My life depended on it.

PETER WYATT

I shouted – "If we stay on the track we know where the live rail is, run in a straight line." Jerry can't run anymore and he turns left and climbs over a wall. We have to follow him. We scamper into a bus shelter and squeeze in there for what seemed like a very long time. After more than an hour we walk back to the station.
I told the others – "Pretend we are different geezers from the ones that ran away." How we would do that, I don't know. But in any case by the time we got there, the skinheads had gone, but so too had our last train. We ended up having to get one of them milk trains at well after midnight.

DERMOTT COLLINS

After Southampton I felt invincible.

JERRY ZMUDA

I finally got home at 6 a.m. - no shoes, painful blisters on the soles of my feet, caked blood down my school shirt, ripped jacket. My mother looked at me horrified - " My god what on earth has happened to you?"

"Mum I've just had the best day of my life."

PETER WYATT

Of course The Jam played three nights at The Rainbow three weeks later. Much easier to get to, but not nearly as much of an adventure.

BURNING TANK-TOPS

JERRY ZMUDA

Suddenly it all became clear. How could I have not seen it before? The reason why everybody took me for a jerk was nothing to do with me. It was these horrible cheap and nasty clothes my Mum gave me to wear. They were hand-me downs from the woman who lived two doors down. I was wearing, I can still hardly believe it - round collared shirts - bright stripey tank-tops, a brown safari jacket - and worst of all, 12 inch flared Delamare jeans. No wonder people took the mickey!

Could I get away with wearing this as some kind of ironic anti-fashion statement? I'd seen Pete Shelley of the Buzzcocks wear a stripey tank-top on Top of the Tops. No! I couldn never pull that off! I got myself a Saturday job in Safeway to save up and get some decent clothes - a Harrington and some loafers.

DERMOTT COLLINS

I'd got used to Jerry dressing all silly, made me laugh. But I could tell getting this whole new look was important to him. So what's the best thing a friend could do? I nicked him a pair of tassled loafers from Kingston Market.

PETER WYATT

Hush Puppies and Harringtons - that's what I wore in them days.

JERRY ZMUDA

I didn't approve of Dermott's methods - but I appreciated the sentiment. Pretty soon I had enough money for a Harrington - Peter was lending me his jeans, and so finally I went up to my Mum and said "THIS IS THE END! I am not wearing these cast-offs any longer." A few days later my Mother is packing the clothes up - she's planning to give them to my cousin.

I said "Mum No! This chain of ridicule and humiliation ends right here."

I took the clothes down to the end of the garden and burnt them. Mum thought I had gone insane, but it was the first time in my life I'd ever properly stood up to her.

RECORDS THAT CHANGED MY LIFE

SARAH BAXTER

The first time I heard it on the radio I was amazed, it sounded so different. This was like the beginning of a new type of music. I had the urge to dash out and buy the record then and there. Denise told me that I should get the full 12 inch which goes on for nearly fifteen minutes - they won't stock that at Woolworths. There was a shop in the precinct called Record Scene that stocked all the 12 inches and imports.

PETER WYATT

Hanging out down Record Scene as usual one Saturday afternoon, I couldn't believe my eyes when I see the lovely Sarah Baxter standing by the counter.

SARAH BAXTER

This over-excited sheep-dog strides over, going to me - "Sarah - I didn't know you were into this music."

PETER WYATT

She said - "I'm not. I'm here to buy *Rappers Delight* by the Sugarhill Gang." I'd forgotten that Record Scene specialized in all that as well. I was tongue-tied for a bit and then I said - "That's quite a good record." But she'd gone by then.

TERRY SOUTH

I left Feltham in the summer of '79. My biggest regret was that I never gave Dermott and his two mates the hiding they deserved. I should go back and pay them a visit.

SARAH BAXTER

At 15 I was thinking about boys, like all the time. But not the boys at school - they were just too young, too silly. I wanted to meet a sexy mature older boy at a classy disco somewhere. So me and my best friend Sam decides we are going to dress and go up to Cheeky Pete's in Richmond. Dad was always too stingy to give me much money, so we had to make our own disco clothes. What if people laughed? Oh No!

Sam comes round and we start playing all our favourite records to get us in the mood - *Contact* - Edwin Starr, *Dance, Dance, Dance* - Chic *In the Bush* - Musique. Then I start fretting, what if I meet a guy and he wants to French kiss me? I've never done it before. So we started practicing on each other. We weren't dykes or anything - we just didn't want to mess up our first French kiss with a bloke.

PETER WYATT

I'd heard of Cheeky Pete's in Richmond. It was supposed to be the pumping heart of West London's jazz funk scene. I wanted to go, but I couldn't go with the terrible twins - they'd just show me up. So I went twice on me jack, in the hope of seeing Sarah, but she never showed either time.

SARAH BAXTER

The maddest situation in the world. We go to Cheeky Petes, it's amazing, I'd never heard this music played so loud before. I get to kiss a boy I really like, Sam is snogging his friend. He's nicely dressed, smells nice and got a car and everything. We tell them to meet us in the car park, while we go to the lav and freshen up. With them waiting for us outside round the back - we do a runner! I was still only 15. I guess I wasn't ready yet.

After blanking those guys at Cheeky Pete's we thought it best not to go back there for a while, so we started hitting - wait-for-it, big fanfare - The West End. This place called Crackers. I saw this really good-looking boy - but he looks familiar. I knew he was cool because he was wearing baggy jeans with coloured piping - and he could really dance. He complimented me on my blouse. I made it myself and I was so flattered. He turns out to be Terry South, the year above me from school - he had left in June. I come all the way to Soho to meet a boy from Feltham School.

RYAN LEAVES HOME

FRANK COLLINS (Dermott's father)
>When Ryan first mentioned it to me, I laughed. Then when I realised he was serious, I begged him to change his mind.

DERMOTT COLLINS
>My brother never explained why he got so upset about me wanting to put a roof over Angela's head. I thought Angela to him was just a girl he had gone to a few gigs with - why should he care? He hardly ever spoke to me after she stayed that one night. Then a few weeks later he declares he's off to join the army.

FRANK COLLINS
>"But you're Irish!" I tell him.
>"No I'm not - I was born here."
>I was pleading with him - "They'll take the mick - literally. They'll make your life hell."
>A few days later Ryan comes home with a face like a smacked arse. "What's up my boy?" The army wouldn't take him. His record of arson at Kennington Manor among other things. What a feckin' relief.

DERMOTT COLLINS
>After the army rejected Ryan, he's still dead set of getting away from all of us, so he signs on to join the Kabutz. I was hoping for some emotional good-bye. I wanted him to tell me he didn't really blame me for Mum's death - that it was all alright, but he didn't - just off and gone. But he did leave his guitar and his record collection, and I finally got a bedroom to myself. So shouldn't complain really.

FRANK COLLINS
>Considering the tragedy that hit my family, I think we managed pretty well. My eldest – Connor, and youngest - Dermott are two very pleasant and up-standing characters. The middle child Ryan was the one that gave me all the trouble. Ryan was good soul at heart, but it didn't always show. Boy was it rough sometimes having him in the house.

THE SLUSH PUPPY MODS

JERRY ZMUDA

In my spanking new clothes I was ready to join the young faces. Announce to the world know that I'm here - young, proud and valiant. We needed a patch - some corner of the world we can hang out in and claim as our own. The place we chose was the Slush Puppy stand at Woolworths.

PETER WYATT

So we're standing around, trying to look hard, knocking back the Slush Puppies, when these five rockers in their grubby leathers - our age - walk in. I give them the glare, but that was it. But Dermott dashes over to them and says something about King Herod. I thought - what the fuck? One rocker gets angry, jabbing his finger at Dermott and Jerry. Then Dermott comes back in a bad Scottish accent - "yer noh swawping that Kung Foo ahnewal." What? Has someone spiked my slush puppy with mescalin?

DENNIS MCBRIDE (from Primary School)

Everybody grows up and moves on - but not Dermott Collins. He was still being the cheeky chappie winding everyone one up - the insecure class clown. Him and his mate Jerry had got into Mod and The Jam. Another reason for hating them. I liked real music.

DERMOTT COLLINS

Thought Dennis would laugh off the whole King Herod thing, but he were having none of it. He properly hated us, and dressing like mods didn't help. Then he threatened to get his gang of rockers onto us. Let him try it, we've got Cobra and Peter on our side.

PETER WYATT

Then this rocker said – "Get down the Cowey Sale Fair - Bank Holiday Monday." The gauntlet had been thrown down. We needed to get a firm together, and I badly needed to release some aggression.

DERMOTT COLLINS
>When I told Cobra about the fight with the rockers on Bank Holiday Monday, he rubbed his hands with glee. "Let's have ourselves a rumble."

PETER WYATT
>Dermott had roped in all sorts of people for this ruckus. He had even got that lad Pig-Sty Jake into a Fishtail Parka - telling him we were now calling ourselves the Slush Puppy Mods.

JERRY ZMUDA
>I wasn't keen on this at all. I went round Smike's and told him about it, and he said in his mellow soothing voice - "What do you care if Dennis is into Iron Maiden and Rainbow and not the Jam? That's no reason to hate him." And he was so right.
>I wasn't going to do it, I wasn't going to join the gang and fight those rockers. I was going to phone in and say I had the flu. So I phoned Peter first. He'd already set off - so I phoned Dermott.

DERMOTT COLLINS
>Cobra was round my house when he called. Jerry dribbling on about having the flu - not feeling up to the fight. I passed him over to Cobra. Cobra went all quiet - listening to him, then he said –
>"I see, I see. That's quite alright Jerry - as long as you get a note from your mother."
>Then he turned into the real Cobra - "YOU CUNT! DO YOU WANT A SLAPPING? Listen you pathetic slug, you are not chickening out on your mates...." Jerry had to turn up now.

PETER WYATT
>About a twenty of us gathered on the other side of the bridge, wearing parkas, harringtons, and flying jackets. I could see Jerry was pale, shaking. I put my arm around him and told him it was going to be alright.

JERRY ZMUDA
>I really appreciated that, I felt protected. But then Cobra came up to me and insisted I lead the charge. I could feel my insides loosening up.

PETER WYATT

> We start marching down the Cowey Sale Fair. We walk in amongst the crowd, families with their kids staring at us, they could tell trouble was a-brewing. Then we see by the dodgems a bunch of long-haired rockers, in battered leathers, long hair - there's only about a dozen of them, but they look hard, one of them was Dennis.

DERMOTT COLLINS

> I told Cobra about Dennis McBride and his Mum saying - "yer noh swawping that Kung Foo ahnewal." He found this dead funny and we all started chanting it as we squared up to the rockers. The rockers looked puzzled and I pointed to Dennis and goes - "Yeah - he knows."

DENNIS MCBRIDE

> If they thought chanting - "you're not swapping that Kung Fu annual" in a stupid Scottish accent - was going to phase me, they were right. Something in me snapped - I tore at Dermott, all my pent-up hatred making me scream at the top of my lungs.

JERRY ZMUDA

> I'll never forget it - Dermott shouted out - "NOW! Fight like Apes!" I instantly stopped being so scared.

PETER WYATT

> If you've never experienced the adrenalin rush of getting into a big ruck yourself, you're just going to think the whole thing is potty. But I swear it really is a thrill when it kicks off, yes - you're in a danger - yes - someone could bash you at any minute - but I guess that's the excitement.

DERMOTT COLLINS

> Dennis starts laying into me, Cobra pushes him off. "YOU CUNT! DO YOU WANT A SLAPPING?" At first I thought this isn't too bad - we outnumber them about two to one. We're chanting away - "yer noh swawping that Kung Foo ahnewal." People watched, women were screaming. Then the Orcs appeared on the horizon.

PETER WYATT

I heard them first. The loud roar of serious motorbikes being revved up, I look up to see a gang of about eight bikers ready to rumble up by the bridge. Within seconds the bikes are down amongst us, knocking us about with chains. Some of them get off to whack us, others swing their chains from the comfort of their bikes. I got hit right across me back. The pain went right through me like a charge of electricity and I fell to the ground.

DENNIS MCBRIDE

We had planned it this way. The mods, rude boys whatever they call themselves, would find us, the young kids, steam into us - thinking they've got us outnumbered. Then the heavy brigade would show up and lay them all to waste. And believe me, this lot knew how to fight.

JERRY ZMUDA

What was I thinking when all this was going off? I am too young to die. We started to run but I stayed close to Peter and Dermott. When I heard the first police siren I thought there was hope.

PETER WYATT

As soon as the old bill arrived the bikers split, but one had got knocked off his bike, as he ran back to his bike he got a hold of Dermott and knocked him to the ground. From under his jacket he took out this little hatchet and as Dermott lay helpless on the floor, drove it into his side.

DERMOTT COLLINS

This rocker had a dirty great big axe which he whacked straight into my stomach. I froze, went numb couldn't feel a thing, then sparked out.

JERRY ZMUDA

I ran towards Dermott, the biker got on his bike and rode off. As more police arrived on the scene, all of our lot just disappeared. It was just us three left, with Dermott bleeding from the stomach, on the ground. The police surrounding us.

PETER WYATT

I told Dermott not to move, but he was out cold, blood was pouring out of his side. The Old Bill came over to arrest us. I said "Whatever - just get a fucking ambulance for Dermott."

IT WAS A BLOODY HATCHETT!

DERMOTT COLLINS

I came to at St. Peter's Hospital, my stomach stitched up, thinking - thank fuck that's over, remind me not to get into any fights with any rockers anytime soon.

PETER WYATT

It was shocking to see Dermott hurt like that. But I was also shocked myself with how much I cared. As soon as I saw him get hit, I forgot all about the pain across my back.

JERRY ZMUDA

He made the front page of the Surrey Comet. "BOY 15 - AXED BY MOTORCYCLE GANG." IT WAS A BLOODY HATCHET! He was going to be insufferable now.

TERRY SOUTH

Sarah handed me the Surrey Comet with the picture of Dermott and his axe wound. I said - "About bleedin' time."

DERMOTT COLLINS

It seemed so nice and peaceful at the hospital - the nurses were really beautiful. I thought I should milk this - get meself under observation a few days longer.

DENNIS MCBRIDE

Dermott had it coming. You shouldn't mess with us. But I felt bad. I went to see him in hospital.

DERMOTT COLLINS

I wasn't prepared for a visit from King Herod, I thought he was coming to finish me off. But he came with a bunch of flowers, some grapes and a copy of *Bomber* by Motorhead. He said - "Do yourself a favour and listen to some decent music." I were choked up.

DENNIS MCBRIDE

I said – "I still think you're a cunt, I just came to check if you're alright."

DERMOTT COLLINS

As he left, I called him back - he looks over I say - "yer noh swawping that Kung Foo ahnewal." My way of saying thank you.

JORDI KNOWLES

I got a phone message - it was from Dermott. "If you talk to Angela - tell her I'm at the St. Peter's Hospital."

DERMOTT COLLINS

It was bliss in that hospital - watching telly in between long rounds of kip. Then I wake up and feel there's somebody by my bed, I thought it was a nurse but it's Angela. I thought I was dreaming - but I rubbed my eyes and she was still there, saying - "You silly boys always feel the need to get into fights." I was agreeing with her, she nursed me back to sleep. When I woke up again she'd gone.

JERRY ZMUDA

Dermott in hospital gave me the opportunity of getting on with my revising. My 'O' levels were just a few months away.

DERMOTT COLLINS

My Dad brought me my brother's guitar, now mine of course. Jerry and Peter came round and we had a sing song. *All or Nothing* we sang. Marvellous. And Dennis was right - that Motorhead album was alright!

JERRY ZMUDA

The three of us doing that *All Or Nothing* sing along in hospital was a stirring, unifying moment. Dermott could actually play the guitar a little bit. It planted a seed in my brain.

CAREER OPPORTUNITIES

JERRY ZMUDA

> The careers guidance counsellor was a fool. I wanted advice on a career where I could give a full reign to my artistic abilities. When she asked me what those artistic abilities might be, I went blank. She gave this huffy laugh which angered me and I said - "Isn't down to you people to bring it out of me?"
>
> After that she suggested some jobs I could go for - administrative assistant at the head office of United Biscuits, warehouse supervisor at Marlin Lighting, trainee manager at the Spar.

NATALIE ZMUDA

> I told Jerry - that is why you absolutely must stay on and do your 'A' levels. To get a decent job.

JERRY ZMUDA

> But what is a decent job? I couldn't see a place for me at all in the adult world. But how could I think about a job-stroke-career when I still hadn't done it with a girl yet? Get your priorities right.

DERMOTT COLLINS

> This career guidance bird goes to me - "What are your goals in life?" I was trying to be a smart-arse and said – "The only goals in my life are the football goal-posts we hang around at break-times." I thought that was a clever answer.
>
> But then she said - "But after June you won't have those goal-posts to hang around anymore. What then?"
>
> That stumped me.

JERRY ZMUDA

> My proudest achievement at Feltham? In all my five years I never once defecated in the toilets. I always held it in until I got home. That's iron self-discipline.

PETER WYATT

> Obviously I wasn't going to stay on and do my A levels with all the boffs. Fuck that! Get a job, get a car, get a bird. I wasn't worried

about it. I may not have been Einstein at school, but I wasn't thick either, somebody was going to hire me. I was still thinking that Record Scene were going to call.

JERRY ZMUDA

RCA in Sunbury on Thames had a careers open day, inviting school kids to have a look round, talk about job opportunities. When they asked if anyone had any questions, I asked if working for RCA meant you got free Elvis Presley records, and tickets to David Bowie concerts. The man treated me with complete derision. I walked out in the depths of depression and dragged myself over to the precinct and to Record Scene.

Staring at that wall - the display of all those glorious 7 inch picture sleeves, The Jam, The Stranglers, The Clash, Sex Pistols, X Ray Spex, Siouxsie & The Banshees, Generation X. My favourite bands in all the colours of the rainbow.

I had my Road to Damascus moment.

Who makes these records?

Who writes these songs?

Who plays the instruments?

PEOPLE LIKE ME.

And right there I saw my future - joining my heroes there on the wall.

GRANT WILLIAMS (Record Scene manager)

I thought he'd gone insane. But then I thought - why not? I told him loads of bands come from this part of the world. Sham 69 were from Walton, so were the Lurkers. The Jam were from down the road in Woking. I encouraged him - that's what punk is all about. Get off your arse. He left the shop all fired up.

JERRY ZMUDA

Dermott and Peter would be the perfect accomplices. What a great idea. I would be the lead singer/songwriter and they would be my backing band. I went home and looked at my *All Mod Cons* album. I read all the lyrics on the inner sleeve, and I thought to myself - I'm a deep and sensitive person like Weller - I'll have a go at that. So I'll start scribbling down lyrics in an exercise book. But I didn't want the others to mock me. I needed to choose my moment and pitch them the idea.

FAREWELL TO FELTHAM

PETER WYATT

I'd spent five years, five fucking years - trying to get Sarah Baxter's attention. A quick smile here, a passing conversation there. But as I came towards my last day at Feltham, I decided - I WAS GOING TO ASK THIS GIRL OUT.

JERRY ZMUDA

I was late with all that. I had just turned 16 and was still scared of girls. Peter was seeing girls and had his campaign to win the heart of Sarah. Dermott fooled around with girls and had his weird thing going on with Angela. But me? I just had a few well hidden magazines.

DERMOTT COLLINS

On that last day at Feltham I strolled past that school gate, I felt something really weird - I was going to miss school.
Loads of kids were running around, swearing at the teachers, flicking the Vs at them - saying stuff - "You can't do nothing about this now." I wasn't like that at all. I hate to admit it, but I was sad. Plus I was a little worried - like what the fuck do I do now? I guess that school counsellor got me thinking.

JERRY ZMUDA

When I first came to Feltham I was repelled and horrified, but bit by bit over my five years I grew to accept the place - and eventually it became part of my identity. Feltham Made Me what I am today. The bleakness now felt like home, almost reassuring.
And I was staying on for two more years to do my A levels. That was going to be different, because as Mum pointed out all the dodgier kids in my year won't be staying on - that included Dermott and Peter.

SARAH BAXTER

It was like the last day of primary school all over again, but this time we're all a bit bigger. It's natural to feel sad on your last day of school. So we all brought in our cameras, and sure enough pretty soon the water-works began to flow. It was the end of an era.

JERRY ZMUDA

But on that last day of the fifth year, everyone was in the mood for a party, but I felt an urge. There was a world outside that Feltham School playground and it's about time I saw some of it. So on the last day I felt strongly we should not be parochial, we should celebrate by hitting the big city.

PETER WYATT

So I walked into school with only one thought on my mind. Sarah Baxter. I was shaking, trying to calm myself down. Then I saw her. She was standing with her friends by the canteen cupboard, they were hugging each other, all teary-eyed. She sees me and smiles, gives me this lovely warm embrace - my heart went into over-drive.

SARAH BAXTER

He said - "Can I have a word - in private?"
His face was all serious and I thought he was going to tell me something like - I've only got six months to live. Then he said –
"I've been in your class five years now, I've always thought there was something very special about you, something very wonderful".
I blushed. Then he popped the question.

PETER WYATT

She smiled, my heart sang, then she put her hand on my fore-arm.
"Peter you're really very sweet. But I am already seeing someone."
"Who?"
"He's an older guy - it's actually Terry South".
Then the sky went black.

JERRY ZMUDA

Peter was inconsolable. I suggested a wild night in the West End, go to a gig, hit a night-club. That would take his mind off Sarah and cheer him up.

PETER WYATT

I wasn't going to give up. I wasn't going to let go. There was the end of term disco happening that night, I knew Sarah was going. I was going to go there and stake my claim for her heart.

JERRY ZMUDA

Are you serious? The Feltham School end of term disco? WE ARE
THE SLUSH PUPPY MODS, Cowey Sale survivors - Remember
Southampton? We can go wherever we want. And you want to go to
some lame school disco? "But Sarah Baxter is going to be there."

DERMOTT COLLINS

So we turn up to the disco, and Argh! The disappointment. The disco
has been cancelled, the teachers had got so pissed off with the
behaviour of some of the dustbin lids, myself not included for once,
they refused to staff it.

PETER WYATT

Somebody must be having a house party where Sarah is going. So I
went around asking as many people as I could, but because I was
Dermott's friend - no-one would tell me anything.

JERRY ZMUDA

I jumped in here, leave Feltham behind. Let's jump on a train and have
a big adventure in the West End. Peter seemed to go with this. But
then he found out about this party.

DERMOTT COLLINS

And this house party is a real sodding wet blanket. They're playing the
Police, and there's this square hairy type trying to dance like it's
reggae. I said to Jerry – "Meet your new friends - this lot that are
staying on to do their 'A' levels."
And everyone's tense because I'm there. Where did I get this
reputation?

JERRY ZMUDA

Then Cobra turns up at the party. "I'll take you to the West End boys
in my new car". I thought anything is better than staying here all night.
So just as we're about to leave Dermott hurls the coffee table through
the glass door. Making an almighty crash, fragments of glass flying out
into the garden.

DERMOTT COLLINS
> I had to do it. They had just put on Supertramp. So we had to race out of there pretty sharpish.

PETER WYATT
> Cobra had this really battered motor, it didn't look too healthy and sounded really dodgy. Plus as you would expect Cobra drives likes a lunatic. I started realizing this wasn't such a good idea.

JERRY ZMUDA
> I was squashed in the back seat, terrified, but I thought at least we're getting out of Feltham.
> We're motoring up the road, with the devil himself behind the wheel. I swear I could hear him cackling. Then the engines splutters, and dies. We get out. And guess what? I'm standing just by the road-sign for Feltham. Am I ever going to get out of this place?

DERMOTT COLLINS
> Then the old Bill pull up and get out of the car. They ask who the owner of this vehicle is. Cobra says fuck all, so we all say fuck all.
> The two coppers press us – "Who is the owner of this vehicle?"
> Then Cobra does a runner, jumps over the wall and into Feltham Park. One of the coppers give chase. This is bad. If he gets away, we get pumped for questions, if we say anything - anything at all, Cobra is going to kill us. So I said to the others. "Scarper."
> So all three of us run in three different directions.

JERRY ZMUDA
> The second policeman chased me, I ran into a garden, climbed over the wall, and into a shed.

PETER WYATT
> This was in the days before mobile phones, so when we all split up like that, we had no way of knowing where each of us where. So I made my way home.

DERMOTT COLLINS
> I didn't fancy going home just yet - so I went over to Peter's house, just wait for him there.

FELTHAM MADE ME   93

JERRY ZMUDA

> After all of us running in different directions and splitting up, our instinct was to head straight round Peter's. Like homing pigeons.

PETER WYATT

> The most amazing thing. I get home, and waiting for me by the front door are my two buddies. Mum is out as usual. We didn't really drink in them days, but we cracked open a bottle of me Mum's Remy Martin - her feller had given it to her.

JERRY ZMUDA

> I thought this is my moment. Music was playing, we were laughing and getting on. And out it came – "Why don't we join our heroes up on the wall of Record Scene? Why don't we form a band?"

DERMOTT COLLINS

> It was the greatest fuckin' idea in the world. I was getting quite good at strumming the guitar, and it answered my earlier question - what the fuck do I do now?

PETER WYATT

> I went along with it. We were a great bunch of friends, so why wouldn't we make a great band? Count me in.

JERRY ZMUDA

> And so we shook on it. The as yet un-named band was born.

Chapter 4
The Life & Times of Septimus Grundy

AFTER SCHOOL – WHAT NOW?

PETER WYATT

Leave school and get a job. Sounds straightforward, don't it? First thing Monday I get down the job centre and look at the cards - washer-upper, bin-man, kitchen cleaner. Of course what I should have been doing was learning a proper, decent trade - builder, car mechanic, something like that. But I wanted money fast.

SARAH BAXTER

I loved making clothes, so I thought I'd make a go at doing it for a living. There was a course in fashion design at Richmond College. Dad wasn't into it, he thought I should get out into the big bad world - be a secretary, and get bossed around by some grumpy old git. So me and Mum did a number on him.

PETER WYATT

Then I saw the card - "Want to make SERIOUS money? Do you want that FAST car? Live in the that BIG House?" I thought - I wouldn't mind. The job was selling carpet cleaning door to door. They interviewed me over the phone and I must have made a good impression because they told me I could start straight away. Then they asked if I had any mates who could do the work - and I immediately thought of Dermott.

SARAH BAXTER

What was a lot harder was persuading Dad to let me go on holiday in Spain with Terry. Even Mum didn't approve of that. In the end I made up a terrible lie - and told them both I was going to the Norfolk broads for a week with Samantha. I had to steal my passport out of Mum's drawer. God! I hate lying.

DERMOTT COLLINS

The first Monday after I left school, Dad pops in and says - "So what are you up today?" I said - "I dunno, get down the DHSS and get me dole sorted out I guess."

FRANK COLLINS (Dermott's father)

There is no way any son of mine was ever going to be drawing dole. I know what people say about the Irish - lazy good for nothing. Well we ain't. We work twice as hard, and I wasn't going to let Dermott give the bigots any ammunition.

DERMOTT COLLINS

Then I picks up me brother's geetar. Remembering what Jerkski said on Friday night - about forming a band. I spent the whole morning playing along to *Rocket to Russia*. Over and over again. Cobra comes around saying - "The sun is out, let's get out on the lash." I said - "Easy brother I'm really getting into this."

FRANK COLLINS

So later that week I sorted Dermott some work on the site. Just carrying and lifting, going to the shops. Nightmare!

DERMOTT COLLINS

The first thing them navvies on Dads's sight get me on was the kettle detail. I ain't no mug - I made the tea so badly - they never asked me again. Then I had to help knock down a wall.

FRANK COLLINS

We started him on the easy stuff. Dust and debris everywhere - in our hair, face and eyes.

DERMOTT COLLINS

Peter told me how builders would always gee up the new lad on the site. Make clowns out of them by sending them on errands for a long stand. Make them wait in the corner and say - "There you are - you've had your long stand." Or send them to the suppliers to get a tin of stripey paint, and they get laughed at. Well they weren't going to do that to Titus .

This builder asks me to get down the yard and get some rubber gromitts. I told him to stick his rubber gromitts up his arse - the fucking wind-up merchant.

FRANK COLLINS

The last straw was when he told one of my top men, to fuck off. He only asked him to get some rubber grommets.

DERMOTT COLLINS

The builders on me old man's site had a meeting. The shop steward then went and saw me Dad. They told him - either you sack your son, or we go on strike.

FRANK COLLINS

So I said to Dermott - "OK enough. I'll support you for a couple of months while you work out what you want to do. But do not draw dole."

DERMOTT COLLINS

Then Peter calls me, he's a got a job for me selling carpet cleaning door to door. I was like – "Oh fuck! Do I have to?"

MAKING PLANS FOR JERRY

JERRY ZMUDA

When my sister Magdalena went to University, the Zmuda household plunged deeper still into a world of gloom. Now an eternal stony silence ruled over the house as my Mother and Father barely said a word to each other. Many women get post natal depression, with my Mother it seemed to last decades, and her constant sour-face was really getting me down - "pull your socks up" - "get your act together." Who wants to hear all that when you're 16?
I saw a video of Joy Division on Saturday morning TV - *The Music Factory* I think the show was called. Joy Division wore expressions of despair and looked Eastern European. Being of Polish descent I related to that. After lunch, I dashed down to Record Scene to buy the record, and told the bloke behind the counter that I was up for going to see Joy Division live.

GRANT WILLIAMS

You'll need a Tardis for that mate, I said. A bit heartless I know. He didn't know the lead singer had just topped himself.

JERRY ZMUDA

I went home all upset and tried to scribble down some lyrics about it. I've still got them in an old exercise book somewhere. They go like this -

From an abandoned warehouse,
All dressed in grey,
Your song was sad,
But it brightened my day.
I want to go to a concert,
To watch you play.
But now I never will,
Now I never will.

MY DOG CAN HAVE ANY DOG IN HOUNSLOW

PETER WYATT

With this door to door carpet cleaning lark, they give you a couple of hours training, then this seedy looking geezer in a crumpled suit takes you in his car out in the middle of the sticks - they won't tell you where. I felt like I was in the mob about to do a hit. On the way there he makes us go over the sales script again and again –
"We have our carpet cleaning team working in your area. While we're here, we'd thought we'd give you a call for a no obligation, totally free quote."
You had to memorize that and, very important, you had to remember to smile. Then they let you out, and you had to go knocking on every door in the street.

DERMOTT COLLINS

Never stuck to the script. The geezer who drove us there just buggered off so we were left to get on with it. I was knocking on the door and saying stuff like "Any chance of a cuppa?" "Your garden looks nice." Pretty soon the locals were calling the Old Bill.

PETER WYATT

It was tough work - some people were quite nice and smiled back, but a lot slammed the door in my face. The supervisor picked us up at lunchtime and took us to some boozer. He was a bit of a geezer this one. One of these types that doesn't seem to able to talk about anything else other than himself. He was telling us - "My dog can have any dog in Hounslow."

DERMOTT COLLINS

Turns out the supervisor geezer is into his dogs. I joke - "Aren't we all after a few drinks?"

I said to him - "Your dog should meet my mate's dog Belzebub - he's the hardest dog in Feltham." I made this dog up, but he was up for it - this clash of West London dog titans. We were arranging a time and a place for the bout when the Old Bill show up, looking for the suspicious geezer who had been knocking on doors and scaring the locals.

PETER WYATT

So Dermott got sacked after the first day, while I stuck it out.

I made a sale on my second day. It was an elderly couple who were just too nice to say no. I was supposed to be happy, but I felt dirty. I was thinking - is this my life? My future? Am I going to end up in a couple of years bragging to my sales team about my dog being hard? I packed it in on my second week.

DERMOTT COLLINS

So there I was - back at home, strumming away, learning some chords. Was I getting good at the guitar? I dunno. Nobody else had heard me apart from Cobra, who weren't interested. The other two hadn't said anything about the band since that Friday. I was just playing to myself but I wanted to know what it sounded it like to others. Especially Angela. Would Angela really like me if she heard me play guitar?

THE LIFE AND TIMES OF SEPTIMUS GRUNDY

JERRY ZMUDA

The bad news envelope came through the letter-box in July. I nearly got there first but Mother swooped it up like an eagle.

Trust her to focus on the negative. I had achieved passes in every subject bar one - Maths. This was something of a drawback on account I was supposed to be doing Maths 'A' level. So there was nothing else for it - the dreaded re-sit.

NATALIE ZMUDA (Jerry's mother)

He was whining and whining about having to do a summer job and now having to do re-sits when he's trying to write songs. I told him that he has to live in the real world - and the real world is Maths 'O' level re-sits in September.

JERRY ZMUDA

Eddie Cochrane was right - there ain't no cure for the Summertime Blues. Being made to do some awful summer job at the Feltham industrial estate and now having to prepare for my re-sits. I was trying to come up with some lyrics about re-sits, as I was walking past the eerie graveyard we used to hang out in when we were 12. And then it hit me - the name of the band - SEPTIMUS GRUNDY!

DERMOTT COLLINS

I wanted to call us the Slush Puppy Mods - but then I thought only mods would come and see us. So when Jerry came in with the name Septimus Grundy - I was up for it.

PETER WYATT

The other two were so into being called Septimus Grundy, I thought - yeah it's a bit weird, but why not? Let's be different. My Mum goes away for the week-end - again to see her mysterious boy-friend, so I said – "Come round and we'll have our very first jamming session."

DERMOTT COLLINS

So I turn up with my brother's guitar, which of course is mine now. And I start playing and singing along, Peter is trying to keep up with an acoustic guitar playing the bass parts.

JERRY ZMUDA

Dermott is trying to take charge assuming he's going to be the lead singer. He strums his guitar and sings dead flat - "I went to a party at the county jail - caught my knob on a rusty nail." Completely pathetic and not even remotely amusing.

DERMOTT COLLINS

Jerry looks at us, with that soppy doe-eyed look of his, saying "What do I do?" Then he gets it out. His notebook of lyrics.

PETER WYATT

The poor mite gets out his exercise book and is reading out his lyrics. Dermott starts laughing.

DERMOTT COLLINS

Unforgettable lyrics. Do you want hear them?
        The Kids on the Street ain't got nothing to do,
        They're just trying to live their life - what else can they do?
Yup! You can always rely on Jerkski to be a top fucking ponse.

JERRY ZMUDA

I never wrote any lyrics about Kids On The Street. Dermott made all that rubbish up - like he makes everything up. It was teenage stuff about wanting to meet girls, and having to face re-sits. Painfully embarrassing - I'm not denying it. But nothing about Kids on the Street.

PETER WYATT

I told Dermott to stop laughing, "come on let's listen to his lyrics, give the poor kid a break." They were pretty shit though - stuff like -
        Government Leaders telling us what to do,
        Don't listen to them - they're not better than you.
I figured well - when you go and see a band live, you can hardly ever hear the lyrics.

GET YOUR TATS OUT (FOR THE LADS)

DERMOTT COLLINS

Cobra sez to me - "a geezer ain't no geezer until he gets himself some tats." Cob had them all over his body, including the famous Cobra on his neck. His catchphrase - *you cunt do you want a slapping?* That was on his chest. He offers to take me down to Hastings for a summer day out and see a tattoo artist he knows. I said - "Great - how about bringing my buddies along?" Cobra goes - "That Peter's alright - but not that Jerry. Jerry ain't shaking with the snake."

PETER WYATT

That was out of order. Cobra was trying to drive a wedge between Jerry and Dermott. I said I wasn't going either. But then on the day I was getting edgy about what Dermott would get up to with Cobra. So I decide to go along and be his protector.

DERMOTT COLLINS

We get the train down. The day starts off OK. Tins of beers - having a laugh - reminded me of our famous day out to see The Jam.

PETER WYATT

Halfway through the journey Cobra knocks back another beer and says - "So who's up for getting hold of some brass later on?"
I was puzzled - was he talking about adding to his coin collection? Then I twigged and I froze in horror. I was a sixteen year old boy, in love with Sarah Baxter, and I wasn't going to get hold of any brass - and certainly not share one with Cobra.

DERMOTT COLLINS

Leave it out! The very thought of waiting my turn on some bird while Cobra pounded away at her turned my stomach. Cobra steam-rolls you into things, but no way was I going to do that.
Then Cobra was cracking on at me about what tattoo I was going to have. I wanted the Big Bad Wolf, but he wanted me to have a snake - so I could be "shaking with the snake." He says to me - "If you don't have a snake - it's going to be another battle of Hastings." But I wasn't going to give in that easy.

JERRY ZMUDA

I didn't want to go with Cobra to Hastings. OK, I hadn't been invited, but I was happy to stay at home and try and write some more teenage angst anthems. I was trying to be all political, writing stuff about Tory MPs and religious leaders telling us what to do. Then I thought - when has a religious leader ever told me what to do? I was stumped, what the hell do I write about?

PETER WYATT

As we walked down to the tattooist near the pier, with each step you could feel the heightening tension. I was squirming. It was like one of those fair ground rides – higher, higher, higher – you know inevitably it's going to go off, any second now. Cobra was still insisting that Dermott had a snake tattoo, and Dermott was standing firm - and so he should. It was his body, it was down to him to choose what to have grafted onto him. The row kicks off right outside the tattooist.

DERMOTT COLLINS

Cobra grabs hold of me. He's shaking me - properly shaking me like a rattle. He gives me the catchphrase – "YOU CUNT DO YOU WANT A SLAPPING?" I soaked my pants.

PETER WYATT

I tried to get Cobra to let go and he turns on me. "YOU CUNT DO YOU WANT A SLAPPING?" I was about to punch the guy when plod jumps in - blows his whistle and puts his hand on Cobra's shoulder. It was time to scarper. Since that film Quadrophenia had come out - the police were always around the seaside resorts. So in the blink of an eye, more police were on the scene. Cobra was taking them all on. While me and Dermott scurried away like the Three Stooges, and sneaked underneath the pier.

DERMOTT COLLINS

We went to the pub to calm our nerves, wondering what the hell was going to happen to Cobra. And more importantly, what was he going to do to us when the Old Bill release him. Then Peter gets that serious look on his face he always gets when he wants a serious chat.

PETER WYATT

I told him that Jerry was his real friend, his proper friend - and Cobra had just shown us what he's all about. Hang out with him and you'll end up in prison.

DERMOTT COLLINS

I kept on trying to change the subject - but Peter kept bringing me back. "Jerry is your mate - Cobra is a bad influence." In the end I just had to agree with him. But I felt bad about Cobra. I'd decided I was going to splash out and have two tattoos - a wolf <u>and</u> a snake.

PETER WYATT

You sure about this? Two tattoos in one day. You sure? The pain....

DERMOTT COLLINS

Fuck the pain! Coupla more beers and I won't feel a thing. Tattoos don't really hurt - they're just like sticking red hot needles into your skin.
Course when it came down to it - I was howling in pain - but I didn't pipe. My eyes were bone dry. After my orgy of agony I said to Peter – "Let's go to the nick. Chances are, that's where Cobra will be." I needed to nip this one in the bud and make sure that Cobra wasn't going to come after us when he got let out.

PETER WYATT

Sure enough Cobra was in the cell, due up before the beak on Monday. We found out his real name - Graham Cobb. The police let us see him for five minutes and Dermott showed him his forearm all bandaged up - saying "I got it done Cob - a snake <u>and</u> the big bad wolf." Cobra was so moved he had tears in his eyes. This was all too weird for me.

JERRY ZMUDA

While Dermott and Peter were having their seaside special with Cobra, I was at home trying to write down some serious heart-wrenching lyrics, but I was still staring at a blank page. I scoured the book shelf for ideas and I found a copy of *Crime and Punishment*. I'd seen the TV production with John Hurt a year or so before. So I thought - I'll write a song about that.
After about fifteen minutes I had something written down -
> *Hey brother have you heard the word? 'Bout St. Petersburg?*
> *I'm not mad, I'm not crazy,*
> *I have decided to do in my landlady.*
> *When she's gone I won't have any fears,*
> *Because I owe six months arrears.*

Complete rubbish. I know that now. But I felt the exhilaration of creativity, I thought I had found my voice. Please remember - I had only just turned 16.

DERMOTT COLLINS

When we got back Peter made me phone and Jerry and apologize for not inviting him down to Hastings and letting Cobra call the shots. Jesus - Peter was like your old man sometimes.

JERRY ZMUDA

I knew Peter had made him call, but I appreciated it. Peter always knew about doing the right thing.

WE COME FROM GARAGELAND

PETER WYATT

Jerry had his 'A' levels, but you could tell he was only doing them to keep his Mum happy. All three of us were teenagers thinking - where the fuck do we fit in this world? But when we got together to do the music, everything fell into place. It wasn't about wanting to see our mugs on the cover of Smash Hits or anything. Just playing along and improving each day was an end in itself. The hours whizzed by.

DERMOTT COLLINS

All that time spent out of work, laying about on my back-side had started to pay off - my guitar playing was really coming along. It was a real nice feeling to be able to pick up me guitar and knock out a riff and not have to stare at my fingers as I tried to find a chord. Peter had bought a really cheap second hand bass and was doing alright. And Jerry well, he was still fucking hopeless at singing and guitar.

JERRY ZMUDA

I was having real difficulty singing and playing the guitar at the same time.

DERMOTT COLLINS

He couldn't do both at the same time. Couldn't do one at a time neither. He was dragging us down like a dirty great big bottle of Domestos round our necks.

PETER WYATT

> So the line up was me on bass, Dermott on guitar and Jerry singing and strumming the occasional chord. We needed a drummer, so we put a notice up in Record Scene.

GRANT WILLIAMS

> Peter came into the shop with a big smile on his face, asking to put a notice up. I said to them – "You serious about this band lark?" They'd even given themselves a name - Septimus Grundy. I said - "Change it. It sounds prog rock - like Jethro Tull."

PETER WYATT

> Only one person called. Stuart Martin.

BUCKLE AKA STUART MARTIN

> I'd been drumming in a band that played R'n'B covers. I was younger than most of them by nearly ten years and I wanted to do something young and fresh. I saw the notice in Record Scene and I thought I'd give it a go.

PETER WYATT

> We didn't tell him that he was the only drummer we were auditioning.

BUCKLE AKA STUART MARTIN

> They're holding auditions in this lock-up garage. So I knew right away it wasn't some big time outfit. We jammed along to a few Jam and Clash songs - and it was pretty clear that I was a lot more advanced musically than that lot. I mean Jerry didn't even know how to hold a guitar. I should have been auditioning them.

DERMOTT COLLINS

> Buckle may have been a bit fat - but he was fucking ace. Hearing my guitar with his drums underneath gave me a top fucking buzz - geezah!

PETER WYATT

He was shit hot and he knew it. After a couple of songs - I just offered him the gig then and there. He asked - "Don't you need to audition other drummers?"

"Fuck the other drummers," I said, "you're our drummer!"

BUCKLE AKA STUART MARTIN

I said I'd think about it. But only because I didn't want to tell them to their faces I thought they were no-hopers. But I went home and played the Clash's first album - the track *Garageland* came on. We'd played that at the audition. I started thinking - those boys have got spirit, they're what punk was all about. I'll take the job, and being older, more experienced, I'll take charge.

DERMOTT COLLINS

I was made up to hear Buckle had taken us up. I could see him clicking with us instantly. I'd already given him a nick-name. Buckle as in Fatty ArBuckle. Of course I told him it was because he was wearing a belt with a big buckle.

LONDON AFTER MIDNIGHT

JORDI KNOWLES (Angela's brother)

Dermott would call me up every couple of weeks to find out if there was any news on Angela. He even gave me a letter to pass onto to her. All I knew was that she was staying in a series of squats in London and she didn't have a phone. She'd call me from a pay phone from time to time, and I met up with her in the Chelsea Potter one Saturday afternoon and passed Dermott's letter onto her. I have no idea what it said.

FRANK COLLINS

Angela Knowles phoned one Saturday afternoon and left a message for Dermott. It was - 'be at the Dead Kennedys concert at the Music Machine, Camden on Monday night.' Dead Kennedys? I didn't like the sound of that one bit.

FELTHAM MADE ME   107

DERMOTT COLLINS

After months of not hearing anything at all about Angela, I went ape-shit when Dad told me she called. I kept telling myself all the way on the train to Camden Town - "She must like me if she wants to meet up."

JORDI KNOWLES

What Angela was up to in squat land, I could only guess. Thieving? Drugs? Sex? More than likely. I didn't want to know. Mum was still heart-broken but we hardly ever talked about her. I wanted so much for my sister to come back home, but I knew that would never happen now.

DERMOTT COLLINS

I turn up at the Dead Kennedys concert - and surprise, surprise it's full of punks. Leather jackets, studs, crazy colour hair. Smuggling in little bottles of Vodka under their jackets. I was wearing my Ramones T-shirt and Harrington. I'd put soap in my hair to make it stick up, but I still felt out-of-place. The place was an old music hall from the good old days that had gone downhill. It's massive, so I just walk around and around through the crowd, trying to spot my Angela.

PETER WYATT

I'd offered to go with him to the concert, because I quite fancied seeing the band who did *Holiday in Cambodia*. But he said he wanted to meet Angela alone.

DERMOTT COLLINS

I went near the front to watch the support band - UK Decay, I think they were called. And there she was, right near the front. She looked at me, dashed over and hugged me. I smelt her smell again, I'd forgotten she'd had her own smell, unique to her - not like BO - smelly but nice. Then she introduces me to her friends. All punks - all squatting in London. I told her about Septimus Grundy - I thought she'd be really impressed, but she just patted me on the back. Then the Dead Kennedys came on and it all went loopy. I was grabbing hold of her - determined never to let go.

GRANT WILLIAMS (Record Scene Manager)

    I was at that gig. Working at Record Scene you get loads of record company freebies. Punk was creatively dead at this point, but the Dead Kennedys were amazingly good, really tight sound. I caught sight of Dermott at the gig, I dived behind a pillar.

DERMOTT COLLINS

    During the set she shouts at me - "Where are you going later?"
    "Dunno. Catching the last train I guess."
    She shouts back - "No you're not. You're coming to a party."
    "Sounds good to me, where?"
    Over the loud music I got her to repeat the address five times - it was a squat in a place that sounded like Great Witch Field Street. I was going to a party with Angela after midnight. I was the happiest teenager in the world. I were grinning from ear to ear, something you don't often see at a punk gig.

GRANT WILLIAMS

    The Music Machine was a good venue for punk gigs. The stage was quite high so a lot of that spitting didn't reach the performers. Although some still managed. The punks were trying to rush the stage from the very first number.

DERMOTT COLLINS

    Each time a punk got on stage the security would either push them back or grab them and take them to the side. It was quite funny watching this all happen until I saw Angela up there. This bouncer came up to her, and she tried to knee him in the nuts. The security went berserk and it took two geezers to turf her off stage. In a panic I went to the side of the stage spluttering - demanding to know where the bouncer had taken her.

PETER WYATT

    I told Dermott if anything happens or you get stranded in London, get to a payphone and give us a call. I'll get Mum to come and pick you up.

DERMOTT COLLINS

I was yelling at the bouncer – "Tell me where she is." He grabs hold of me and throws me through a side-door. I look around and I'm in this dark alleyway. "Angela?" I cried out pathetically. I run round to the front of the venue, desperately looking for her. The gig finishes and I'm going up to strangers - all punks - "Do you know Angela Knowles?" "Have you seen her?" Some tried to help - others just laughed. Then I remembered the party in the squat in Great Witch Field Street. I ask about that. This girl tells me I probably mean Great Titchfield - that's Central London, it's down towards the Post Office Tower.

So I head for the Tower, panting heavily, I'm Desperate Dan, running down this main road with the Post Office tower in the distance ahead of me, slowly getting closer, when this geezer pulls up in his car. "You seem lost Boy." He says rolling down his window - "Jump in I'll give you a lift."

He's about 30 - and asks me if I've been to the punk gig. I tell him all about Angela - and what she means to me, and I say I want to go to this squat party in Great Titchfield Street. He tells me instead "I know where your Angela will be. I'm taking you to Soho."

GRANT WILLIAMS

The last train to Walton went at midnight - but there were trains all through the night going to Kingston, so after the gig I grabbed one of those, trying not to fall asleep, and called a cab at Kingston.

DERMOTT COLLINS

"So you know Angela?" I asked. Yes he nodded, I was suspicious - but I was clutching at straws. He takes me down to this real seedy basement bar in Soho, I look around and there's six people in there - all geezers and none of them Angela. I shout at the geezer – "She's not here - and you don't know her." He gets me to calm down and buys me a beer. It tastes funny, he's put whisky in it. Then he puts his hand on my leg. I punch the guy square in the mush. He grabs me by the collar of my harrington, five other guys bound over - it's looking bleak for our Dermott. Time to remember some Bruce Lee. I kung fu kick the biggest poof and he goes down, then I double punch another - I then make a dash for the fire exit door. I crash through them - I'm free. But what about Angela? I was desperate to find her so I make my way to that Post Office Tower.

PETER WYATT

It's 3 AM. Mum is home for once. The phone rings, eventually I pick up. It's Dermott - he's stranded can we pick him up? Mum doesn't want to go. I insist - it's Dermott - he's family.

DERMOTT COLLINS

She wasn't there. Or was she? I saw some blonde girl snogging in the corner, it could have been her - but I didn't want to see. I waited and waited, in this burnt out squat - ankle-deep in wasted punks all over gaff. London after midnight felt scary, weird. Eventually I get to a payphone to call Peter. I wait outside in the freezing cold and eventually this car pulls up - I saw this man inside smile at me - but when I saw it was Peter, I knew I was safe.

VERONICA GETS SERIOUS WITH ROY

PETER WYATT

Mum comes home one evening. She's quiet for a bit, then she goes to me - "There's a man I want you to meet, he's called Roy." I knew she had a boyfriend but she'd never mentioned a name. This was serious.

ROY HOOKE (Veronica's boyfriend)

Boy was I nervous. Do I try and come across all wealthy and successful? Or do I try and be one of the lads? Or a bit of both? It was hard enough trying to win the trust of Veronica, but now her teenage son?

PETER WYATT

So she wants to go out to dinner, and I said "OK but I want my buddies along as well."

DERMOTT COLLINS

I felt sorry for this geezer Roy. Peter was glaring - and me and Roy were trying to lighten things up. Talking about football and the telly. Roy talked about what he used to listen to when he was our age - Rock'n'Roll. He saw Billy Fury play the Walton Hop and it was the

FELTHAM MADE ME   111

best gig of his life. He'd also seen Johnny Kid and the Pirates. I was getting into all this music myself - Eddie Cochrane and all of that, so I was jabbering ten to the dozen with him. He offered to lend us some of his albums - while Peter just carried on glaring.

ROY HOOKE

I wish it had been Dermott I was trying to win over. He was an enthusiastic, gregarious soul who loved classic rock'n'roll. But Peter just glared at me as if I was the Yorkshire Ripper. It made Veronica very uncomfortable.

PETER WYATT

Why was I giving Roy such a hard time? Dunno really. It certainly wasn't out of loyalty to me old man. It just didn't feel right.

ROY HOOKE

What do you do when somebody's son makes it clear they don't want you to carry on seeing their mother? But I wasn't going to stop seeing Veronica - my intentions were honourable. And a man isn't meant to be alone - even at 42. I was getting over a painful separation, losing custody of my two children - I needed companionship. Female companionship.

LATE NIGHT AT THE PETROL STATION

PETER WYATT

The whole Mum seeing some geezer bit had really wound me up. I felt the need to break away, get myself some independence. Get a good job and then buy myself a motor. No decent job was on the horizon, so I wound up a cashier at the Apex all-night petrol station in Feltham. It paid alright, it'll do for now.

JERRY ZMUDA

Peter was not his normal happy-go-lucky self as Christmas '80 was coming up. I went over to see him at the petrol station - it was daunting. Round the back you had the kids off the estate hanging around. At eleven' o'clock the pubs shut and it's armagideon time - with all the drunks making for the petrol station like moths round a flame - shouting and whooping, swaying around. Buying crisps and

Mars Bars and stuffing their inebriated gurning faces. I asked Peter whether he'd seen anything crazy or amusing in his time working there. He says blankly – "Nothing - nothing at all." Then this guy walked up and gently tapped on the glass. Peter turns and explodes with rage. I never heard him shout like this before.

"Fuck Off. I said Fuck. I won't tell you again. Where's my box of Toblerone you cunt? Don't you dare piss on my forecourt. I'll give you a slap you'll never forget!"

This job at the petrol station was bringing out Peter's dark side.

PETER WYATT

The Sunday morning before I'm at the petrol station listening to a tape of Greg Edwards' Soul Spectrum. This geezer taps on my glass - he's got a wild look in his eye and he's talking in a strange rasping voice.

"Ere mate - you've got let me come inside and have a piss."

"No mate."

"I know you've got a khazi in there."

"Yes I have, but it's not for the public."

"Come on mate - I'm desperate for a piss."

"No - you live over by the flats don't you?"

"I won't get there in time - I gotta have a piss."

So eventually I unlock the door and let him in. I started serving a customer and next thing I know - the geezer grabs a box of Toblerone and runs out the back door. He didn't even go for a piss.

DERMOTT COLLINS

Peter was working at the petrol station most Friday and Saturday nights. We went over there most of the time, what else did we have to do? But I loved Sundays afternoons the best - that's when we got together for our jamming sessions.

PETER WYATT

I was working like a mother-fucker at that petrol station. Well I call it working - you're really just sitting around most of the time counting and re-counting the stock. But I was putting the hours in. Pretty soon I had enough money to buy a car.

DERMOTT COLLINS

He bought it out of the Exchange and Mart for two hundred barr. A real pussy magnet. Every morning he'd find a dozen cats sitting on the bonnet.

PETER WYATT

Yes it was a shitty little rust bucket which cluncked every time I changed gears. But it was my first car. I was so excited and I felt I was finally going places. But I was about to bite the hard concrete of reality street.

JERRY ZMUDA

We were at the petrol station listening to John Peel when a bright purple Ford Capri pulls up. Inside is Sarah Baxter - with Terry South in the driving seat. Peter dashes out, all out to impress, and Terry and Sarah were smirking at him because he was working at a petrol station. Peter then showed Sarah his car, and she and Terry burst out laughing because Terry was driving a considerably more expensive car.

TERRY SOUTH

We weren't laughing at him because he had a shit job and a shit car. But what do you do when some geezer who's after your bird comes up to her and tries to impress her with one hundred pounds worth of scrap metal? We weren't being nasty - we just couldn't help it.

PETER WYATT

The laughing - they were both laughing. It echoed in my ears as I went to bed that night. I was determined to get even.

MOONBOOTS IN MOLESEY

DERMOTT COLLINS

I'd planned on spending another Friday night in practicing on the geetar, when I get a call from Cobra. "I'm going over Molesey tonight. I need you to come with me." I had to go - I was in the Brotherhood of the Snake.

PETER WYATT

I'd heard a number of times Cobra mention his 'fence' in Molesey. I played football once a week with some lads from Molesey - they all knew Cobra.

DERMOTT COLLINS

Cobra's driving soundtrack at the time was *Suspect Device* by Stiff Little Fingers. We're singing along, going fairly mental, when Cobra turns to me -
"Are you ready for things to get a bit tasty later on?"
"What's that Cob? You taking me to a restaurant?"
"No you plank" he said "it's likely to kick off. We are going into enemy territory."

JERRY ZMUDA

Molesey is a residential area just by Hampton Court. It's actually green and pleasant, but it's got this reputation.

DERMOTT COLLINS

So me and Cobra are in this pub, propping up the bar and this geezer walks in with his mates. He's all Pringled up, smart looking. He goes to up to Cobra –
"You've got some front showing up here."
Then he points over to me and says - "Who's this Cobra? The boyfriend?"
Cobra replies - "So what if he is? At least he's not wearing moonboots." Moonboots? What the fuck is going on?

PETER WYATT

I got a lot of pointers about how to dress from the Molesey boys. I don't know if they were being called casuals then, I remember the term dressers being used a lot.

DERMOTT COLLINS

Moonboots? Moonboots? What the fuck is going on? They start talking - it's looking bad - I offer to buy them both a drink. The Molesey boy accepts., but Cobra waves me away. Then a big platoon marches in, but instead of khaki and army gear this lot are decked out in Sergio Tacchini, Pierre Cardin, Henri Lacoste. It was like a walking

FELTHAM MADE ME   115

talking shop window. I look down at my hands - are they shaking? Better not let Cobra see. Then Cobra and this Molesey lad shake hands - then they hug. Friends again. Phew! I ask Cobra –

"So what's this all about? A drug deal? Someone's a grass? What?"

He tells me - last week-end this Molesey boy's girlfriend turned up wearing Moonboots and Cobra took the piss. The girl was crying and Cobra refused to apologize.

"You don't do it," he said "you don't let your girlfriend show you up by wearing Moonboots."

Anyway it's all blown over now - thank fuck. They call last orders - Cobra and me get in the car, he drives by the pub and the Molesey boy is outside with about a dozen of his mates, Cobra pulls up and rolls the window down - sticks his head out. He yells –

"This geezer's girlfriend wears Moonboots - and he lets her get away with it. MOONBOOTS!"

And speeds off. I was quaking, realizing I was going to have to avoid the Molesey area for quite some time.

HEY! HEY! WE'RE THE GRUNDY

ROY HOOKE

I'd arranged to go to an Italian restaurant with Veronica and I called round for her. To my dismay she was late at the hairdressers and Peter was in on his own. So I sat in the living room alone with him, and it was tense - real tense. I asked him, just to cut the silence –

"How's it going?"

PETER WYATT

I don't why - but I just blurted it all out. I told him about Sarah - the new car, the laughter - and he listened.

ROY HOOKE

Peter said that he had tried to talk to his two best friends, but neither of them knew anything about the opposite sex. I told him that I was hardly an expert. Now this was really difficult, but I was delighted the ice was thawing.

PETER WYATT

He told me – "Don't get angry - get even. Girls will always judge you on how much money you earn, the car you drive, your status in life. That's just how they think and you won't change that. Be patient. Work hard and get yourself a decent car." I don't know if I agreed with everything he said, but at least he listened and came up with something.

ROY HOOKE

A few weeks after that, myself and Veronica sat down with him. We told him Veronica wanted to move out of Egmont Court and live with me. He is more than welcome to come and join us.

PETER WYATT

I turned them down. I still wasn't happy about all of this, and besides I liked the idea of having the flat at Egmont all to meself.

JERRY ZMUDA

It's normally the teenage son that moves out - not the mother.

DERMOTT COLLINS

Uh Wah Hah Hah! It's Monkey time! Me and Jerry practically moved in when Peter's Mum moved out. The first couple of weeks were insane - blaring music out of the window late at night, getting Smike and all our reprobate buddies round. We were like Cheech and Chong, but we weren't fucking hippies and we listened to The Jam.

JERRY ZMUDA

A few weeks later, Peter made us look around the place and handed us some dustbin bags and J clothes - it's time for a tidy up. He was right - the place had become a filth-ridden mosaic of beer cans, Mars bar wrappers, cigarette ends. Stink - and dust everywhere.

DERMOTT COLLINS

Ha! You thought I was going to be the slob. But no. What with not having a mother and all that - Dad always made sure I cleaned up and tidied after myself. He was very strict on that, he made all the brothers do it. Jerry on the other hand was throwing his dirty clothes on the bathroom floor and wondering why they didn't appear as if by magic all fresh and clean in the clothes draw.

JERRY ZMUDA

I used to think that when Mother used to wash my clothes each time after I'd worn them, she was doing it just for the sake of it. I didn't realize quite how smelly you can get.

PETER WYATT

I laid down the rules, you can stay here as much as you like - but you have got to keep the place clean and tidy. Yep! I even set up a cleaning rota.

DERMOTT COLLINS

Peter was the Man About The House - whatever he said went.

FRANK COLLINS (Dermott's Father)

I knew Peter - he was a sound lad. I knew that while Dermott was staying round there, he wasn't doing drugs or thieving.

DERMOTT COLLINS

I saw a future of us living forever altogether in that house - having wild adventures like the Monkees.
"Hey!Hey We're the Grundy! People say we Grundy around!"

PETER WYATT

Pretty soon we were decorating the place – our way. Grant from Record Scene gave us loads of old record promo material - posters and stuff.

DERMOTT COLLINS

He gave us a life-size cardboard cut-out of Walt Jabsco the Two Tone guy. That held pride of place in the living room over the TV.

JERRY ZMUDA

Every day was fun filled. Laughter was easy and unabating. Even mundane events like going to the shops, going to the Kentucky or doing the cooking. Living together had brought us closer - this was our honeymoon period.

THE JAM SECRET GIG

DERMOTT COLLINS

'Course one of the reasons me and the lads were practicing on our instruments so much was because there was fuck all to do round these parts. The only thing on for the youngsters was the Walton Hop - which is fine if you don't mind getting buggered by a bunch of dirty old geezers. Think Jerry went a few times.

JERRY ZMUDA

I never went to the Walton Hop - not my scene at all.

DERMOTT COLLINS

So imagine our excitement when we hear that the Jam were doing a series of secret gigs in their home town of Woking - just a short jaunt down the railway track. We just had to be there.

PETER WYATT

The Jam playing a secret gig in Woking? And somehow we've been tipped off? This has got to be worth checking out.

JERRY ZMUDA

Then I had a brainwave. We should use this gig to further the career of Septimus Grundy. Make a tape and give a copy of it to one of The Jam over a pint.

DERMOTT COLLINS

So we went about recording our four best songs - hang on - our four only songs, in the garage. Don't laugh, but I think we even slung on the theme tune from *Rainbow*.

JERRY ZMUDA

We recorded a shambolic version of a dire song called *Hullo Cruel World*. It sounded like a cat drowning in the bath. But we thought it was amazing and was obviously going to get us a support slot on the next Jam tour.

PETER WYATT

We went down there early in the day to make sure of getting in. Turns out this secret gig wasn't that much of a secret. Half the kids in Surrey had put on their bowling shoes and got there before us.

DERMOTT COLLINS

In no time the pub was packed to the rafters - mostly kids dressed like mods. Some kids were trying to get in through the toilet windows. I was pushing them back - saying "Sorry there's too many in already."

PETER WYATT

There's Weller over there dressed up in a smart boating blazer - talking away to some kids - but we couldn't get over there. It was so packed, I couldn't even lift my arms to scratch my nose. Then I see Dermott's talking to Buckler. The band go on stage and I said to Dermott – "Did you tell him?"

DERMOTT COLLINS

Tell him what? About the band? Shit I totally forgot.

JERRY ZMUDA

The gig was fantastic - being so close to our favourite band, I could actually see the hair on Paul Weller's nose, the spit fly as he sang out the words. After the gig we went to the bar next door to cool off, and there was the manager John Weller - unmistakable with his blond quiff. This was our chance. I gave the tape to Peter and said – "You do the talking."

PETER WYATT

John Weller was very nice. He tells me straight - "I get loads of young bands trying to get support slots with The Jam." He'd try to give it a listen, and try and get Paul to listen to it and all - but he couldn't promise anything. He holds up the tape and read out the name of the band on the label. SEPTIMUS GRUNDY - just to hear him say out loud the name of my band was an honour.

FELTHAM MADE ME   120

JERRY ZMUDA

Peter's phone number was on the label on the tape. We waited for the phone to ring.
Nothing.

GREAT EXPECTATIONS WITH LYDIA

LYDIA DANCEY (friend of Magdalena, Jerry's sister)

So how did I get to be the brainy bird? At what point? Is it too late to switch? I fancy being the sexy girl for a change. I blame all those books I was reading when I was 12 - and now at 16, I'm type-cast. I'm going to start dressing sexy - that's it. But what if they laugh?

NATALIE ZMUDA (Jerry's mother)

Alarms bell started ringing again when Jerry's report came through. A litany of mediocrity - and most disappointing of all - he was struggling with his English. If he was going to pass his 'A' levels - he needed extra tutoring. Magdalena had a friend who was studying her 'A' levels in Brooklands - she was a star in English Lit. I asked her if she'd like to help Jerry - and obviously I'd pay her for her trouble.

LYDIA DANCEY

So I bought this top, well it was more like a string vest. I thought if I wore a bikini bra underneath - it might set a few male pulses racing. This is what I was wearing when I went round to give a lad called Jerry Zmuda a tutorial in English Literature.

JERRY ZMUDA

I couldn't concentrate, she was talking about Dickens and *Great Expectations* and while she made it interesting, I had Great Expectations of my own. I kept looking at her bra, her tanned chest heaving through that vest. Fantasising about cupping her breasts in my hands.

LYDIA DANCEY

> I could see his hard-on through his trousers - I wanted to stroke it. Then he jumped me. We became a fireball of exploding pent-up teenage sexuality, we literally ripped each other's clothes off.

JERRY ZMUDA

> Then I remembered - Oh-my-God. Mum is downstairs.

LYDIA DANCEY

> So we forgot about Dickens for the rest of that afternoon. We did it quietly - slowly so his Mum wouldn't hear. Jerry grunted a few times and I bit my lip, then I bit his arm - and he yelped in pain.

JERRY ZMUDA

> Her smell, her taste - I was in the wonderful world of all things female. And I felt fully accepted. I held her in my arms and studied her, every little freckle, every little spot - I just took all of her in. I felt privileged to be close up to someone so beautiful.
> We talked afterwards. She told me she had written a novel when she was fifteen and she was about to send it out to publishers.

LYDIA DANCEY

> Such a lovely boy! Plunging cheek-bones to die for. I wanted to tell him everything. I told him about my dreams of living the wild life in the big city and leaving the dreary suburbs behind.

JERRY ZMUDA

> Her novel was called *Radiate Sunshine* and was all about a young girl who runs away to the big city and becomes a world-wide fashion icon. It was based on this girl called Edie Sedgwick who used to hang out with the Velvet Underground. "It sounds fantastic, can't wait to read it," I said.
> "You'll be the first one," she replied, and I felt very honoured.

LYDIA DANCEY

> After I told him all about *Radiate Sunshine*, he's looking at me adoringly. Then he pulls open the bottom drawer. I thought he was going to show me his porno mag collection. But no - it was an exercise

book of his teenage angst-ridden lyrics. It really was a case of - I'll show you mine, if you show me yours.

A BOTLEY CREW

JERRY ZMUDA
> I used to see Botley once in a while at school - said Hello - but we'd basically lost touch. I felt bad because every time I saw him, he was alone.

PETER WYATT
> We were down the pub watching the Home Internationals and Smike came in asking - had we heard what Botley had gone and done?

JERRY ZMUDA
> Some of his classmates had decided to have an end-of-term summer outing to Hampton Court, and Botley had found out about it - but it seemed they didn't really want him to go.

DERMOTT COLLINS
> So they're all at Hampton Court, having a look round and Botley goes for a slash and these fuckers go and hide - to try and lose him. Botley comes out of the toilet all upset and goes looking for his so-called buddies that have deserted him. He finds them in the pub by the river. They're all laughing and he goes up to them, he punches one kid in the kidneys, throws a chair at another kid and then knocks him in the river. Then he throws a pint over the girls and all through it he's shouting "I'M BOTLEY! I'M BOTLEY!"

PETER WYATT
> This was classic. We just had to hear this from the horse's mouth. So I bell him up. He's all sheepish, and I ask if he fancies coming out for a beer.

JERRY ZMUDA
> He seemed really moved when we met him. After this incident he must have thought he was going to be branded forever a weirdo, and no-one was going to talk to him ever again. But his freaky behaviour

found solid friends and admirers in us three. I wrote a song in tribute to him called *I'm Botley*. It went like this -

> *I'm Botley,*
> *Don't walk away from me.*
> *I'm Botley.*
> *You don't even know me.*
> *Just gimme a chance,*
> *- gimme a chance,*
> *Give me a chance to know you.*

It had a real angry punk rock rage to it.

AIN'T YOUR MUM GOT NO GHERKINS?

PETER WYATT

In all weathers we played our music in that ramshackle lock-up garage. In the winter we froze our nuts off - and in the summer we baked to a frazzle - but there was no place on earth I'd rather be. And that's where Septimus Grundy really came alive in the summer of '81.

DERMOTT COLLINS

Saturday mornings were sheer bliss! Peter would open up the garage, sling the kettle on. We'd chat, play some records and then pick up our instruments and jam. All day just playing along. In the afternoon Botley and Smike would come over, and we'd play for them. Buckle, I mean Stuart had made all the difference.

JERRY ZMUDA

Saturdays were wonderful - in the morning playing with the boys and in the afternoon - another "English" session with Lydia.

BUCKLE AKA STUART MARTIN

I was really starting to enjoy jamming with the boys. I had helped to improve their playing and they treated me with a lot respect. They even gave me a nick-name - Buckle. On account of the large buckle I wore on my belt.

DERMOTT COLLINS

Little did he know.

BUCKLE AKA STUART MARTIN
> I would play music with these boys - but I would never, I mean never, go out with them socially. Peter was always suggesting gigs to go to, but each time I politely made my excuses.

LYDIA DANCEY
> Jerry would often talk about the boys, tell me about what they got up to - and I was intrigued. I was dieing to meet them, but Jerry seemed reluctant.

DERMOTT COLLINS
> Jerry told us he had a girlfriend. We didn't believe him.

LYDIA DANCEY
> Kay was a friend of mine from class at Brooklands - her parents were moving into a large house in St. George's Hill. Only the ultra-wealthy can afford a house there.

DERMOTT COLLINS
> Me old man did some building work in St. Georges Hill. Mansions bigger than schools, he told me, but obviously not 'orrible like Feltham.

PETER WYATT
> St. Georges Hill - home to the rich and famous. The Beatles used to live there - or at least John Lennon and Ringo Starr did. I heard that you would often see the music hall comedian Tommy Trinder walking his lion.

LYDIA DANCEY
> So when Kay invited me to come over and have a look at the new house, I jumped at the chance. Her parents hadn't moved in yet - they had the decorators in, and the carpet hadn't been laid down. But it was spectacular. It was modern, split level, with this wonderful marble spiral staircase in the middle. I instantly pictured a swinging sixties gathering with Peter Sellers, Jean Shrimpton and David Bailey. I said to Kay – "You simply must have a party here."
> So I feel somehow responsible.

FELTHAM MADE ME   125

JERRY ZMUDA

Life is bewildering enough when you're a teenager. You've got raging hormones, and all the stress about finding your place in the world. You don't need drugs to throw into the mix.

LYDIA DANCEY

Kay said - "The party would give us the chance to meet your new boy-friend that you're telling me so much about."

JERRY ZMUDA

I'd planned to spend Saturday afternoon with Lydia, while the rest of Septimus Grundy practised without me. I felt bad, so I called them and said – "Do you boys fancy coming to a party in a big house in the Hills this evening?"

PETER WYATT

Smike came round the garage that afternoon. Under his arm he had a Brian Eno album he wanted to 'open us up to.' He also had a bag of these things he called Magic Mushrooms.

DERMOTT COLLINS

It was always nice to get a visit from Smike.

PETER WYATT

It was a hot and sunny afternoon, we started on these mushrooms not thinking too much about it - pretty soon the craziness began. Dermott said "Uh! Me Rockfords" impersonating a friend of his Dad's. It's rhyming slang - Rockford Files - Piles. We all laughed like lunatics and we found that we couldn't stop.

DERMOTT COLLINS

One minute we're talking about getting the right bass sound for Peter. Then I see little traces of things moving out of the corner of my eye. I thought they were rabbits. Then all was madness. Then Botters shows up. It seemed a shame to have him miss out on the fun - so Smike obliged with a few more of them mushrooms. Then Botley starts drawing in spray paint on the wall - it was like a kid's drawing - you know from primary school.

He drew a sad-faced dog, a grinning wolf and a large orange bear.

PETER WYATT

It was his picture of us. How he saw us. Jerry was the sad-faced dog, Dermott the laughing wolf and I was the big bear. I was touched - I'd stopped laughing, now I was crying, crying with the beauty of it. I told Botley I loved him, and then I told him that his drawing would be the front cover of our album. Then we all started laughing again.

JERRY ZMUDA

Lydia and I got to the party early and I was mightily impressed - real luxury. A world away from the egg-box coloured semi-detacheds of Sunbury, or the hovel that is Egmont.

PETER WYATT

It got to about 6, and I said – "Get your glad rags on lads, we're going to a party in the Hills."

DERMOTT COLLINS

Peter said we have to bring a bottle or something. I grabbed a can of lager from the fridge. I gave it a proper shake and we walk all the way there. A coupla miles.

PETER WYATT

And all the way there, Dermott is kicking this can of lager along the street. "Just wait till this baby goes off," he kept saying. I swear I saw him turn into Willie the Wolf before my eyes, hearing his throaty chortle with this can of lager at his feet.

JERRY ZMUDA

People started showing up - nice polite kids - all my age – all doing 'A' levels. Lydia introduced me to all of them but I felt...out of place. They were talking about their 'A' levels and what 'uni' they were going to. I kept changing the subject, asking if they were into punk - and whether they'd seen The Jam. I wasn't really clicking at all, and I was looking forward to my pals turning up.

LYDIA DANCEY

Three guys turn up - walking up the drive. Two of them are pushing this guy up in a wheel barrow. The guy in the wheel barrow has got this most austere haircut - like something out medieval times - and the other guy with the deranged stare was saying to Kay - "Where do you want your Botley delivered?" The large fair-haired boy was the most amenable of the three - he introduced himself as Peter. He said - "We've come to see Tommy Trinder walk his lion."

JERRY ZMUDA

As soon as I saw them with Botley in that wheel barrow I knew something was up. Something was different. Dermott and Botley always act strange, and so it was Peter who gave it away - he was all flushed, staring into space.

LYDIA DANCEY

At first the party guests were humouring them. "What does this Botley do?" They rolled Botley out of the barrow - he stood up and said "Uh! Me Rockfords" - and the other two fell about laughing. Just those two.
I mean, in what universe is that funny?

JERRY ZMUDA

Their strange behaviour was getting too much for me - I needed a drink. I found a can of lager on the mantelpiece and I opened it up. It gushed like Mount Etna all over Kay and her boyfriend. They were furious - and soaking wet. She was screaming at me because she thought I did it on purpose. I escaped the scene into another room, to find Botley and Dermott painting the walls. They scrawled on the walls - Ain't you Mum Got No Gherkins?

LYDIA DANCEY

Ain't you Mum Got No Gherkins?

PETER WYATT

Pretty soon a paint fight had started - we thought we were starring in our swinging 60s movie. Then I saw the look of horror on this girl's face.
I explained to Jerry - "Spike has Smiked us." The penny dropped. Jerry went loopy - "Get the hell out of here then - I don't want you lot showing me up." "I think the horse has long bolted out on that one," I told him.

LYDIA DANCEY

>It was at around 11 that the police showed. Just two of them, nothing heavy. It was nothing to do with the noise, they had received a report of a stolen wheel-barrow.

DERMOTT COLLINS

>When I saw the roozers, I cracked one of my favourite jokes -
>Two prostitutes - one says to the other "Have you ever been picked up by the fuzz?" "No but I've been swing round by the tits." We laughed a little too loudly and got stared at by the Old Bill. Then we ran and hid in the woods.

LYDIA DANCEY

>Kay was beside herself when the police arrived. She called the party off and sent everyone home. I stayed to console her, while Jerry sat like a lemon in the kitchen.

DERMOTT COLLINS

>After about an hour - we thought it was safe to come back. The party had finished, and the girl whose house it was, was in tears. I said "Don't worry girl, we'll help you clear up". She started screaming "GET OUT! GET OUT! GET OUT!". Calm down it's not as if we'd smashed anything.

PETER WYATT

>A coffee table got smashed, Botley had done it by jumping on it when he was singing "Uh! Me Rockfords!"

DERMOTT COLLINS

>Peter's getting mixed up with another party. We definitely didn't smash anything at that party.

LYDIA DANCEY

>Kay was screaming at the Botley crew, and all three of them ran away into the night. Just leaving me and Jerry to clear up all the mess - empty cans, cigarettes and broken glass. So I finally got to meet your friends Huh?

FELTHAM MADE ME   129

JERRY ZMUDA

I tried to explain – "My friends are crazy. But they're not usually THAT crazy."

PETER WYATT

We walked all the way back to the garage. We needed to calm down, so we called Smike and he came over and built a large spliff. We watched the Sun rise over Egmont Court. Beautiful. Then Dermott said "So we finally got to meet Jerry's girlfriend. Do you think we made a good impression?"

DERMOTT COLLINS

Them mushrooms didn't really affect me.

BACK TO THE OLD SCHOOL

PETER WYATT

I couldn't help noticing how much Jerry changed when Lydia came along. He wasn't, I dunno, such a drip. He came out of himself a lot more. It was good to see.

JERRY ZMUDA

With the vast improvements made by Septimus Grundy, and Lydia now part of my life, it was nigh on impossible for me concentrate on my boring old 'A' levels. In hindsight, taking Maths turned out to be bad advice. My mind is literate - not numerate, I can't even remember the number of buses. I had been over-exerting myself on my Maths and getting nowhere. It was totally unrewarding.
So instead of studying I would often stay round Egmont. I'd wake up thinking - I don't fancy going to Feltham School today. Dermott would be there as well and he'd say - "Let's go and visit your girlfriend in Brooklands."

DERMOTT COLLINS

Yup! Having bugger all to do all day was ace, but I missed school life. So when Jerry says he's going to see Lydia at the sixth form college - I jumped at the chance of tagging along.

LYDIA DANCEY

When term started at Brooklands in September '81, I remembered thinking - this time next year I'll be studying in London - and I'll be leaving the boring cotton wool suburbs behind - forever. But it became clear that Jerry was not attacking his education with the same ambition as I was. I tried to explain to him that it was his escape route.

JERRY ZMUDA

So we'd take a stroll down to Weybridge - green and peaceful. Brooklands was set in its own grounds – with tree lined walk ways. The kids all nice and polite. Why did I have to go to school in the grey brutality that is Feltham?

LYDIA DANCEY

I was happy to see Jerry when he visited Brooklands. But it felt wrong - shouldn't you be at your own school? What was weirder was when he'd come over with Dermott. I told him to keep a low profile because I don't think Kay would be especially thrilled to see him.

DERMOTT COLLINS

I loved it there - even sat in on some of the classes.
This teacher bloke saw us in the common room - smoking and chatting with some pot-head types - he gets suspicious. He comes over –
"You're not studying at Brooklands are you? Why are you here then? You're dealing drugs - is that it?"
"What? Me? Dealing drugs? No fucking way. I ain't no low-life sleazy drug dealer." But it gave me an idea.

LYDIA DANCEY

It was Kay that reported Dermott as a suspected drug dealer, and he got escorted off the premises.

DERMOTT COLLINS

I go and see Cobra and told him about my idea - selling puff to the kids at college. Cobra puts his arm around me and says "Why didn't you mention this earlier?" He gives me a lesson in drug-dealing. It's all about blending in and being discreet. This is coming from a geezer with a large snake tattooed on his neck.

PETER WYATT

I was still doing long hours at the petrol station, Jerry was supposed to be doing his 'A' levels, and Dermott? All of a sudden he's real flush - getting the rounds in. You don't have to be Sherlock Holmes to work out what's going on. Then I find a massive stash of puff round Egmont. It's still technically my Mum's gaff - so I'm none too happy.

DERMOTT COLLINS

So I had my circuit - Brooklands, the Food Tech, Esher College, then over to Richmond College. I was making money, making new friends - nice polite kids who laughed at all of my jokes. On Cobra's advice I didn't go by my real name - I got them to call me The Wolf. The Happy Life of a college drug dealer! Good Times!

But I still missed Feltham - the craziness, the wind-ups, the laughter. So one afternoon I thought I'd take a stroll down Memory Lane and take a look around, maybe sell some puff. I went to see Mister Sea-lion himself, Mr. Dunne the metal-work teacher.

MR. DUNNE (Feltham School teacher)

What was it like seeing Dermott a year after he'd left school? Troubling. It was like - they've let you out into the big bad world? How are you coping? How do you live? What are doing for money? He said he does OK - and if I needed some good Black Leb - he could sort me out. I laughed, thinking he was joking - then I realised...

DERMOTT COLLINS

In places like Brooklands and Esher College you can walk around chat up the girls - and it's all fine. At Feltham School these herberts came up to me.

"What are you doing here? You ain't from this school!"

"No I left."

"Well fuck off."

"No you fuck off - I'm an old boy - I used to rule this playground."

"Well we rule it now - FUCK OFF!"

FELTHAM MADE ME   132

Then they lay into me. Getting roughed up by a bunch of 15 year olds when you're 17 is not good for the old ego. I had to face facts - this world was not my world any more.

THE BIG LOG SHED SESSIONS

PETER WYATT

I told the boys that pretty soon we'd be good enough to take the old feller out on the road.

JERRY ZMUDA

You mean Septimus Grundy? Play live? To an audience? Listening to my songs? That was my dream. The very thought made me itch and girate with anticipation.

PETER WYATT

Why not? We're racing through the songs in practice, one or two fluffed notes, a bit out of tune here and there. But we've got to make that move from garage to stage at some time.

DERMOTT COLLINS

I was having a laugh just playing in the garage with Jerry and Peter - and Botley hanging around. Playing live? Yeah why not? Everybody knows I love an audience.

JERRY ZMUDA

From the moment Peter said that, we didn't practice any more - we REHEARSED. Rehearsed our live set. It upped the stakes and gave us something to aim for.

PETER WYATT

Botley was our audience, our advisor. We played a song to him in the garage and he'd go - "It needs a bit more drumming" or "The chorus isn't quite there". Or quite often - "That sounds too much like The Jam."

BUCKLE AKA STUART MARTIN

Once again it was down to me to tell the Clueless Trio how the music scene worked. YOU NEED TO RECORD A DEMO - IN A PROPER

STUDIO - NOT ON A CASSETTE TAPE IN YOUR GARAGE. A selection of four or five of your best songs. Chris Logan, a mate of mine, had a little studio over in Chertsey. We'd have to pay him a couple of hundred, so start saving.

DERMOTT COLLINS

We thought we were going to be recording in some plush mansion house. Turns out it's some geezer's garden shed. And we had to make our own tea.

JERRY ZMUDA

We get to the studio-stroke-large garden shed and predictably Dermott is giving it, as he would say, the north and south. Telling the guy that we want our banquet at 12, and send the groupies in at 2. He wasn't acting like a rock star - he was acting like a cretin.

PETER WYATT

We put a list down of our strongest songs. Jerry had just written a quite good one called *The Stranger*, which goes -
> *I was born here, but I feel that I don't belong,*
> *I was raised here, but I just don't seem to be able to get along.*
> *I am Stranger - a Stranger in my own land.*

DERMOTT COLLINS

I never liked *The Stranger* - what a dreary load of old shite.

THE BIG LOG (OWNER OF TERRAPIN STUDIO)

The mouthy one asked my name - I said Chris Logan. By mid-morning he was calling me the Big Log. Cheers guys - I make you sound like The Who and you call me the Big Log.

JERRY ZMUDA

I learnt so much from that day with the Big Log. He introduced me to the concept of dynamics. Don't sing a song the same way all the way through - change the mood half way through - whisper a line, then scream it. Wow!

PETER WYATT

He made us sound pukha! Finally nailed my bass sound. I still wasn't the geezer out of Chic - but after a few beers I swear you couldn't hear too much of a difference. My bass lines were... fluid.

THE BIG LOG

What I couldn't help noticing was the way the mouthy one was always smiling when he played his guitar - smiling and looking around. I asked him about it. He said that when he watches these hairy rockers on the Old Grey Whistle Test, they'd be playing their guitars and pulling faces like they're having a real hard shit. But he wanted to make it look easy. I was impressed with that attitude.

DERMOTT COLLINS

I told the Big Log straight - I don't want you making me sound like some pub rock bozo. He got me to go easy on the effects pedals and hit them at the right time. He made me sound fierce! In no time I was hanging on his every word. The Big Log knew his shit.

THE BIG LOG

I suggested filling their sounds with some keyboards. The mouthy one threw his guitar down and declared -
"No Way! The Who never had any keyboards."
The diplomatic fair haired one said - "I think you'll find they did."
"Not on any of the good stuff!"
"*Baba O'Riley* and *Won't Get Fooled Again* - they're good." And they nearly had a fight. Working with those boys was draining.

PETER WYATT

At the end of the session we played back the demo - again and again and again. We sounded so 'professional' - like a proper band. Driving home I was made up. Botley was with me and he said - "I don't why you're so surprised - I always knew you could sound like that." Cheers Botley – you're a gent.

JERRY ZMUDA

Botley was our biggest fan. Our only fan. Our inspiration - the runny Evostick that bonded the woobly Airfix plane of our friendship together.

FELTHAM MADE ME   135

PETER WYATT

The songs we put on the demo were *The Stranger*, *Do the Stranded*, *Mr. Frospawn Hates Punk Rock*, *I'm Botley* and an instrumental track called *Donkey Planet*.

The stand out track was *Do The Stranded* - it was nothing to do with Roxy Music, it was a rare example of Dermott and Jerry working on lyrics together, and it was all about when Dermott was left stranded in London looking for Angela. A powerful song, though to be frank I thought Jerry's vocal were a little weak.

DERMOTT COLLINS

I wanted to sing *Do The Stranded* - it was my story. I really got into playing it and I would give it loads of backing vocals - thinking about my Angela.

PETER WYATT

After the thrill of recording the demo had died down, we all sat in my living room saying – "who the fuck do we send it to?" We made a list. John Weller - manager of the Jam. It took us a couple of minutes to think of someone else - Polydor, The Jam's record label. Then John Peel. Who else?

LYDIA DANCEY

They played me the demo - and I thought it was quite good - surprisingly. I was mildly impressed. But just that - mildly impressed. But being good is not enough in this world. You need to work hard - and know the right people. But - my God these boys were clueless about the music business. I had to come up with a hit-list for them - record companies, The NME, Melody Maker, Sounds.

JERRY ZMUDA

We needed feed-back on the demo. It sounded good to us, but what was it like really?

PETER WYATT

The only person we knew in the misc biz was Grant at Record Scene. So I take the tape down there and give it to him and say – "go on, put it on."

GRANT WILLIAMS

"I can't put it on now," I told Peter. "I'll lose all my customers. Ha! No but seriously." I promised I'd play it at home. I oozed insincerity. I felt obliged to show support to these young kids, but really I wished they wouldn't bother.

When Peter came back the next week asking what I thought. I said it had "potential." I lied again. Hadn't even listened to it. I mean it was bound to be shit. Obviously.

JERRY ZMUDA

So a good demo - and nothing. The spider of harsh reality bit me hard - nobody in this world is interested in me and my crappy little band.

OPERATION SARAH - THE STRATEGY MEETING

PETER WYATT

I had been going out with the girls - but nothing serious. I still had a thing for Sarah. I decided I was going to do something about it. NOW! If I left it any later, eventually I'd hear the dreaded news that she was marrying Terry South. With the Big Log session coming out so good, I was brimming over with confidence and ready to take anybody on.

DERMOTT COLLINS

I told Cobra that Peter was ready for some dirty tricks.

PETER WYATT

Cobra came round my place to hold a strategy meeting.
"We attack from two angles," he told me "you have to impress Sarah - that's down to you. But you've also got to get her to hate Terry."
"How?" I asked.
Cobra did that sly grin of his "Dirty tricks - me boy, dirty tricks."

JERRY ZMUDA

What the hell was Peter doing getting advice from Cobra? I thought he knew better than that.

PETER WYATT

I don't play dirty tricks on people. But this was Terry South - the dead leg merchant from my first day at Feltham. The man who laughed at my car, in front of Sarah. Revenge was brewing, so me and Cobra hatched a plan.

TERRY SOUTH

If I was to steal some cars - why would I park them in the slip road behind my back garden? Why? Why?

SARAH BAXTER

He lost it. Terry really lost it, accusing all sorts of people that he was set up.

TERRY SOUTH

The Old Bill couldn't prove nothing. All they had on me was that three cars had been stolen from the showroom at work. Somebody tips them off that they were parked round the back of my house. Someone was trying to fit me up. Who?

SARAH BAXTER

It was a great relief when the police announced they didn't have enough evidence to press charges. But I saw a side to Terry I didn't like.

DERMOTT COLLINS

Cobra was a real mate. When you nick a car - you run the risk of doing bird. So if you're going to run that risk you've got to make sure it's worth it. When Cobra stole them cars, he could have sold them on for a well decent wedge. But he didn't. Instead he planted them round the back of Terry South's house. That's a real mate for you.

A FRIGHTENED WOLFF

DERMOTT COLLINS

So I'd been serving up puff to the students of Surrey for a couple of months now. Minding me own business not doing anybody any harm, when one day outside Brooklands a big black car pulls up. A dark-skinned meaty geezer with frizzy hair gets out and slings me in the back of the car.

PETER WYATT

I told Dermott to stop dealing - it's dangerous - a mug's game - all the usual bit. Does he fuckin' listen?

DERMOTT COLLINS

Even scarier than the guy with the frizzy hair is the geezer in the driving seat. "What's your name?"
"They call me The Wolf."
"Don't fuck around - you cunt!" He yells. "What's your fucking name?"
"DDDDDDDerrmotttt CCCCCCCCollins." Was it plain-clothes? Was I looking at a stretch of bird? When he gave me a whack across me chops with his chunky ringed hand, I twigged they weren't Old Bill.
He gives me a warning - "Stay off this patch - stay off any patch. If I see you dealing again, you'll spend the rest of your miserable life in a wheelchair. Understand?"
I nod feebly and they let me out. I went round Cobra's and he was going - "I'll find out who they are - I'll have words."
I said - "Leave it - I've had it. This wolf is retiring from the scene."
Cobra's screeching - "You can't back out at the first sniff of bother. Where's your bottle? You need bottle to live this life!" I told him - "I ain't got it" - and walked out.

PETER WYATT

Cobra called him a coward. But I was delighted Dermott did the right thing. On the downside, it was a drag having Dermott back to having no money again. I said to him – "Didn't you save any fucking money when you were dealing?"

LYDIA CHOMPING AT THE BIT

LYDIA DANCEY

I never felt comfortable when I went round Egmont. It was Dermott - he was always strange with me. I sensed he was looking at me while

I was looking the other way. Then he'd show off and act as if I wasn't even in the room. Like it was only the boys that mattered.

DERMOTT COLLINS

Lydia Dancey? A damn fine girl. Too good for Jerry. Real nice looking - in a horsey kind of way.

LYDIA DANCEY

Dermott would say things to me like - "I bet you're chomping at the bit to be living in London" or something about me being in a "stable" relationship. Then I realized what he was doing. He was referring to me looking like a horse. It was intimidating and hurtful.

PETER WYATT

Lydia - what a sweet girl. It was great to have her come round, because otherwise we're just a bunch of geezers talking geezer stuff. She was real intelligent, and knew a lot about music, which is unusual for a girl. Jerry had really lucked out there.

LYDIA DANCEY

Peter was always a perfect gentleman. He spent the first few months trying to convince me that he wasn't really a tripped out freak who turned up to parties with stolen wheel-barrows. He was always bringing me into the conversation and offering me cups of tea. Dermott on the other hand was always shutting me out of the conversation and trying to get me to make the tea. Peter tried to make me feel comfortable - but it was nigh on impossible with Dermott in the room.

LOSING OUR MUSICAL VIRGINITY

PETER WYATT

March '82 - and I was itching to play our first ever gig. I had the boys round my house and we sent out demos to all the venues in the music papers. Then I got hold of the yellow pages and sent demos to all the pubs in the area. Naive or stupid? You decide.

DERMOTT COLLINS

How many envelopes did I stuff? I didn't join a band for this.

JERRY ZMUDA

A big row kicked off when Dermott said "this is bird's" work and told Lydia to get packing. I stepped in and told Dermott to get lost. I ended up having to pack most of them myself.

PETER WYATT

Botley - God bless him - ended up stuffing most of the envelopes.

PETER WYATT

So after sending out literally hundreds of demos, we waited for the phone to ring. Nothing.

DERMOTT COLLINS

The Airman is a pub right close to where we went to school. Typical geezer's boozer - every Thursday night they used to put on this Blues Brothers type band called Past Caring. They were completely shit, but quite good in a "I've-got-my-beer-on-the-sideboard-here" way, if you get my drift. So I went and saw the Guvnor about playing a gig there.

PETER WYATT

So we finally get a gig. Of all the places in the world to lose our musical virginity, I wouldn't have chosen a Feltham boozer. But it's a gig. Our first gig. Would Sarah come along?

JERRY ZMUDA

I was thrilled when Dermott said he'd got us a gig at the Airman. This will sound pathetic but for the next two weeks I couldn't think about anything else. 'A' levels? Stuff the 'A' levels - I'm playing the Airman in Feltham.

PETER WYATT

And of course Botley was as excited as the rest of us. I told him he could be our roadie, and he was chuffed to bits.

JERRY ZMUDA

The afternoon of the gig I was more nervous than I'd ever been in my whole life. There I was at home pacing around, playing records, thinking about taking up smoking, waiting in agony for Peter and

Dermott to come over in the van, When they finally turn up - hours late, instead of going straight to the venue to set-up, we drop off at a caff for a late lunch. I was palpitating with panic.

DERMOTT COLLINS

Made me laugh, Jerkski getting all edgy over some gig at the Airman. Course I wound him up - you have to, haven't you?

PETER WYATT

We turn up at the venue and something's not quite right. The young barman, a studenty type called Dave, said he knew nothing about a support band playing tonight.

JERRY ZMUDA

As soon as we got there I wanted to finally set up, and rehearse our set before the audience turn up. But oh no! What's going on? Dermott's demanding this thing called a Rider from the young barman - which apparently is free drinks for the band.

DERMOTT COLLINS

This herbert wouldn't give us our rider. Knackers! Then he starts giving it the NME north + south about how guitar music is dead, and that drum kits would be museum pieces soon. Like we're all going to be listening to bollox like the Human League. His choice phrase was - "it's all been said with guitars and drums." I told him what hadn't been said before with guitars and drums – "DAVE THE BARMAN IS FULL OF SHIT! That's our opening song."

JERRY ZMUDA

I stepped in - "Don't mouth off to the staff." I told him. When Dave goes to change the barrels, the next thing I know, Dermott jumps over the bar to help himself. It was when Dave was chasing Dermott round the pub that the Guvnor was mentioned for the first time.

PETER WYATT

So while them two were squabbling with the barman, it was down to me and Botley to set up Buckle's drums kit. Buckle couldn't get the day off work, so he was going to join us later. Then this long-haired type, Sonic the sound-man, shows up.

FELTHAM MADE ME   142

DERMOTT COLLINS

> This bozo was more like a dungeon and dragons type. He was wearing a Past Caring road-crew T-shirt and starts bragging about him being the thirteenth member at the controls. Wow!

PETER WYATT

> Sonic tells us Past Caring have got a big following. "You're guaranteed twenty to thirty people wherever they play." He boasts.

DERMOTT COLLINS

> Call that a following? I get a better turn-out to watch me play snooker.

PETER WYATT

> What was really worrying was that Sonic the sound guy also knew nothing about any support band. We winged it and told him we were definitely playing, and he agreed to soundcheck us.

JERRY ZMUDA

> It was really dodgy, this Sonic chap said that there is never a support band for Past Caring. When I considered the guy who booked the gig - Dermott Collins - something was definitely amiss. Anyway Peter does the talking and eventually, at long last, we are doing OUR FIRST EVER SOUND-CHECK. Two-two-two.

DERMOTT COLLINS

> Sonic the hairy one behind the controls is reading the paper while we're sound-checking. I shout in the mic –
> "Sonic! Sound geezer! Can we check our levels please? Sorry if we're keeping you from your dungeons and dragons."
> That got him all red-faced. "I haven't played dungeons and dragons in almost three years!"

JERRY ZMUDA

> I looked to Peter to calm the situation - we need this Sonic guy! Then a much bigger problem, showed - THE GUVNOR.

FELTHAM MADE ME   143

PETER WYATT

I'm sweet-talking Sonic apologising for Dermott, when a large dark shadow appears behind me. I look round and gasp. This huge bear of a man is behind me. "Who are you?"
I smile – "We're the band."
He doesn't smile back. "You're not Past Caring."
"No we're not."
"Past Caring are the only band booked to play tonight."

DERMOTT COLLINS

I talk to the Guvnor. He denies telling me we could play. Actually come to think of it he probably didn't, he said come down on open mic night and do a turn then. I let Peter do the talking - he's good at this.

JERRY ZMUDA

This gig meant everything - absolutely everything - to me. Peter Wyatt to the rescue - he'll sweet talk him into it.

PETER WYATT

I was saying – "A short set, you don't have to pay us. Fifteen minutes and we're gone."
The Guvnor is a rock. He isn't having any of it. Then Jerry comes in all desperate - "Please let us play." The Guvnor walks away - Jerry calls him back.

JERRY ZMUDA

I said – "This may sound desperate. But we'll pay YOU to play."
The man puts his arm around me - squeezes me in an uncomfortably tight grip, he says - "I'll give you desperation mate - on a life support machine. Got it?"
Then he gives my face a firm pat. Menacing or what?

PETER WYATT

Then he walks off - saying "I am going to my office - if you're not out of here by the time I come out again - THERE WILL BE SERIOUS TROUBLE." What can you do?

JERRY ZMUDA

As he walked off, I was devastated - no gig tonight. Then abject disappointment turned to anger. At who? Dermott of course. He gives the north and south at every person we come across, but when it comes down to it, when we actually need some front - he backs down.

PETER WYATT

I had to break them two up. I said - "Come on - there's nothing else for it. Let's get the equipment in the van."
Sonic goes home to get changed, but when Buckle our drummer shows up, things took a whole new direction.

BUCKLE AKA STUART MARTIN

I turn up and the boys are taking my drum kit down. I wasn't having it. I hadn't arranged with MY guvnor to leave work early, just to have some geezer say we can't play. Where is this GUVNOR geezer? Jerry points a shaky finger to his office door.

PETER WYATT

I followed Buckle into the office. Buckle goes - "Is it you who says we can't play?" The Guvnor's not even looking up - "Yes haven't you gone yet?" Then Buckle says something I still can't believe to this day...

BUCKLE AKA STUART MARTIN

"Let's go outside to the car park and discuss it."
The man gets up and he's a mountain. Oh Fuck!

PETER WYATT

We got out in the car-park. "Alright then mouthpiece," the Guvnor taunts him. Buckle, like a crazy rhinocerous, head-charges him.

BUCKLE AKA STUART MARTIN

The guvnor bats me back – but I head charge him again. This time right into his stomach. I feel his great weight go down as he grabs me into a headlock. So there's me grappling with him – he starts to pummeling my head and I think – this isn't right, there's four other blokes looking on here – and they're supposed to be on my side.

DERMOTT COLLINS

The Guvnor turns into a wild animal – shouting "Who do you think you're dealing with? You're out of your league!"

JERRY ZMUDA

With trepidation we dive into help out. It took all five of us to get the Guvnor pinned to the ground. Buckle shouts - "Get the gaffer tape." Botley runs to the van. It's a fierce struggle, arms and legs flailing, but eventually we've gaffered him up - mouths, hands and legs. We lift him up and throw this massive weight into our van.

DERMOTT COLLINS

We slam the van door shut on him – and laugh it right up. Back in the venue, we're larging it. When Sonic comes back changed into his Past Caring gear we tell him that the Guvnor has said we can play. All this time while the Guvnor is struggling, all gaffered up in our van. We look out the window and the van is shaking from side to side. What a top fucking cackle!

PETER WYATT

In the pub we were laughing heartily, buying round after round for Buckle, the man who made it all possible.

JERRY ZMUDA

I on the other hand was not quite so celebratory. I hated to think of the consequences of all of this. But I just knew that at last we were going to finally play to an audience. Albeit to a handful of people.

PETER WYATT

The place is very slow in filling up, a lot of our so-called mates hadn't showed. Maybe it was a good TV night. In fact Botley - our only true mate - was the only one that showed. It gets to about 8 o'clock and there's barely a dozen people in. But we thought we might as well hit the stage.

JERRY ZMUDA

My opening words to the audience were – "Good evening ladies and gents - we are definitely <u>not</u> Past Caring."

DERMOTT COLLINS

"This one's called 'Dave The Barman Is Full Of Shit!'"
Then Uh! Me Rockfords! Who the fuck let the fucking Guvnor out? Someone must of have seen the shaking van. He appears in the doorway, snorting flames and makes a charge straight at us.

PETER WYATT

We had to get out of there double sharpish. Me and Buckle grappled with the Guvnor - while Botley, Dermott and Jerry slung what they could in the van – guitars, amps and pieces of drum kit.

DERMOTT COLLINS

Past Caring who are all dressed up like the Blue Brothers start getting involved. I was fighting them off with the mic stand.

JERRY ZMUDA

The only thing that mattered now was getting ourselves and our equipment out of there.

PETER WYATT

I drove out of there like a bat out of hell. Past Caring and the Guvnor tearing after us. So that, ladies and gents, was Septimus Grundy's debut gig.

CARPET STAIN ANTHOLOGY

JERRY ZMUDA

I was getting constant bad dreams about having to sit exams and not having revised properly, making me wake up with ill feelings. Did nothing about it though. When it came down to it I just couldn't be bothered with the 'A' levels, so I knew I was going to do badly.

DERMOTT COLLINS

The Sulphate Crash course is what Jerry needed to do. Cram a whole two years of revising in just a coupla hours.

JERRY ZMUDA

Then the bad dream came true - I sat at the exam desk, knowing little or nothing of what the exam papers were asking of me.

My Sulphate crash course in History helped though. I wrote an excellent essay, the only trouble was I'd scrawled it all down on the desk - none on the exam paper.

DERMOTT COLLINS

Fuck exams. Who needs 'em?

JERRY ZMUDA

But how badly was I going to do? Bad enough to go to a fifth rate college? Or bad enough that no-one would take me? In August the envelope came - an E and 2 Fs. I told my Mother that E stood for Excellent and F stood for First Class - and she was happy for a time.

NATALIE ZMUDA

When I found out from a friend what an E and 2Fs really meant - I was crest-fallen. I hate to say it - but this really was the last straw.

JERRY ZMUDA

Over the years Father had become an increasingly distant figure. In one sense this was Ok because when my 'A' level results came out, he didn't care one way or the other. But Mother - well she never forgave me after that.

LYDIA DANCEY

He could have done better if he had really tried. He was trying to act all cool and unaffected by it. Dermott held a drinks party in the garage. But it was all a bit pathetic really. My 'A' level results came through and I did better than expected - an A and two Bs - I was off to study Media Studies at the Polytechnic of Central London.

JERRY ZMUDA

I felt proud that Lydia had done so well. Proud and threatened at the same time.

DERMOTT COLLINS

In honour of Jerry's exams, I came up with a riff of an E chord and two F chords for him to write his drippy lyrics to.

JERRY ZMUDA

I tried telling myself I didn't need exams where I was going on. I threw any hope and ambition I had into Septimus Grundy.

But what could I do for the short term? I looked to my parents for guidance, but it was clear they really didn't want anything to do with me any more. So I hung around people to whom exams didn't matter - Botley, Dermott, Peter and Smike.

LYDIA DANCEY

I told Jerry to move out - live in London. At that time there was a big squat scene and you could get dole and housing benefit relatively easily. I really pushed him to leave the suburbs, but he was rooted to his mates.

JERRY ZMUDA

So I completely moved into Peter's place in Egmont Court. I took out the last of my belongings from my parent's house. I looked around my bed-room for the last time, I had been happy here once, as a young child. A time of Rupert Bear Annuals and games with Ruben - but that was now far far away, just a faded hazy memory. I looked down at the stained beige carpet. Each stain had a story to it. That's when I got the idea for the *Carpet Stain Anthology* album - each song told the story behind the stain.

PETER WYATT

When Jerry finished school - a new Jerry came out. It was like this cloud wasn't hanging over him anymore - he could be himself. He didn't stoop so much. But the biggest change was in the garage when we rehearsed. Before I always thought he was the weak link in the band. But now instead of straining to sing - he shouted more, just really belted the song out. Like he didn't give a fuck. And he started standing up to Dermott.

DERMOTT COLLINS

Me and Jerry had a big row over the song *Do The Stranded*. Jerry wanted to rework it and re-name it *London After Midnight*. We were nose to nose, inches away from a bust up if Peter hadn't stepped in. 'Course Jerry was right - *Do The Stranded* is a pathetic name for a song and *London After Midnight* was much better. But couldn't back down - could I? So I goes to Peter a bit later – "Tell him we can change it."

BUCKLE AKA STUART MARTIN

Dermott was always taking the piss but suddenly this new Jerry was standing up to him. I remember once Jerry was reading out his new lyrics and Dermott was supposed to come up with a riff to go with it.

DERMOTT COLLINS

Taking the Arthur, I started playing along to his lyrics with the riff from *Black Betty*. Jerry instead of singing his own lyrics, starts singing "Wow-oh oh Dermott he's a cunt. Wow-oh oh Dermott he's a cunt. If he was black I'd join the National Front."

PETER WYATT

Dermott he's a cunt - to the tune of *Black Betty* - hilarious.

JERRY ZMUDA

Dermott was really starting to rankle me. This band was now my life - my entire life, and he was still treating it as an opportunity to clown around. Even his Basil Brush laugh didn't do it for me anymore. Monkey Time can go to hell.

If Septimus Grundy doesn't get anywhere, well it doesn't bear thinking about.

Chapter 5
'Muda The Brooder

BRITISH STEEL

PETER WYATT

Dermott says to me - "They put bands on at the Feltham Football club. Why not give them a call?" After what happened at The Airman he'd passed on gig arranging responsibilities to me. So I phone up, and the manager goes -
"As it happens you can play this Friday, the support band has just cancelled."
"Oh yeah? Who's the headline?"
"British Steel."
"Never heard of 'em."

JERRY ZMUDA

We turn up to Feltham Football Club and the headline band are sound-checking. But right away we sense something amiss. Was it because all the headline band had shaven heads? The union jack t-shirt on the guitarist? The Swastika tattoo on the lead singer' arms? Or was it the song they were singing? A charming little ditty. The lyrics made a lasting impression -

> They try to brand us criminal, violent and psychotic –
> But what they fail to realize –
> We're just being patriotic.
> British Steel - British Steel.

LYDIA DANCEY

I got a panicky call from a pay-phone. Jerry whispering
"Whatever you do, do NOT come to the gig tonight."
"Why?"
"They're all Nazis!"
"Who?"
"The headline band, the entire audience - they're all Nazis."

PETER WYATT
>This lot were like the mob who came after us at Southampton train station.

BUCKLE AKA STUART MARTIN
>I told them straight - there's no point playing to an audience like this.

DERMOTT COLLINS
>I said – "Why not? They might like us". Then Botley chips in - "If they like us, we might get saddled with a following of Nazi skinheads coming to all our gigs – like Sham 69."

BUCKLE AKA STUART MARTIN
>These people are the arse end of humanity - they just spend all their time kicking people in. If we play - they'll nick our equipment - they'll gob at us.

DERMOTT COLLINS
>Gob at us? I don't fancy that at all. Spreads germs. OK - let's call it off. But I couldn't leave without given them some kind of a performance. So I ran on stage.

PETER WYATT
>We put all our equipment in the van, I left the van running as Dermott ran back in and onto the stage. He shouts into the mic "So what do you lot all think about the Pakis?"

DERMOTT COLLINS
>I look out into the audience - a sea of boneheads and tattoos. They're puzzled - some shout back. Then I say –
>"I think they add so much to our community. Just like us Irish."
>I was expecting an angry tidal wave of boneheads, but they just stared and scratched their heads. Like "what's he saying?" I exit stage left - and straight into Buckle's van and off we go.

JERRY ZMUDA
>Just when I'm ready to write Dermott off as complete waste of time - he pulls something like that out of the bag. I loved him for that. We laughed merrily all the way home.

PURPLE RA-RA SKIRT

SARAH BAXTER

It wasn't the car stealing thing that split me and Terry up. It was actually all over a purple ra-ra skirt. I'd bought it from Top Shop and showed it to Terry - he hated it. But worse than that, he told me I was not allowed to wear it. Not in public not around the house - not ever. I told him to stick it. I was much too young to end up being "her indoors."

TERRY SOUTH

Sarah stuck with me throughout the whole car stealing set-up. I really appreciated it. But the thing with Sarah was that she was still into going out - dancing, drinking. But I'd had enough of all of that. I mean you don't want to be doing all of that in you're twenties. You have to grow up - settle down. Otherwise - what's the point?

SARAH BAXTER

So that was it. I moved out and went back to live with my parents. Having lived away from home for over a year, this was a real shock. Having my dinner cooked for me, having to eat it at set times, having to tell my folks when I'm going out - when I'm going to be back. Dad asking me to turn my music down because they're trying to watch *Surprise Surprise*. I couldn't hack it - I decided as soon as my course is finished I'm off out to get a job. Then Peter called.

PETER WYATT

I asked her out on a date. She said No - she had only just split with Terry and wasn't ready to start seeing anyone again. But I wouldn't take No for answer - I wasn't going to put that phone down until she said Yes.

SARAH BAXTER

I admired his persistence. Eventually I had to say Yes - but I said - "We're just meeting for a drink OK? That's it. This ain't the start of anything."

PETER WYATT

After seven years I was finally out on a date with Sarah. This is imy big chance. I needed to impress her. I would get a fancy suit and hire a car for the day.

DERMOTT COLLINS

I told him that if you need to impress Sarah - Cobra can steal you a Spaz Chariot to order. She'll find it hilarious. I mean who wouldn't?

JERRY ZMUDA

So where does Peter choose to take Sarah on his dream date? Ah! The Romance. Staines.

DERMOTT COLLINS

Get rid of unsightly Staines.

SARAH BAXTER

I was worried at first that Peter was going to be all creepy and intense - like "at last - we're together." But he wasn't like that at all. He was very relaxed and he made me feel very relaxed.

PETER WYATT

We had lots to talk about, seeing as we both went to the same school. There was loads to catch up on. We met at this wine bar, and just talked and talked and talked.

SARAH BAXTER

Everything seemed right with Peter. So upbeat and cheery - and he loved my purple ra-ra skirt.

PETER WYATT

We missed the start of the film, and Sarah says - "There's place round here called Jacksons - they play Jazz Funk. I've always wanted to go." I said of course.

SARAH BAXTER

When I first started seeing Terry he would take me to a lot of the soul and jazz funks dos, but after a while, he couldn't be bothered.

Just wanted a pub and a pint - or staying home and watching the telly.
But everything seemed reckless and spur of the moment with Peter.

PETER WYATT

My musical tastes have always been very open, and I liked what I heard
at Jacksons. I heard a record with this amazing slap bass sound - I dash
up to the DJ - "what's this mate?" "Level 42." I was going to try a bit
of slapping on my bass.

SARAH BAXTER

We danced and talked. Talked and danced. Of course we did a little
bit of drinking in-between. It turns out he's still going around with
those two loser clowns from Feltham School. The way he talked
about his friends - real warmth. I was quite moved. I told him I thought
they were pratts - I had to.

PETER WYATT

That night with Sarah, dancing in a club in Staines - one of the best
nights of my life.

SARAH BAXTER

He walked me home and he asked me if I would see him again. I said
of course. We kissed good-night and it felt so nice to be 18 again.

OUT OF THE ARMS OF LYDIA AND BACK INTO THE CLUTCHES OF DERMOTT

JERRY ZMUDA

Dermott said to me - "When your Lydia starts going to college in
London, we can go up and see her." I thought - Ah! No you don't.

DERMOTT COLLINS

So the sneaky sod goes up to the smoke to see his bird without telling
Titus. Once again leaving us, the true heart and soul of The Grundy,
to rehearse in the garage without him. A real shame - I were planning
on giving The Wolf a come-back on the London college circuit.

LYDIA DANCEY

In my first year I was staying in the halls of residence. But the room I was in was really cramped. Like not big enough for a hunchbacked rat.

JERRY ZMUDA

I got on the train and watched the grey rooftops by Hersham station pass away in the distance. I was off to see my girlfriend in London town.

LYDIA DANCEY

It wasn't really an option to have Jerry stay in my bed, it was just a single and very small at that. My friend next door, had an inflatable double bed, and when her boyfriend had stayed last week - they'd both slept on that in the store room. Trouble was - they gave it a bit of a hard ride, and it now had a slow puncture.

JERRY ZMUDA

The night consisted of us, and two of her drab friends, going to some grim student union bar - thread-bare foam-filled chairs and dog-eared posters stuck with blue-tac. They had a juke-box and we all got drunk on snake-bite and black and the girls danced to Sister Sledge. Not that inspiring really, and hardly better than a Friday night out in Hersham. I told Lydia that - and she got all tetchy.

LYDIA DANCEY

The conversation with the girls turned towards the hated Thatcher - would the Falklands factor keep her in?
I was talking about Thatcher's monetarist policies, but Jerry seemed rather clueless. I got the impression he got all his political views from Jam lyrics and NME interviews with Paul Weller. I made the mistake of making a joke about this.

JERRY ZMUDA

I said something about the Tories and she said to me with that hiccupy derisory laugh - "Is that the gospel according to Paul – Paul Weller?"
I looked at her, I didn't see an 18 year old girl - I saw that frumpy middle-aged careers advisor. I told her to get lost - she'd shown her true colours.

LYDIA DANCEY

Jerry could never hold his drink, and that night he was a nightmare. Ranting on about how being a student wasn't that fantastic - and he was glad he failed his 'A' levels. I could tell that already he had terrible chip on his shoulder about it.

He was blind drunk by the time we got back to the halls of residence. I put him in the store room, and I thought about the slow puncture. If I slept on it with him, the bed would get deflated much sooner. So I left him to the air-bed and I slept in my own room.

JERRY ZMUDA

I wake up Saturday morning, in a freezing cold cupboard, aching all over because I'd been sleeping on a hard floor - the air bed had deflated right down. Lydia meanwhile had slept in the comfort of her room. Who wouldn't be annoyed?

LYDIA DANCEY

I look in on him to ask what he wanted for breakfast. And he greeted me by calling me a bitch. I shuddered - he'd never used that word before - and such venom. I tried to explain about the slow puncture, and how I was actually being considerate. But he wasn't listening. So we split up all over a puncture on an air-bed.

JERRY ZMUDA

Sleeping on the hard floor - it made me fume, it was treating me like dirt. I got that from my Mother, from school, from employers. I'd had enough. Lydia was a snob, looking down on me because I wasn't a student type like her. She had a photograph of me in her room. I ripped it up.

LYDIA DANCEY

He tells me he wants to break away from the suburbs - but he does nothing, absolutely nothing about it. The only pro-active thing he does is look for new things to whinge about. It was over - good riddance.

PETER WYATT

I was really sorry to hear that Jerry and Lydia had split up, I offered Jerry the chance to talk about it, and he goes on this ramble about student discos and air-beds. I tried to be a good listener but my mind was elsewhere. After all this time, Sarah and me were together.

JERRY ZMUDA

With Peter spending all his time with Sarah, I was now in one hell of a situation - out of the arms of Lydia and back into the clutches of Dermott. Talk about regression. I had Dermott trying to cheer me up with his Basil Brush impersonations, and me laughing like a drain. Monkey Time all over again. Cobra had lent us a Video Cassette Recorder. Girls - who needs 'em? Not when you've got a VCR.

DERMOTT COLLINS

We watched some pornos and hired some films from the shop, but we really got into taping and watching programmes over and over again. But Peter was missing out on all of this, he was out there in Sarah land.

JERRY ZMUDA

We watched The Jam on the Tube - over and over. *Fawlty Towers* as well. I was bent double with laughter. Then Dermott and I both got into the *Young Ones* - I saw a bit of myself in Rick - made me realize what a pratt I could be.

THEIR FIRST EVER INTERVIEW

JERRY ZMUDA

She was called Yvette - what a sweetheart. Big eyes, peroxide hair, and PVC mac - she came up to us after a gig at the King's Head, Putney, playing with her hair, fidgeting with enthusiasm.

DERMOTT COLLINS

She fancied me the most. They always do - being the Grundy sex symbol. I knew I was in there.

PETER WYATT

She wanted to interview us. Us? Septimus Grundy? Are you sure?

JERRY ZMUDA
> Her fanzine was called NOTES FROM THE UNDERGROUND -
> she'd taken the title from the story by Doestevysky. I was really into
> this.

DERMOTT COLLINS
> It was a bunch of photocopied pages stapled together.

JERRY ZMUDA
> Of course I kept the interview - it was our first ever.

DERMOTT COLLINS
> So she met us backstage and got out her dictaphone then and there -
> and off we went.

TRANSCRIPT

There is strange atmosphere backstage at the Kings Head, Putney. The band
Septimus Grundy have gone down well to a small but appreciative audience, but
the boys are distracted. It seems Buckle their drummer has once again hastily
said his good-byes and chosen not to stay for an après-gig drink with his fellow
band-members. Dermott their fiery extrovert guitarist is speculating why.

DERMOTT COLLINS
> It's you (pointing a finger at Jerry the band's singer.) You put him off.
> He thinks you're a tosser.

JERRY ZMUDA
> Why would he think I'm a tosser?

DERMOTT COLLINS
> Why should he be different from anyone else?

Peter the band's fair-haired and amiable bass player chips in.

PETER WYATT
> He probably thinks we're all tossers. But who cares? As long as Buckle
> does a good job.

YVETTE

So why do you call him Buckle?

DERMOTT COLLINS

After Fatty Arbuckle - the silent comedian. You know because he's a
bit on the large side.

YVETTE

That may be why then.

DERMOTT COLLINS

No - he thinks we call him Buckle on account of him wearing a large
buckle on his belt.

JERRY ZMUDA

So do you want to do this interview then?

YVETTE

We already are - the tape's running.

JERRY ZMUDA

Can you please delete all that stuff about Buckle?

YVETTE

So what are your influences?

DERMOTT COLLINS

Alcohol, puff, cleaning fluid.

YVETTE

No I meant...

JERRY ZMUDA

We're open to all influences, we're not derivative of any...

DERMOTT COLLINS

Uh derivative.

FELTHAM MADE ME   160

JERRY ZMUDA
      Shut up. For me it all began with Punk. That's when I first got into
music.

DERMOTT COLLINS
      Yes the Electric Light Orchestra was the first band Jerry got into it.

JERRY ZMUDA
      No it wasn't.

DERMOTT COLLINS
      He cried when his mother wouldn't let him go to an ELO concert.

JERRY ZMUDA
      Shut Up! This is supposed to be a serious interview.

PETER WYATT
      I like disco and soul - as well as punk. We like all types of music and I
      hope it shows in what we play.

YVETTE
      Thank you Peter.

JERRY ZMUDA
      Just for the record - my sister once had an ELO record, which was
      kept in my room. I only played it a couple of times.

YVETTE
      What do you think of the music scene of the eighties?

JERRY ZMUDA
      We feel like outsiders, we feel disenfranchised by what's going on
      around us. I've just written a song about this - the lyrics...

DERMOTT COLLINS
      Me and Peter turn our instruments up really loud so you can never
      hear Jerry's lyrics.

JERRY ZMUDA

Dermott! Shut Up! I was talking here. The Thatcher government has made us all feel alienated - we want nothing of this consumer culture...

DERMOTT COLLINS

I want to consume another lager. Going to the bar Jerry?

PETER WYATT

I'll go.

YVETTE

No stay - I want to interview all three of you together.

DERMOTT COLLINS (shouting at the door)

Botley! Get us a pint of Hofmeister will ya? Lovely! Ta

JERRY ZMUDA

We're all being brain washed and conditioned into a way of thinking. Consumerism is like drug addiction - yes you get your highs - but ultimately it ends in...

DERMOTT COLLINS

Is he still going on about Thatcher?

YVETTE

He was on a roll on then. Come on Jerry you were saying.

JERRY ZMUDA

I can't. He (points a finger at Dermott) is putting me off. Maybe we should do this alone - you know just us two.

PETER WYATT

Hey - super smooth.

YVETTE

No - I like to do all three of you together.

DERMOTT COLLINS
> (unzipping his trousers) Why didn't you say so before? You wanna see my dictaphone?

YVETTE
> You know what I mean. It's interesting to interview all the band members together, because then I get a picture of the group dynamic. So Jerry you were saying?

JERRY ZMUDA
> Well I've written this song about how religion is fading away, and being replaced by the cult of consumerism.

YVETTE
> So how do you feel about religion?

JERRY ZMUDA
> I'm not into organized religion...

DERMOTT COLLINS
> Stroll on. What the fuck does that mean? You're into disorganized religion?

PETER WYATT
> Yeah - you turn up to church and the vicar's late and everyone's got different hymn books.

Enter Botley with a tray of beers, to the sound of loud cheers.

DERMOTT COLLINS
> (singing) I'm Botley don't walk away from me.

PETER WYATT
> Yvette meet Botley. He's the heart and soul of this band. Ask him some questions.

BOTLEY
> Pleased to meet you.

YVETTE
So what do you do Botley?

BOTLEY
They're my friends. I go to the gigs, watch them rehearse. I have lots of fun.

Meanwhile Jerry and Dermott are rowing over Dermott's supposedly ruining a serious interview.

YVETTE
So what have you got to say about Sepitmus Grundy?

BOTLEY
They could be the best band in the world, if only they stopped squabbling.

NEW YEARS EVE – A FREAK SHOW FOR FREAKS

PETER WYATT
1982 had been a brilliant year. What with Sarah coming into my life, and Septimus Grundy playing live, I thought I'd celebrate it by having a New Year's Eve Party. I didn't want to hold it at the flat in Egmont - it'd get wrecked. So I held it in the lock-up garage where we rehearsed as that was pretty wrecked already.

ROY HOOKE
I visited Peter with Veronica at Christmas, he seemed really cheerful and I got to meet Sarah. He was right, she was a smashing lady. He mentioned his New Years Eve party - and half heartedly invited me. I knew it wasn't a real invite, but I was pleased to get it none the less.

SARAH BAXTER
I'm telling you that New Years' Eve party at the garage was a freak show for freaks. Sam and the girls were having their own party over in Bedfont, but out of loyalty to Peter I had to go to his. You had Botley - I never got the Botley thing, and this long-haired one they called Smike - he was the one who had all the drugs.

PETER WYATT

I'd really gone to town with this party, laid out a spread, and decorated the garage with a Christmas tree and paper chains. Botley put up some of his paintings.

JERRY ZMUDA

We had a big row over Smike's name. It was me that called him that in the first place. It was because at Feltham he looked like a Dickensian urchin - so Smike out of Nicholas Nickleby.

DERMOTT COLLINS

It was because his real name was Gary Carmichael. Michael - so Mike. Then Smike cos he smoked pot all the time. Thing is, Smike couldn't remember himself - that's puff for you. Then Jerkski starts sulking.

SARAH BAXTER

That monster Cobra was there, but thankfully someone told him the Molesey boys were going to show, so he left early. As soon as Septimus Grundy played a live set - Buckle bailed. He was only the sane one there. We were left with the weirdo convention. I couldn't understand Peter hanging around with them.

PETER WYATT

It gave me a happy glow to see all my friends together at New Year.

SARAH BAXTER

It was doing my head in. Dermott had obviously taken something, he was even stranger than normal. The argument now was why Bungle the Bear out of Rainbow wears a towel over his bits when he comes out of a shower, when he's naked the rest of the time. This really rattled Botley's cage. Then Peter stopped the music and did this little speech - and he came over all warm and fatherly. I realized that despite all this nuttiness around him, I was falling in love with him.

PETER WYATT

Jerry didn't seem too happy, he went over to the flat to use the phone.

LYDIA DANCEY

My parents had just bought an ansafone for Christmas - they had been waiting for their first message. We got a slurred drunken message at around 1 AM from Jerry - telling me that he missed me. Not a good way to create a good impression with my parents.

JERRY ZMUDA

I remember feeling sorry for myself and talking to Botley about dieing young. About leaving the party early. Leaving before it got boring. Not wanting to get old. Those stupid adolescent words to Botley will haunt me for the rest of my life.

THE GILBERT AND SULLIVAN SCENARIO

ROY HOOKE

I had a well-paid, respectable job - a sales Manager for a shipping company. But my God it was boring - oppressive even. My amateur dramatics was my escape and of course this was where I met Veronica - the love of my life. My big break for the Manor Players came when they gave me the part of Pooh Bah in the *Mikado*. It was the day of my first performance, and I was at work. The clock on the office wall hit four and I was so excited, in my mind I was already on that stage singing to the blue rinse brigade of Sunbury-On-Thames. The Managing Director came in to my office and says that there's a crisis with a shipment that needed sorting.

PETER WYATT

Mum asked me to go and see Roy sing at the Church Hall in Sunbury. I said - "OK, if I have to. Can I bring my mates?"

ROY HOOKE

I had to work late, it got close to 7 and I was getting anxious, I asked my MD if I could be excused - if somebody else could stay late to deal with this problem. He asked me why. I told him. He said –
"You have to decide what's more important. Your job - or your amateur dramatics."

JERRY ZMUDA

Gilbert O' Sullivan? No thanks. You have to draw the line somewhere.

PETER WYATT

The place was full of old dears moaning and moaning because the curtain was supposed at go at half seven and it was now gone eight. Then eventually Roy came on - he was very good - he trembled a bit when he sang - but he had a good set of lungs on him. Not my kind of music obviously. We went to see him back-stage after the show.

ROY HOOKE

I was delighted that Peter had come along - he was even polite enough to tell me I was good.

I told him I hope I was good. I sacrificed a lot to be here tonight. In the aftermath I was sacked at work and had to rent out my house. So I had to move into Egmont with Veronica.

DERMOTT COLLINS

When Roy and Veronica moved back, it was assumed that me and Jerry would move out. No fuckin' way. We'd been here ages - we had our rights.

JERRY ZMUDA

It made me feel awkward having Roy and Veronica round all the time, but I couldn't go back to my parents. I really was persona non grata there.

ROY HOOKE

Sharing a flat with that lot put a real strain on my relationship with Veronica. She lost a lot of warmth towards me. I tried making a joke about it - "Saying you're the sole bread winner now - can you handle it?" Not amused. It gave me a jolt to get a new job sharpish. And eventually I did - another shipping job. I rented somewhere for me and Veronica to live. But one good thing came out of all this.

PETER WYATT

He blew a well-paid respectable job to perform his music. I respected that. Even though it was some soppy Gilbert O'Sullivan nonsense - I respected the choice he made.

DERMOTT COLLINS

There was a big huff of relief when Roy landed himself a new job and moved out.

MAN ABOUT THE HOUSE – THE CREATIVE EPIPHANY

PETER WYATT

I got a phone call from my old man saying - "Did you see me on Top of The Tops last night?"
"No I didn't. What the fuck are you talking about?"
"Yes I was doing that record *Shipbuilding*." Of course he meant Robert Wyatt - who had the same name as me old man. Only Dad goes by the name of Bob. Bloody fool! This got me thinking.

JERRY ZMUDA

Peter came to me with some scribbled lyrics he wanted help with. First time ever he'd written anything down. It was called *Man About The House*.

DERMOTT COLLINS

I thought Peter's song *Man About The House* was a dig at Jerry. About how he used to pretend to have seen the TV programme just to get in with the kids at school. But it were a lot more personal than that.

JERRY ZMUDA

The lyrics as I recall went something like this -
> You're just a tinny voivr on the phone,
> Stupid jokes make me groan,
> Geoff Hurst is not your mate - neither am I,
> I can barely look you in the eye
> You let us down, you foolish clown.
> You left me to be The Man About the House
I looked at Peter and said – "This is all about your Father isn't it?"

PETER WYATT

> I was quite proud of that song, it sounds up-beat with a strong bass-line, but if you listen to the lyrics – it's well bitter.

JERRY ZMUDA

> So Peter's song got me asking myself the question –
> What is really going on in my life?
> What are the real issues in my life?
> I realized it was stuff like - losing Lydia, Cobra driving a wedge between me and my oldest friend. And him of course - Dermott Collins - whose shadow I have lived under for so long. And If I wanted to write lyrics that was true to my heart, it should be about things like this. That's when I had my creative epiphany - I wrote *(There Goes A Man Walking) The Wrong Road* and *Feltham Made Me.*

PETER WYATT

> Jerry sung us his new songs. Half way through *(There Goes A Man walking) The Wrong Road* - he starts yelling into the microphone, like yelling at the top of his lungs. I felt the hair at the back of my neck stand on end. At last he was singing from the heart.

DERMOTT COLLINS

> I knew that song *Wrong Road* was about me - straight off. So I answer back with my own song about Jerry called - *Everybody thinks Zmuda Is A Cunt. Yes We Do - Yes We Do - Yes We do.*

JERRY ZMUDA

> The song *Feltham Made Me* was my five years at secondary school, crammed into a three minute pop song. It starts off with me on that first day, frightened and intimidated, but builds in confidence, and by the end, that thing I was so scared of is now a part of me, a part of my character. The lyrics goes like this...
>> *You see a place that's bleak,*
>> *But this is home to me,*
>> *And I'm here to say -*
>> *Feltham Made me,*
>> *What I am today.*

FELTHAM MADE ME   169

PETER WYATT

    I now saw Jerry in a new light. I never knew he had all of this in him.

DERMOTT COLLINS

    'Muda' the brooder is always trying to find stuff to mope about. When we were kids, I remember going round for him and his Mum's at the door - "Jerry can't see you today - he's too upset because Petra the Blue Peter dog has died." I mean for fuck's sake.

THE BIG LOG (OWNER OF TERRAPIN STUDIO)

    I got a phone call from Peter Wyatt – all up-beat and enthusiastic - "We've got some great new songs we are simply dieing to put on a demo."
    I said - "That's great boys - you know my rate, once your cheque is cleared I'll book you in."
    I had to admit it - the new songs showed real progress and I was really impressed with how they had got so musically proficient in such a short space of time. Peter flashed a grin at me and says - "We don't get out much!"

PETER WYATT

    The new songs on the demo were - *Wrong Road, Man About The House, An E and two Fs, Feltham Made Me* and a totally re-worked version of *London After Midnight*.

DERMOTT COLLINS

    This new version of *London After Midnight* had an ace intro - with sound effects of the big city at night - passing cars, police sirens - then the bass and drums kick-in - absolutely amazing. Best of all me and Peter give it loads of backing vocals. We sounded like The Clash!

THE BIG LOG

    They even dressed differently - they were smartly turned out. There was definitely something about this lot - they now looked like a band going places.

PETER WYATT

    And Jerry's vocals wasn't the weak link anymore.

FELTHAM MADE ME   170

Can I describe it as an English Neil Young? OK perhaps not. And Dermott - well Dermott was now a wizard. On *An E and two Fs* - he'd start off with choopy bar-chords - stop and then pick at the strings...it was breath-taking...

JERRY ZMUDA

After we'd finished the demo, amazing though it was - we still faced the same old problem. Who do we send it you? Who the hell cares? I sent a copy to John Peel with a hand-written covering letter about how much his show meant to me. It went like this –

Dear John,
Listening to your show late at night has kept me out of the pubs and away from the off licences. For that I am eternally grateful. Now we are proud to make our humble contribution to the world of music. Here is our latest demo. Hope you like it. Thank you for everything
Lots of Love Jerry (Septimus Grundy).

SEND IN THE CLOWNS – THEY'RE ALREADY HERE

JERRY ZMUDA

Euphoria! That's how I felt after we recorded these new songs. Pure Euphoria! Treasure that moment - it's not something you feel every day. Now I was itching, to play these amazing new songs to an audience.
I asked Peter to set up a local gig at the Hand & Spear in Weybridge, just near Brooklands - Lydia's old college. Pathetically, I was hoping she would show up.

PETER WYATT

We got a decent crowd last time we played there. So the owner was happy to have us back. The crowd is even bigger this time. Some of the Brooklands lot, mostly girls came along - and some of the Molesey chaps had showed. Me and Dermott looked great in this clobber Cobra had given us. Like a band of casuals.

DERMOTT COLLINS

Jerry on the other hand looked a total spaz in this Joy Division trench-coat and a home-made Polska t-shirt.

JERRY ZMUDA

I felt a spiritual yearning to get closer to my Polish roots, discover a new identity. I tried talking to my Father, but he wouldn't even give me the time of day. I wanted him to contact one of our uncles about sending me a Polish football shirt. Nothing doing - so I made my own.

PETER WYATT

We were getting ready to go on stage when I clocked this geezer with a beard - staring like Charlie Manson at Jerry and Peter. I said – "Do you know him?"

JERRY ZMUDA

It was Mr. Heyward our old form teacher from primary school. I went up to him with a smile, but he just glared back.

DERMOTT COLLINS

Then we got on stage. Jerry's about to sing but Mr. Heyward rushes up the front and grabs the mic out of Jerry's mitts. He starts shouting - "Send in the clowns - they're already here." Shouting not singing.

JERRY ZMUDA

We just stopped playing, looked at him and laughed. The audience thought it was part of the act. Then he said - "Now you know what it's like to have your performance wrecked. That's karma." He jumps off the stage and walks out into the night.

DERMOTT COLLINS

Everyone's clapping - though they weren't sure what they had seen.

MR. HEYWARD

I was trying to make a point. But people like that - they just don't get it. God I hope they die!

DERMOTT COLLINS

We couldn't stop laughing about it afterwards - we were singing Send In the Clowns in the van back home.

PETER WYATT

The rest of the gig was a blinder. Towards the end of *Feltham Made Me*, we were all supposed to play out the riff that Dermott had come up with. We're doing this, but then Jerry grabs the mic and starts singing

- *"Never had too much to sing about before,*

- *but tonight tonight tonight Feltham Is Mine,*

- *Feltham Is Mine, Feltham Is Mine, Feltham Is Mine."*

We even had people in the audience singing along. Then Botley got on stage with us and started bashing his tambourine. I looked over at Dermott and we grinned at each other - we'd cracked it.

JOHN PEEL PLAYS THE GRUNDY

PETER WYATT

I thought Charlie Manson had put a curse on us - but the most wonderful thing happened the next night. I still get a tingle when I think of it.

JERRY ZMUDA

We were in the garage winding down after a rehearsal - the radio is on - then it happened. John Peel said the words "Here's a new band who show a great deal of promise - and thank you Jerry for your letter - I like to think of my show as a healthy alternative to alcohol. This is Septimus Grundy."

PETER WYATT

I was in heaven - heaven when I heard Peely play *London After Midnight*. That's my bass on there - that's you Jerry singing, now Dermott's taking to the bridge - and Buckle bashing away - it's us - being played on the radio. In session that night Peely played some other new band called The Smiths - we switched them off.

DERMOTT COLLINS

Septimus Grundy on the radio!!! Fuckinell!!! I called Cobra and he shot round with a bottle of Jack Daniels. He was made up for us.

JERRY ZMUDA

After we got played on Peel I expected to get deluged with phone calls, congratulating telegrams, offers of blow jobs. Didn't happen. But it was still a thrill. Thanks Peely - I will love you forever for that.

PETER WYATT

To me - just getting played on Peel was something special - something to treasure. We used to listen to his show when were nippers, getting into music for the first time. And now we were part of it.

LYDIA DANCEY

I got a phone call at the halls of residence from Peter.
"Peter why are you calling?"
"Jerry wants me to tell you that Septimus Grundy were played on John Peel last night."
"Wow! That's wonderful - why couldn't he tell me himself?"
"You know how he is".
My curiosity was piqued. There was this spotty anorak kid on my floor who was always asking me to go to gigs with him. He taped the John Peel show religiously. I listened to his recording of the show and this time I was suitably impressed by Septimus Grundy - the production was superb. But to be honest I was even more impressed by this new band in session - The Smiths.

JERRY ZMUDA

I was simply dieing to get back with Lydia. She was coming back to Sunbury-on-Thames for the week-end to see her parents - so I knocked back a couple of shots of Jack Daniels and I called her, and trying to sound suitable nonchalant, suggested meeting up.

LYDIA DANCEY

I'd met other boys in the time that I'd split with Jerry. It made me realize he wasn't all that bad. Most guys are emotionally stunted, self-absorbed idiots. The last guy I had been with used to grunt stuff like – "Get In There" - at the beginning of sex. Most off putting. Compared to him, Jerry was an angel.

JERRY ZMUDA

So we met up and after a few drinks, I kissed Lydia and I went into spasms when she agreed to give me a second chance. Riding a wave of optimism I made a drunken declaration – "I want our relationship to be special. Why should I waste time chasing other girls, when I have found THE ONE? You - Lydia Dancey - the love of my life."

DO IT YOURSELF

JERRY ZMUDA

The General Election was coming up but Peter didn't seem bothered, his line was - "they're all the bleedin' same." Naive. So in desperation for some astute political debate I turned to Dermott - his contribution was "Margaret Thatcher - Lager Snatcher!" It was Milk Snatcher - you cretin. He couldn't even get that right. I didn't want to talk to Lydia, for fear of some "gospel according to Paul Weller" remark, and I didn't want a row so soon after getting back together. So I was internalizing everything - and putting it down in my lyric notebook.

PETER WYATT

Septimus Grundy didn't set out to sound punk, it's just how it came out when we started learning our instruments. But the 80s wasn't a time for people like us. It was the age of the ponse - you know the Human League, ABC, Duran Duran - all dressing and sounding like ponces. That is why we never really fitted in with the music scene of the time. So I woke up one morning and thought - Fuck It. If those music biz fuckers won't take any notice - we'll fucking do it ourselves.

THE BIG LOG

Peter called, asking about contacts for pressing a 1,000 seven inch singles. He wanted to put the demo I did with them on an EP.

PETER WYATT

I priced it all up, it was about £750 for the records - a thousand of them - £500 for the sleeves if you wanted them in colour, which we obviously did. Artwork would be free - we'd get Botley to do one of his drawings.

JERRY ZMUDA

Peter sat me down, he was fired up with a sense of purpose. But I didn't like the idea, if we were good enough, surely a record company would pick us up eventually. Putting the record out ourselves is what they call vanity publishing.

PETER WYATT

I explained to him –

"Why should we wait around asking for permission from some record company git to exist as a band? If we press our own record then at least Septimus Grundy is leaving something behind - literally a record that we existed. Something to give to our friends, family. But also for DJs to play at gigs - a promotional tool."

JERRY ZMUDA

Can't we do that with a cassette tape and save some money? I wasn't into this at all - but Peter was on one his missions and very persuasive. But when he talked about the record sleeve I put my foot down.

PETER WYATT

It seemed perfect - get Botley to do one of his drawings of us. Like the one he did in the garage.

JERRY ZMUDA

No way! People will think it's a record made by retarded people. And why was I a sad-faced dog?

DERMOTT COLLINS

I liked being a crafty looking wolf.

PETER WYATT

It was important to keep Botley involved - made him feel part of the firm. I was still worried about him. He had no proper job since leaving school, just temping. We were his only friends - now that was REALLY worrying.

JERRY ZMUDA

OK that's nice Peter, you're a compassionate soul. But that doesn't mean he has to draw the cover for our record.

PETER WYATT

I said – "If we each stump up £500 we could do this record thing."
But Jerry was being such a stick in the mud, going "Uh - I don't where
I can hold of that kind of money." In the end I thought - Fuck It!
Shame.

ROY HOOKE

He should have come to me - I would have happily put up ALL the
cash in a heartbeat. Anything to win Peter's trust and acceptance.

PC HELL

LYDIA DANCEY

I moved out of halls of residence to a flat in Battersea with two friends
- while Jerry was still at that tip with Peter in Egmont Court, Hersham.

JERRY ZMUDA

I wanted my relationship with Lydia to be special, to rise above the
problems of other relationships - jealousies, dominance, lack of
communication. But very soon I'd often find myself with nothing to
say to Lydia and a long silence would fall upon us. Was the silence
because we didn't need to be talking all the time, that we had some
kind of psychic connection? Or was it the same kind of empty silence
that my Mother and Father put me through at home? Sometimes I
couldn't wait to get back on that train back to Hersham and relax
again.

LYDIA DANCEY

Jerry was always talking to me about the song he was trying to write,
reading out lyrics to me. Trying to act like the enigmatic artist all the
time. I wished he could drop the act and just be himself.

JERRY ZMUDA

Lydia and I did the typical things that studenty couples do - like the
Notting Hill Carnival. I was disappointed because I was hoping to be
in on some *Police and Thieves* Clash-style riot. But instead I was
surrounded by loads of fat women dancing with policemen. I said to
Lydia - wouldn't it be funny if I went up to a gang of raggas and said in

a posh Basil Brush accent - "I say! Do you happen to know where the nearest cash-point is? I've only come out with a oner!" She didn't find it funny at all.

LYDIA DANCEY

He said – "Dermott would find that funny." I said – "Go out with Dermott then."

JERRY ZMUDA

I didn't like the girls that Lydia had moved in with. One giggled all the time - mirthless and nervous. I nicknamed her 'giggle factory'. The other one was built like a Russian shot-putter, only ever wore dungarees and looked like Ronnie Barker in drag.

LYDIA DANCEY

The advice I got given was, when you start college, join several clubs and societies - and that's how you meet people. And I met Amy and Felicity at some left-wing affair - I can't remember which. When I heard Jerry make snidey remarks about them I saw red.

JERRY ZMUDA

She started calling me a sexist pig over the Ronnie Barker in drag observation. Apparently I was criticizing her because she was "a woman who didn't conform to the idealized objectification of women." I said to her Dermott would have found that funny.

LYDIA DANCEY

I leapt to the defence of my friends. But in my heart I was disappointed with them. When I signed up at the Polytechnic of Central London - PCL - otherwise known as PC Hell, I had visions of being caught up in a whirlwind of glamorous parties - and meeting a parade of exciting people. Living like a 1980s Edie Sedgwick - but without the self-destruction and hard drugs.
But with Amy and Felicity it wasn't really happening. Going to the Social Sciences end of term disco fundraiser hardly compared to a wild night at the Factory. That's where Jerry could have helped - if he moved to London we could go out more - go to clubs and find out what's really going on in London.

JERRY ZMUDA

Look I know I was tosser when I was teenager. But who wasn't? But Lydia said something that still riles me to this day. The row about my comments about Giggle Factory and Shot Putter extended into her telling me I had no right to write lyrics because I hadn't lived. I lived in "fluffy cotton wool" land in the suburbs and I hadn't suffered enough in life. Cobra had once said something similar and gave me his hard luck story. So in a fit of anger I wrote this song called *Hard Luck Story*.

DERMOTT COLLINS

Hard Luck Story was one of my favourite Grundy songs - the lyrics are quite funny.

> Please your honour, take it easy on me
> My dad used to sodomise me while I watched TV
> He was shooting himself up at the very same time
> While I watched Hector's House - to take it off my mind
> Every time I hear that theme tune I relive the horror,
> Thank Fuck they don't show Hector's House no more.

A TALE OF TWO BANDS

JERRY ZMUDA

In the months after being played on John Peel, we carried on gigging, going down well. In the meantime this other band The Smiths, had signed to Rough Trade and had a series of singles out. By the end of 1983 they'd been on Top of the Tops a couple of times and on the front cover of every magazine. The only press Septimus Grundy got in that time was a photocopied fanzine and a short piece in the Surrey Comet. I said to Peter – "How did this happen? The Smiths have become this massive band - and we're still playing toilets to three people and a dog. What have The Smiths got that we haven't?"

PETER WYATT

Contacts. They obviously had contacts in the music biz. As for us - still all we had was Grant what worked in Record Scene.

GRANT WILLIAMS

As soon as the last demo was finished Peter whizzed into the shop, jumping about with enthusiasm, "Just wait till you hear this new demo - it's even better than the last one." "Even better," I said, "that's hard to believe" - playing him along. I hadn't even listened to the last one. I took the demo, with no intention of listening to it.

JERRY ZMUDA

As far as getting any press or record company interest in Septimus Grundy, the silence was deafening. Maybe our covering letters were poorly written. I don't know what it was.

GRANT WILLIAMS

It was something like a whole nine months after Peter stuffed his demo-tape into my hand and I'm out with this girl. I've got a Street Sounds compilation on the car stereo, trying to be up-to-the-minute. She doesn't like it. She takes the tape out and slings in a dirty dust-covered tape she's found on the floor – the hanging off label reads Septimus Grundy. Before I can stop her, the first song comes on, it's London After Midnight. It was a revelation, full of power and determination. I had to stop the car and play the track again. They sounded like the Ruts. Yes that good!

PETER WYATT

So nearly a year after I give Grant at Record Scene our demo, late one night I get an excited phone call from him.
"Your demo is class mate! You sound like the Ruts."
I said – "Who wants to see a band who sound like the Ruts in 1984?"
"Me. I want to see a band like that. And I am coming to your next gig."

LYDIA DANCEY

The Smiths were playing the Hammersmith Palais, and I told Jerry straight - you either go with me to this concert, or I find a myself new boy-friend.

JERRY ZMUDA

What? That bunch of jokers who had their session on Peel the same night he played us? Lydia was dead set on going, so what can you do?

LYDIA DANCEY

I'd been listening to their album over and over. So when they came on stage in a flurry of gladioli, I just melted. The first song they did was *Miserable Lie* with an extended intro. Swoon!

JERRY ZMUDA

I was seething with jealousy when the Smiths came on. The place was packed and the crowd just went into spasms. And there was me - alone and unrecognized. I'm just as good as him - look at me. My songs are just as good - even better. After the gig, Lydia was going on and on and on about how good the gig was. I bit my lip - I didn't want another row. I wanted my leg over.

LYDIA DANCEY

The following week, I was still going on about the concert, Jerry got drunk and this big cathartic torrent of abuse and accusations came out. I was a snob, I was this, I was that.

JERRY ZMUDA

I wanted her to tell me I was quite good, that I had some talent, that maybe I too could play the Hammersmith Palais, if only as just a support band. Nothing was forthcoming so I stormed out of her flat. The idea was for her to call me back, I walked down the road and looked back, but she hadn't come after me.
I waited for about half an hour and then I got on the train and went back to Hersham. We had split up again.

COBRA COBRA-CABANA

DERMOTT COLLINS

Cobra comes round one Saturday and goes - "Come on geez - we are going shopping." But one thing this was clear - Jerry ain't invited.

JERRY ZMUDA

I didn't want to go.

PETER WYATT

I was always worried about Dermott spending time with Cobra. The devil makes work for idle hands. We needed to get Dermott a girlfriend.

DERMOTT COLLINS

He takes me up the West End, all the proper shops. None of your Carnaby Street tat, and he's paying cash for the best gear - Lacoste, Pierre Cardin, Sergio Tacchini. Pukha clobber. I was trying stuff on, and he was going "You like it? you can have it." We were giving it large - like proper gangsters. So what's going on Cob? Where's the money come from? Big score?

PETER WYATT

Dermott looked sharp in these new threads - like a different bloke. It gave his craziness some sort of authority. Cobra had been treating him like a gangster's moll. I said to him — "Hang about Derm where's all this money come from?"

DERMOTT COLLINS

Dunno.

PETER WYATT

Few weeks later, I get a phone call from Graham Cobb aka Cobra, he's asking how's it going with Sarah.
I said "Great - real great."
He says - "You owe me big, me old china."
"How's that Cob?"
"I helped you two get together."
"Well I think it was more to do with a purple ra-ra skirt, but thanks anyway. So what's up Cobra? You after a favour?"

DERMOTT COLLINS

Turned out all the money he'd been spending like water was Bank of Toyland, and Cobra didn't know the meaning of the word discreet. Come to think of it, Cob didn't know the meaning of a lot of words. Any old fucking road - the Old Bill were closing in.

PETER WYATT

Cobra says "I am going to need a favour real bad soon." This is just
about the last thing I wanted to hear. Then he says - "The next time
you hear my voice, I'll be calling you from Brazil. Tara!" And he hangs
up.

DERMOTT COLLINS

He chose Brazil because of Ronnie Biggs. He was going to look him
up and open a bar with him. He was going to call it the - wait-for-it
COBRA-CABANA.

PETER WYATT

A week later - Cobra phones again -
"How's Brazil?" I ask
"Didn't quite make Brazil, Pete - I'm in Brixton Remand - I've been
nicked."
So Cobra had nicked all this funny money. Some shady character had
offered him the forgeries for a sum of money, but instead Cobra goes
over there one night, chivs the geezer and steals the bank-notes This
is why he was spending as much as he could, as quickly as he could.
What he had wanted me to do was get a load of his gear - personal
things - and send them onto him at his hideout in Brazil. Of course I
didn't have to do that now. I tell you what - I was fucking relieved.

DERMOTT COLLINS

So of course I had to go to court to show my support. It was a big
turn-out - Cobra's a popular guy - apart from in Molesey. Oh! And
the firm that did them forgeries weren't too keen on him neither. I
finally got to meet his old man - who seemed alright. Not the sort of
bloke who'd bugger you after a night down the boozer.
Anyway like the hard nut that he is, Cobra put up a real struggle when
he got arrested.
The copper reads back his statement in court, all-matter-of fact - you
know how coppers speak. He comes to the bit when Cobra is fighting
off the coppers – he reads out word for word what Cobra said -
"YOU CUNT DO YOU WANT A SLAPPING?" The place just
exploded, deafening cheers. Cobra milking it. The judge wasn't
impressed - he gave the cunt five years.

FELTHAM MADE ME   183

PETER WYATT

When Cobra got sent down - he called over to Dermott and said "Will you wait for me?" "Of course," Dermott called back.

JERRY ZMUDA

I hate to say it. I was relieved when I heard that Cobra got sent down. He made it perfectly obvious he disliked me and I was always expecting him to do something really unpleasant to me. OK I admit it - he scared me.

DERMOTT COLLINS

I used to go and see Cobra in Brixton every two to three weeks. He seemed fine - fitting into prison life and no regrets. Saying "I'd rather give it large for a day - then live like a cunt the rest of my life." He told me prison wasn't so bad, but I didn't fancy it meself. Then I didn't visit for a month or two and he was well miffed with me.

THE GLC CONCERT – JUNE '84 – WERE YOU THERE?

DERMOTT COLLINS

I messed around with girls but......I was still stuck on Angela.
I hadn't seen her for so long I was worried I'd forget what she looked like. I called her brother Jordi for a photograph. He thought I was weird. I guess I was a bit. But he found one for me, which I kept in my wallet.

JORDI KNOWLES (Angela's brother)

Dermott used to call up all the time. I told him that I had seen Angela a few times, but he couldn't come along because it was brother and sister meeting up. But I did tell him that we were both going to The Smiths open-air GLC concert at the County Hall, London in June.

LYDIA DANCEY

I had just finished my second year at Polytechnic. What better way to celebrate than to see the Smiths play at an open air concert in London? Maybe I'd meet a nice boy there.

DERMOTT COLLINS
> So in the end it's just me, Jerry and Botley going. We get there and
> thousands upon thousands of student types are there. I saw some
> bother over by where the Red-Skins were playing. I think the British
> Steel lot had showed. I didn't get involved though. I had one thing -
> and one thing only on my mind.
> While the Smiths were playing, I climbed up this massive high pillar. I
> only did it so Angela could see.
> The crowd turned towards me and it was a top fucking cackle to have
> all these people look up at me - even though some of them were
> shouting "Jump." There was Morrissey warbling away down below,
> singing about dropping his trousers to the Queen - and me up there
> - taking away his glory.

JERRY ZMUDA
> Everyone was staring at Dermott as he climbed up that pillar. It was
> one hell of a climb and about a sixty foot drop.
> I thought it was pathetic myself. I'm no psychiatrist, but to me this
> was plainly the act of a psychologically damaged show off. This was
> supposedly my oldest and best friend.
> I started feeling something I'd never felt before. I started feeling the
> urge to hit Dermott. Right in the mouth.

LYDIA DANCEY
> I was watching the band and I looked up and there's this nutter who
> had climbed this pillar. He must have been about sixty foot off the
> ground. Then I saw it was Dermott.

DERMOTT COLLINS
> Angela had seen me. When I get down she was there waiting for me.
> She gave me a hug - and a wet warm kiss. But something was very
> different.

JORDI KNOWLES (Angela's brother)
> Angela was moving in new circles, she was looking very different.

DERMOTT COLLINS
> Angela weren't no punk any more. She was dressed straight. She even
> smelt differently - that make-up and perfume. Glamorous - I mean

proper glamorous - she said to me - "Of course I've changed - it's 1984 - punk is over". She was right I guess, but it was still a shock in all the years that I hadn't seen her.

JERRY ZMUDA

Angela always knew how to stand out in a crowd. When she was the ice queen of punk she stood out in school assembly with her peroxide white hair. Now at the GLC concert she stood out in her expensive designer clothes against a backdrop of scruffy students. What had happened?

LYDIA DANCEY

It was the best gig of my life, the Hammersmith Palais was a close second. But there was something about the open air, the political statement, and at that point - the Smiths were the single most important band in the world. At the end of the gig Morrissey threw his blouse into the audience.

JERRY ZMUDA

I begrudgingly have to say that the Smiths were excellent that day. I finally got them. They had taken the position that The Jam used to have a few years before, as the British band. When Morrissey threw his top into the ground I saw this scrum. I thought, if I break off a piece, I can send it to Lydia - as a present - a peace-offering.

LYDIA DANCEY

There was about two dozen Morrissey-crazed people trying to get a piece of this blue and white-flecked blouse, made of this awful synthetic fibre. It was getting fierce but I wasn't going to let go. I mean - this was Morrissey's blouse.

JERRY ZMUDA

I dived in, and as the blouse was ripping, I grabbed a small piece, and then everyone just clawed away at it. It was like a pack of hyenas on some poor polyester gazelle. Then I saw her. Holding a piece of the same blouse.

LYDIA DANCEY

Was this fate? It seemed like it. We both held up our piece of the blouse put them together - and we laughed.

JERRY ZMUDA

It seemed that the Smiths was playing at fate, and insisting we got back together. Who was I to argue?

LYDIA DANCEY

We were talking a little cagily at first, but it was clear that we both wanted to get back together.

After our emotional re-union we went over to see Dermott and Botley. That's where I met Angela. Dermott had a special respect for this smartly-dressed woman. He wasn't all sarcastic and irritating around her. I thought it would be good for Dermott to finally get a proper girlfriend. It might straighten him out.

DERMOTT COLLINS

There was me saying to Angela – "Give us your phone number," dead set that this time I would never to let her go. Then I ask the question I wish I never asked –

"What are you doing for money?"

"I do very well - now."

"Yes, but what do you?"

She gave me a saucy look - raised her eyebrows and then I twigged. I looked back at her and she said –

"It's all high class, men with lots of money."

Like that was supposed to make it alright. I could feel my eyes filling with tears. I was about to choke, trying not to cry. Then I ran away. I ran through the crowd and over the bridge. It was only until I was well away from everyone that I started sobbing by the river, looking at her photograph – when she was a punk.

PETER WYATT

Dermott never talks about his inner feelings. Never talked about his Mum, or anything. After the GLC concert I knew something terrible had happened. I insisted he told me, and eventually he did. All I could do was listen, I couldn't offer any advice. The girl you love becomes a prostitute, this was way out of my experience. All I could say was –

"She's just one girl Dermott - there's millions of others."
"But this is Angela."

'MUDA THE BROODER

PETER WYATT
The geezer at the Hand & Spear got on the phone to us, he wanted us back. I was getting savvy, I knew we were pulling a crowd. I said this time we want a tonne. He said Ok immediately. I should have asked for more. I thought we were on cigar city - one hundred pounds to play a gig!

DERMOTT COLLINS
It was one of the Molesey lads what suggested we did a cover version of a Jam song.

PETER WYATT
Jerry was acting strange before the gig, refusing to drink –
"Is something up?" I ask him. "Is it Lydia? Dermott winding you up? You can tell your uncle Peter."
He says nothing, nursing his coca cola.

DERMOTT COLLINS
I'm the one who should be moody. I was in heartbreak hotel over Angela. But Jerry - he was moping around. I said to him – "I haven't seen you like this since Petra the Blue Peter dog died." Not a flicker of a laugh. Cruising for a bruising that mug.

GRANT WILLIAMS
At the Hand & Spear gig, the band do *London After Midnight* and I'm bopping away - then they stop. We're just about to hit them with some appreciative applause when they picked it up, playing the outro of *West One* by the Ruts - complete with Dermott and Peter giving it the "Shine on Me." I was awestruck. Before I had to time to draw breath, they went straight into their last song - a cover of *Thick As Thieves*.

DERMOTT COLLINS

Big cheer coming from The Molesey Boys when they recognised *Thick As Thieves*. A song they all knew and could sing along to - they went fairly mental.

BUCKLE AKA STUART MARTIN

In the early days of The Grundy Jerry always used to turn his back on the audience, while he tried to play his guitar on the instrumental breaks. And I knew exactly why he did it – because he couldn't really play, and he didn't want the audience to twig. But now Jerry would turn his back start thrashing at his guitar and lock me into his stare. He was like a man possessed as we bashed out the end of the song, in a trance. Wow! Talk about transformation.

GRANT WILLIAMS

They were superb that night. I had no doubt that I was seeing a band that was going to make it.

SARAH BAXTER

I was taken aback. Jerry who I always thought was a drip - was quite different on stage, he wasn't Marvin Gaye - but he could hold a note. It wasn't my type of music - but I could appreciate it. And of course when they finished off with that Jam song, the place went berserk.

BUCKLE AKA STUART MARTIN

The R'n'B covers band I used to play in always used to go down well - I mean you can't go wrong with that stuff. But never before had I played in a band that had gone down as well as Septimus Grundy did that night. They literally raised the roof.

PETER WYATT

Course there's no backstage at the Hand & Spear, so after the gig we sit down at our table next to the stage, the crowd's still cheering, and everyone's coming up to us. One of the Molesey lads says something like – "You saved the best till last." Jerry didn't like that.

DERMOTT COLLINS

Jerry was sulking because our cover version of *Thick As Thieves* went down better than his own songs.

JERRY ZMUDA

> I was <u>not</u> sulking I just wanted to put the whole thing in perspective. Our own songs go down fine, but it wasn't until we played the cover songs that people really got into it.

PETER WYATT

> We went down well with a good mixture of people. There was Lydia's lot, posh Weybridge girls and then you had the Molesey Boys.

LYDIA DANCEY

> I felt I understood Jerry better after that gig. Particularly after the song *Feltham Made Me,* which was obviously very personal. His home in the suburbs was his artistic reference point - and that's why he did nothing about leaving Egmont. If an A&R man had come to that show, there was no way they would have not signed them then and there. I went up to them after the show and told them that, but Jerry was sulking.

DERMOTT COLLINS

> The crowd loved us - who cares about anything else? When we started out we used go down like a Wet Baboon. Now this - Jerry should be bleedin' happy. I was. But what can you do with 'Muda the Brooder? Giving it the moody Jim Morrison act.

PETER WYATT

> That gig at the Hand & Spear was an even better high than getting played on John Peel, and that's something. Even Sarah liked it. I turned to Jerry and he's still all miserable. "SNAP OUT OF IT - YOU SILLY CUNT! WE ARE GOING TO MAKE IT."

GRANT WILLIAMS

> I was blown away. I told them I knew a young A&R scout from MCA. I was going to **insist** he comes down to the next gig.

IT SOUNDS SO NICE WHAT YOU'RE PROPOSING

SARAH BAXTER
> I was teasing Peter saying – "you're more committed to the band than me. If the band takes off you'll leave me behind."

PETER WYATT
> I had to prove her wrong. So I did it then and there, on her Mum's living room carpet.

SARAH BAXTER
> He gets down on one knee and proposed. I was so shocked, but very moved. I said – "Yes, Peter I want to share my life with you."

DERMOTT COLLINS
> When Peter announced his engagement to Sarah, first time in my life I was speechless. Eventually I said – "Peter that's great, but what about us?"

PETER WYATT
> You'll still be my friends, I'm just going to be living with Sarah.

DERMOTT COLLINS
> But what about Egmont?

SARAH BAXTER
> One thing was certain though - there was no way I was ever going to live in that tip in Egmont Court.

JERRY ZMUDA
> I was thrilled and delighted when Peter called with the news he was marrying Sarah. OK that was my official line, but inwardly I was devastated. I thought it would be the end of us as friends. Sarah was a lovely girl - but Peter's too young to settle down. And what about Septimus Grundy? I immediately felt pressure. Something had better happen with Septimus Grundy - record deal or something, or Peter would just quit and leave me alone with Dermott. At that time, that seemed a fate worse than death.

YOU DON'T DO IT - YOU DON'T THREATEN JOHN PEEL

PETER WYATT
You don't do it. You don't threaten John Peel. John Peel of all people.

DERMOTT COLLINS
What the fuck? This was all Jerry's fault anyway. We were in the van and he was telling Botley about how the geezer from Joy Division first met the boss of Factory Records. They were at a gig, and the Joy Division bloke went up to him and says - "You're a cunt you are. Why don't you put us on your TV show?" And that's how Joy Division got on TV. So I thought - if this works for Joy Division, why wouldn't it work for Septimus Grundy?

PETER WYATT
We were outside a gig at ULU - Red Guitars I think it was - and giving out flyers for a Septimus Grundy gig and John Peel was there. I said Hullo and smiled but he was talking to someone so I couldn't butt in. Then Dermott catches him on the way to the tube station. I thought he was going to thank him for playing our demo, but then I see this real nasty look on Dermott's face.

DERMOTT COLLINS
I told him straight – "You look like a hobbit - you're a fucking cunt - you're lucky I don't stick your head in the gutter." "Why? Why?" He was going. I said "For only playing my band Septimus Grundy once on your show."

PETER WYATT
I dashed over to stop it, but by the time I got there Peely had scrambled off. I told Dermott off - but he seemed to think this approach was going to pay off. I wrote a letter apologizing, but Peely never played us again.

JERRY ZMUDA
I didn't find out about this until weeks afterwards. Naturally I was furious. I was considering two options - changing the band's name and/or kicking out Dermott. I suggested this to Peter - but he said "It's alright - Peely won't take it personally." Well he never played us

again - all because of Dermott - this great big albatross round our neck.

A RECORD COMPANY MAN AT OUR GIG? AFTER ALL THIS TIME?

LYDIA DANCEY
> I gave the Septimus Grundy demo tape to the social sec at my polytechnic. I fluttered my eye-lids, played with my hair and went into flirt mode, and so he agreed to put the band on a Friday night in October.

GRANT WILLIAMS
> I knew this guy Warren who used to be a sales rep, but then he landed himself a job in A&R for MCA. I gave him a copy of the Septimus Grundy demo. He thought it was "a little retro - but had potential." I told him how good they were live and he said - OK he'd check them out.

PETER WYATT
> I told the boys – "We got to make this next gig a really good one. Grant's getting a Record Company scout down."

JERRY ZMUDA
> A record company man at our gig? After all this time? I'll believe it when I see it.

DERMOTT COLLINS
> You'd think we were preparing for a royal visit the way Peter and Jerry were going on about it.

JERRY ZMUDA
> I was disappointed with the venue, it was the same scuzz-hole that I'd been to with Lydia a year before. I was dead paranoid about the A&R man not getting in. I felt as though my whole life depended on this A&R man coming to see us. I had a row with the social sec. I said - "This guy has GOT to be on the guest list,"
> and he was saying - "Well it's a free gig, so everyone's on the guest list."

FELTHAM MADE ME   193

"No you don't understand this guy has GOT to get in, even if the place is full."

PETER WYATT

I calmed the situation down by saying that if it's a full house, I would stand on the door and personally make sure the A&R man gets in.

JERRY ZMUDA

With Peter announcing he was getting married I felt this was our last chance, we needed to get a record deal - immediately - like now. Otherwise Peter would drift out of the band and away from us.

DERMOTT COLLINS

Me and Botters were playing penny up the wall, and Jerry shouts at us - actually shouts at us – "STOP MESSING ABOUT!" He was so nervous, he was losing it. This just made us laugh.

JERRY ZMUDA

After the soundcheck I went up to the social sec's office to make a call and we started chatting. He showed me all the demo tapes he'd been sent in the last year. They were in eight beer-crates. He said "I couldn't possibly listen to them all." I stared at the tapes - I realized that Septimus Grundy was just one of thousands.

PETER WYATT

Half an hour before we are due to come on, Grant shows up with the A&R man. He introduces us and we go down to the bar to meet the rest of the boys.

DERMOTT COLLINS

What a plank! He's got a baseball cap with MCA written on it. Then I found out his name is Warren. So out came the old joke – 'what do you call a geezer with 20 rabbits up his arse?' I mean you have to do it.

JERRY ZMUDA

Butterflies in my stomach. An A&R man finally at one of our gigs.

DERMOTT COLLINS

But the worst thing about him was that he was saying things like - "yeah really happening'" or - even worse "there's a real vibe about that band." What a complete ponce.

JERRY ZMUDA

He'd listened to our demo tape and he said it had "potential."

PETER WYATT

When we hit the stage, we could tell the A&R man was still in the audience because of the baseball cap. He was standing by the mixing desk.

JERRY ZMUDA

In between the songs Dermott gets on the microphone - "OK audience - let's play a game - spot the A&R man." I tell him to shut up and just play the next song. But he's not finished.

DERMOTT COLLINS

I said - "You can spot the A&R man because he says stuff like 'happening' and 'vibe'. But the dead give-away is the baseball cap with the record company name on it."

JERRY ZMUDA

Everyone turned to look at the A&R man - I could have died. We play the next song - the next time I look out into the audience the baseball cap - my one beacon of hope - had gone.

BUCKLE AKA STUART MARTIN

We finished our song - and some of the lads are shouting THICK AS THIEVES - THICK AS THIEVES. Jerry is just staring out into the audience.

JERRY ZMUDA

I was scouring the crowd for the chap from MCA. Had he gone to the bar - or had he left? I couldn't see him at all. Then the rest of the band started playing *Thick As Thieves*.

PETER WYATT

Jerry sang it totally differently from the time before - all pissed off - spitting out the words. Then as the song was coming to the end he put his guitar down and he clumped Dermott.

DERMOTT COLLINS

I was looking out into the crowd, smiling, and I felt this fist in my jaw.

PETER WYATT

Some of the audience laughed - others gasped.

DERMOTT COLLINS

It didn't hurt - just took me by surprise - I fell over the monitor. Then he hit me again.

BUCKLE AKA STUART MARTIN

So those two fighting on stage became the encore.

DERMOTT COLLINS

He fought like a girl - sure he got me on the ground - but that was just a lucky first punch. I was about to whack him hard back but Peter broke us up.

JERRY ZMUDA

I wasn't trying to be hard. Something inside of me snapped. I'd just had enough - enough of Dermott being an idiot and holding me back. First threatening John Peel and now this. I'd worked hard on this band - just to have him throw it away with some stupid jibe at an A&R man. Dermott always gets it wrong. You take the mickey out the A&R man after you've signed the contract with the massive advance.

PETER WYATT

Jerry didn't come back in the van with us. It was real quiet on the way back, Dermott just staring ahead. Botley whispers to me - "They are going to make up are they?" I was nodding – "Of course they will."

SARAH BAXTER

Dermott and Jerry fighting on stage? Hilarious! They should have kept it as part of the act. Audiences would pay good money to see Dermott get a punch in the gob.

LYDIA DANCEY

When you go out with someone and they have a row with someone else - you have to take their side - don't you? I mean Dermott is an annoying git - isn't he? But on the way home Jerry was just going on and on about it. I eventually said – "Fine, you've made your statement on stage in front of a crowd of people, let's talk about me now please."

JERRY ZMUDA

There was no way back after this. I was going to go off and form a band with another a bunch of people. I'd come to the end of the road with Dermott.

MOVING OUT OF EGMONT

DERMOTT COLLINS

I was waiting for Jerry to apologize. He wasn't man enough - like he wasn't man enough to throw a decent punch. If it hadn't been for me, that no-mark arse-wipe would have gone through life as Jerry-No-Mates. That fucker owed everything to me.

JERRY ZMUDA

My mind had been made up - I didn't want anything to do with Dermott any more. He had been the person holding me back all this time. I told Peter I would continue with Septimus Grundy but only if we kicked out Dermott.

PETER WYATT

And I got the same thing from Dermott - kick out Jerry and continue without him. But I wasn't going to do either - I told them both straight – "EITHER YOU TWO SETTLE YOUR DIFFERENCES OR IT'S THE END OF SEPTIMUS GRUNDY."

DERMOTT COLLINS

I had a dream around that time. I was in the Music Machine - it's deserted. I'm looking around and eventually at the bar at the very top I see my Mum - she's drinking brandy. I've only ever seen my Mum in a photograph - so I've never actually seen her before - but I just know it's my Mum. She gets me a beer and says - "Be nice to Jerry - he's a good friend." I say back – "But he's the one who won't talk to me." Then she disappeared, and I was all alone again.

LYDIA DANCEY

Jerry was insufferable at this time, he just kept going on about Dermott - on and on. I said to him – "Jerry - he's out your life now at last - please shut up about this." I think he was hoping that Peter would take his side.

PETER WYATT

When I saw the bags packed and on the door-step of Egmont, it really hit home that my friends had fallen out and were moving away. Lydia came along in her Mum's car. Loading it up, I said to Jerry – "Aren't you going to say good-bye to Dermott?" I was hoping that they would get all emotional and sink their differences. Jerry refused, and Lydia drove him away. Later on Frank - Dermott's Dad - came to pick his stuff up. I was left in Egmont alone. My friends had gone. I couldn't stay here any more.

SARAH BAXTER

It was perfect timing really. With his friends off the scene, he could spend more time with me. I mean I don't want to be negative - the band were good - but they were a bit old-fashioned - too punky and loud. Peter needed to focus on sorting his life out and our wedding.

GRANT WILLIAMS

I was gutted when I heard that Septimus Grundy had finished. I was hoping to go down in history as the guy who discovered them.

PETER WYATT

The worst thing was when I went to the garage and all the equipment had gone - just Botley's spray painting as the only reminder of the hours we spent there. I was devastated that my friends weren't friends anymore. But the person it upset the most was Botley.

THE WEDDING

DERMOTT COLLINS

With Cob in prison, I was left to buying my own clothes, so I was rooting around in a charity shop - and I dug out a Kung Fu annual from 1975. It took me right back to primary school. I was just about to nick it and show it to Jerry, when I remembered - we're not friends any more. Guess it hadn't sunk in yet.

I used to play the guitar everyday, but after the split I stopped playing altogether.

PETER WYATT

Months passed without them speaking, but I had a strategy. I was going to use my wedding as a way of getting my buddies together again.

TERRY SOUTH

I heard Sarah was marrying Peter Wyatt from Feltham School. What a waste - Sarah's a nice girl, what's she doing wasting her life on a loser like him? It would never last.

JERRY ZMUDA

I got a phone call from Peter, "How about coming out on my stag night?"

"No thanks - not if Dermott's going" - then he asked me to DJ at the wedding reception.

PETER WYATT

I asked Botley to be Best Man and he said "No - you can't do that - Dermott and Jerry are better friends." I set him straight – "I have no better friend in the world than you Carl."

I did something sneaky. I booked Dermott and Jerry both to DJ at the reception at the same time. The idea being they would DJ together - and become friends again.

ROY HOOKE

I was delighted to get my invite to Peter's wedding. Had he finally accepted me? This was a good sign. He chose to have the reception at the church hall in Sunbury, the venue where he saw my glittering performance in *The Mikado*.

JERRY ZMUDA

Apparently Botley in his best man speech, in between the jokes, said something about how Dermott and I should make up. What he said exactly I don't know because I wasn't at the meal. I knew Dermott was going to be there, but I wasn't expecting him to be DJing at the same time. I said - "Look we still hate each other - but let's work out a system - you play two records - I play two records - and that way we'd avoid interacting in any way at all."

DERMOTT COLLINS

That suited me. Jerry starts playing classic rock'n'roll - music that I got him into. So I put on some punk.

JERRY ZMUDA

Punk? I like punk - but you can't play that at a wedding. I mean you've got the aunties and uncles there. So I put on some Motown. He turns off *Stoned Love* half way through to put on the Ramones.

SARAH BAXTER

I was fuming! Those two clowns seemed dead set on upstaging me on my wedding day.

FRANK COLLINS

The atmosphere was tense, real tense. I though I'd lighten up the proceedings but doing my *Mule Train*. So I got hold of a tea tray and I'm away.

PETER WYATT

We all laughed - well most of us did, when Dermott's Dad did his party piece.

JERRY ZMUDA

That was my cue to slip off into the night. I gathered up my records and exited - didn't say good-bye to anyone.

DERMOTT COLLINS

The party got a lot better after Jerry bailed. I played Elvis, Chuck Berry, Johnny Kid and the Pirates, Eddie Cochrane - a feast of classic music. Peter got me to play some soul and we toasted the happy couple. Jerry? Who needs that whinging cunt?

TONIGHT'S THE NIGHT - FAREWELL TO BOTLEY

JERRY ZMUDA

I lost count of the times Peter phoned me to try and get me to patch it up with Dermott. He even started using the – 'he never had a mother - you have to go easy on him' line.
I was not for turning. Just because Dermott never had a mother doesn't give him the right to go through life acting like a bastard. I had to remind him - I didn't split up Septimus Grundy. It was Dermott, he had become intolerable. I wanted to take Septimus Grundy places - Dermott just wanted to wind people up.

LYDIA DANCEY

They say Christmas is the peak season for suicide.

JERRY ZMUDA

Lydia and I were at a party in Sunbury - I'd invited Botley along. The music in the living room was horrible so I was loitering in the kitchen - knocking back the spirits. Botley came in and asked me when was I going to start talking to Dermott again. I said when "hell freezes over." I thought I was being clever.

PETER WYATT

I had an early night that night - went to bed at 10 - but I woke up with a jolt at 11.45. I heard a strange muffled sound, I thought it was the next door's cat. But that was around the time that Botley jumped. According to the police report - Botley left the party at around 11.30 he walked about a mile to the bridge over the M4. And he climbed over the barrier.

FELTHAM MADE ME   201

LYDIA DANCEY

Jerry was wracked with guilt for a long time afterwards about the things he'd said to Botley about Ian Curtis and suicide being cool. But Botley didn't do what he did it to be cool. He did it because his life revolved around his group of friends. His only friends. When that group of friends fell out - he just couldn't face life anymore.

PETER WYATT

And poor Botley jumped. He timed it so he got hit by a lorry. Splattered all over the motorway.
I found out when Botley's Mum called me to tell me about the funeral. Why didn't he call me? Why didn't I go to that party and stop him?

JERRY ZMUDA

This was the single worst thing to happen in my whole life.

DERMOTT COLLINS

I can't talk about this. I just can't do it.

PETER WYATT

I still get it - even now, every so often - waking up at a quarter to midnight. It's my friend saying good-bye.

FUNERAL FOR A FRIEND

PETER WYATT

Botley I mean Carl's Mum came up to us at the funeral, I gulped, I thought she was going to have a go at us for leading her son astray. But she was managing a smile and said that us three had brought Carl a lot of happiness. We were his three best friends and he talked about us all the time.

JERRY ZMUDA

Peter spoke at the funeral. He's not a man of words - but he said it all –
"When Botley, I mean Carl came into our life - it was breath of fresh air. So many people are cynical and only doing you a favour to get something back. Carl wasn't like that - he was pure and innocent. We first became

friends over music but over the years we would talk about everything under the sun. I was amazed by his memory.

He was so shy, but when you got to know him you felt truly privileged to know someone so special. I can't lie to you. I can't say he's gone to a better place. I hope that he has. But most of all I wish he was with us today. As long as I live I will never forget my good friend Carl."

PETER WYATT

> The funeral was over - we said our good-byes to Carl. I wanted the three of us to get together and be mates. Septimus Grundy was one thing, but our friendship was another - just forgive and forget.

JERRY ZMUDA

> There was no way. No way on this earth I was going to forgive and forget. I needed to get away from Dermott. I just couldn't bear to have him around - even look him in the eye. And seeing him at the funeral was just deeply antagonizing.

DERMOTT COLLINS

> Jerry was acting off with me - as if I was to blame for what happened to Botley. We were all to blame. Especially him. He was the one who talked to him at the party.

PETER WYATT

> I put my arm round Jerry. I said - "Come on - make it up with Dermott. Do it for Carl - it's what he would have wanted."
> Jerry pushed me away.

THE LAST RECORD SALE

PETER WYATT

> I went down Record Scene. Just to catch up with Grant, see what new records were happening. Record Scene had shut down - replaced by a travel agent. It was the end of an era. The end of my youth. Time to forget the past - focus on my marriage and plan a family.

Chapter 6
Acid House And All That

JUNE 1988 - THE PHONE CALL AT 7 AM

PETER WYATT

7 am. I just got Abby, my three year old daughter, to sleep. She had been up all night with a cough. The phone rang, it was Dermott. I said – "You're up early."

DERMOTT COLLINS

"Early? Haven't been to bed yet." Had to talk to Peter. Meant to talk to him the first time I done it. Now I couldn't keep it in any longer.

PETER WYATT

He was very excited, talking ten to the dozen. I hadn't slept yet so I couldn't take it all in. It went something like - "Get on one…strobe flashing…pumping bass…blinding night…sweating buckets…black and white unity…hugging some geezer I never met before."

DERMOTT COLLINS

He told me to slow down - tried but couldn't. I was at a pay-phone in Waterloo, still buzzing, waiting for my train.

PETER WYATT

When a mate phones you up, on drugs, at a strange hour, telling you he'd hugged some geezer he'd never met before - it's all a bit worrying. I told him to be careful. When I put the phone down, I looked at my daughter, finally sleeping peacefully. I thought - yeah there might be some new scene going off out there - but my world is here.

JERRY ZMUDA

Smike had invited me to the Astoria to a night called the Trip. A total revelation, he passed me a tablet that tasted bitter. Beforehand Smike had described taking E as like mixing acid with speed. That sounded pointless - why not just take acid with speed and save the money? He didn't prepare me for this religious experience. Half an hour later I felt a surge of energy and wonder - I just had to dance. For the first time ever I danced without feeling self-conscious or shy - and I felt love for everybody. I mean everybody - even Dermott. But especially this new scene. As I was coming down Sunday night, all glowing, I felt I had to call Peter and tell him about this wonderful, happy new scene.

PETER WYATT

So Dermott calls me off his head early Sunday morning. Eight hours later that same Sunday, Jerry calls me about the self same subject. Fate is playing her hand. She's telling us it's time the boys - the unholy trinity - got back together.

SARAH WYATT

I was gutted when Peter told me he was going out on Saturday night with the Twins of Terror. He's a cabbie and Saturday night was the busiest night.

PETER WYATT

I wasn't bothered about any new scene, trying new drugs. I was doing this to get my pals back together.

DERMOTT COLLINS

That week-end when we both phoned Peter, I'd been down RIP down Clink Street and Jerry had been down The Astoria. RIP was a proper small underground club and a bit hard to get into, they gave first dibs to members. So we decided to have our get together at the Astoria. I was looking forward to seeing Jerry. But I was hoping he wasn't still an arse hole, and wasn't going to rake over old ground about the Grundy.

JERRY ZMUDA

I wasn't sure about any re-union. I had hoped Dermott was out of my life for good. But Smike was going away to Goa the following week-end and I was stuck for someone else to go out with. So, with some reluctance, I said OK.

THE TRIP

PETER WYATT

As soon you got within a half mile of The Astoria, you knew something was happening. There was a massive, heaving queue outside making this loud hum of excitement. You could hear it and feel it. Everyone dressed in baggy colourful clothes. Fuck me, some geezer was even wearing a poncho. Hair was mostly long, some wore hats, Aztec woollen patterns. Dermott was acting like he owed the gaff, and he pushed his way through to the front, people were saying hello to him, even the security shook his hand. The bouncer says - "Be good tonight Dermott."
"No chance of that mate."

DERMOTT COLLINS

Peter wants to get a beer. I slipped him a pill and tell him – "When this baby takes hold, you won't care about beer."

JERRY ZMUDA

The last time I'd laid eyes on Dermott was at Botley's funeral so I felt awkward - really awkward. I needed to relax - badly. I saw Dermott give Peter the E, and I said – "Got any more?"
He said "Of course" and hands over a pill. I said "How Much?" He waves his hand - "On the house."

PETER WYATT

I had half a mind to spit it out. But then curiosity got a hold of me, so I washed it down with me beer. I look around and saw that no-one else was drinking alcohol.
Dermott says – "Let's go upstairs and plot down before it all goes crazy." As I went up the stairs. I felt my bowels moving, I needed to go the toilet. I thought if I dump that pill out the other side, then it won't affect me. That's probably for the best.

JERRY ZMUDA

My strategy was to get off my head, talk to some strangers, get lost in the crowd and then I wouldn't have to talk to Dermott at all. I was determined – determined, not to apologize for anything. And I wasn't going to let Peter make me.

PETER WYATT

After that big dump - I felt relaxed. It's all out of my system now, the drug won't have any effect. Just as well - I was a 24 year old married man - with a three year old kid. Leave the drugs to the nutters.

It was starting off. People jumping around wildly - I supposed it was dancing, strange twisted expressions on their faces. It was like when you see films of a 60s hippy festival, where there's one guy standing up - dancing like a lunatic, while most people are sitting down being mellow. It was like that - but here everybody was acting like that lunatic. Even without coming up on the E it was still powerful. The Music was electronic - but soulful vocals, I heard a piano here and there. It looked weird to me, but there was a good energy to it.

DERMOTT COLLINS

Jerry was acting off, couldn't even look me in the eye. So Jerry is still an arse-hole after all these years.

PETER WYATT

I didn't care about anyone else, I was going to have another beer. As I was waiting to get served I felt this warm tingle. I couldn't stop smiling. I smiled at the bar man, then at the girl next to me - and she smiled back. She asked me my name - I started chatting, looking out across the dance floor. The nutters on the podium weren't nutters anymore. There were my people. My people. I took this girl to meet Dermott. I said to him "Thank you - thank you - thank you for introducing me to this."

DERMOTT COLLINS

After playing some of the soulful garage stuff - *It's Alright, Reachin', You're Gonna Miss* me. Holloway started playing some the darker stuff - *Rock To The Beat, KLF.* There was a massive cheer and the crowd went mental when he dropped *Flesh* - Split Second.

Jerry had scarpered and I thought - good riddance.

PETER WYATT

A big cloud of sweaty BO hung in the air. But I didn't mind, rather it was beautiful, it was our sweat - brought about from dancing.

JERRY ZMUDA

The intense rushing ram-raided on my inhibitions and sent them crashing down. I was now up on the podium, looking around. I felt somebody tug at my trousers. I turn around and somebody is kissing me on the mouth. I can feel their face, it's rough stubbly, it's not a girl. I recognize that distinct sweet sickly body odour. I push him away - it's Dermott and he's laughing. Laughing like Basil Brush. My anger evaporated and I hugged him tight.

PETER WYATT

I could see Dermott and Jerry hugging on the podium - friends again at last. I jumped up and joined them, and all was well with the world, dancing with 1,000 newly made friends.

DERMOTT COLLINS

Some of the acid house purists say that the Trip in the Astoria was shit because it was too mainstream, too big. Well I thought it was fucking pukka. Great soundsystem, great crowd, blinding visuals, and the best music. The only fucking downside - it shut at 3am. Fuck that. Our bodies were shouting at us to keep on dancing. So we spilled out into the streets and we all took the party to the NCP car park by the YMCA.

JERRY ZMUDA

A revolution was happening - in the NCP car park.

PETER WYATT

It's amazing how everybody just talked to everybody. Laughing with each other. Everybody was so wild, we even danced in the all night car-park to some geezer's car stereo. And there was us three - back together again - the three Musketeers. We shook on it - friends forever.

SARAH WYATT

I was worried out of my mind. Peter was supposed to get the last train. As it turned out he got the first train and got home at dawn. He comes in with this soppy mongy smile - looking like Goofy - "Have I told you today?" What? "You are the loveliest girl in the world."

THE AFTERMATH

PETER WYATT
> Come down? There was no come down! I felt great afterwards. Driving my cab round London on Monday morning I found Kiss FM on my dial and discovered that this acid house scene wasn't just The Trip - this scene was growing. Something very exciting was stirring in Old London Town.

JERRY ZMUDA
> Just when I'd thought I'd got away – he's back in my life. The euphoria had made me feel it was all wonderful to be back with my oldest friend. But when that faded, I was still smarting over the Septimus Grundy affair. He still grated on me.

DERMOTT COLLINS
> You didn't have to be Tony Montana to work out there was a pile of cash to be made out all of this. But the Mathematics of the half-arsed drug dealer don't work out. You buy a bag of 20 Es for fifteens. Outlay 300 quid. You take 2, give 2 away - you sell 16 for a score. 320 comes back. You're risking a stretch of bird for a lousy score. I visited Cobra inside and told him I need to get myself connected.

JERRY ZMUDA
> Smike had introduced me to the joys of house music and ecstasy. But he was going to spend the summer in Goa - the bloody hippy. So I did it. I couldn't believe I was doing it. I picked up the phone and called Dermott – "What are you up to this week-end?"

DERMOTT COLLINS
> The great thing about the scene - well there were many great things - but one of them was you could dress up like a right cunt and no-one would bat an eye-lid. No! In fact they loved you for it. There was this geezer who always dressed like a pirate, eye-patch and all, the only thing missing was the parrott. Someone else used to carry a stuffed bear around with him. OK that was a bit much. Me - I liked wearing me deer-stalker. ". People used to shout out - "Oi Sherlock! Elementary my dear Watson!"

FELTHAM MADE ME   209

JERRY ZMUDA

Even after the effect of the pills had worn off, I found that I had a new outlook on life. It wasn't me alone against a world that hated me any more. I felt much more optimistic and confident. And what made it so exciting was that I was just one of thousands of people who was going through this. It was wonderful to discover this new scene and watch it grow before my eyes.

OLIVER MACINTOSH   (Spectrum Boy and budding DJ)

My acid house experience all began on a quiet Monday night. My mate told me that the geezer who runs the Project Club in Streatham was doing a night called Spectrum down at Heaven. I thought my friend was coming on to me, because Heaven is normally a gay club. He shows me the flyer with the psychedelic big eye - and I said – "Yeah looks good" - planning to make a dash for the fire exit if he got frisky. It was only about the third or fourth week - The Theatre of Madness hadn't really taken off yet, but you could tell that pretty soon it was going to break big. So I am very proud to say I was one of the early Spectrum people.

PETER WYATT

A few weeks before doing my first E I had gone past Trafalgar Square in my cab in the early hours of Tuesday morning. There were these kids dancing around the bus stop like it was a totem pole, dressed all colorful. I thought at the time - who let those loonies out? Weeks later I knew exactly where these loonies had been - SPECTRUM! This time I pull up.
"Where to?"
"It's alright mate - we haven't got any money."
"Get in – I'm feeling generous."

OLIVER MACINTOSH

"Hang about he may be a nonce," I warned the others. But there was four of us, so I didn't fancy his chances. He was a young guy and he starts pumping us with questions about the scene. I got a good feeling from him, he was just a nice person who wanted to give us a lift home.

JERRY ZMUDA

At the start of '88 I had found myself a job-stroke-career in that refuge for scoundrels that is Media Sales. Well what else could a no-hoper like me do? It just involved phoning people up all day - and saying the same stuff over and over again. They gave me the DIPADA training - where you ask all these open-ended questions, and then you flog what you've got, pretending it's based on what they've told you. I was living alone in some shoddy bedsit in Willesden Green but I had visions of progressing in this career. Make a go of it - prove my parents wrong. Then this acid house malarky got hold of me, and totally threw things off kilter.

PETER WYATT

To be a cabby I had to do The Knowledge, so I knew all the derelict nooks and crannies of London town. I thought I knew London like the back of me hand, but all of a sudden these different places opened up to me. Parties in snooker halls, warehouses, meat factories - anywhere. London was becoming our playground.

OLIVER MACINTOSH

I was born in 1970 – lived in Ealing all my life. I got into electro-funk – body popping, break dancing when I was 13. But the house music scene was the first scene I was ever really a part of. I was buying the records, saving up for some decks. I used to look over at the DJ, mixing away – lord of all he surveys. And I thought to myself – that's where I want to be.

JERRY ZMUDA

From drinking with my dreary office co-workers I was starting to pile on the pounds, and looking rather unfetchingly porky. But after just a couple of weeks of raving, I was back to being as slim as a rake. Got my cheek bones back. Stands to reason - you're dancing pretty much non-stop for four or five even six hours. It's like running a marathon every week-end. And my filofax - in March '88 - I was 'Billy No Mates' as Dermott likes to call me. Six months later my filo was crammed with people from all over - Enfield, Dagenham, Windsor, Coventry - who are all these people?

DERMOTT COLLINS
>Cobra tells me that Lord William will be getting in touch about boshing out MDMA.
>"Lord William? Is he posh this geezer then?"
>"He's not really a Lord - he's a top bloke - that's just what he calls himself."
>"Where do I find him?"
>"Don't worry - he'll find you. You need to get yourself down Queens Sunday afternoon."

DISCOVERING QUEENS

PETER WYATT
>Cabbying during the day, I would stop off at all the record stores - Black Market, Groove, City Sounds, Red Records, Vinyl Zone and buy all the records. I picked up all the flyers. But Saturday night was the cabbys busiest time and Sarah didn't like me going out then. So nights like The Trip was a one off for me. Then I found out about a Sunday afternoon affair called Queens.

JERRY ZMUDA
>I loved Queens - it was at nightclub-stroke-boating house at the top of a hill.
>Outside on the balcony you had a glorious panoramic view of the reservoir with Windsor Castle on the skyline, Middle England tranquillity. Inside however....

PETER WYATT
>I expected Queens to be a mellow Sunday afternoon affair like the Belvedere in Richmond used to be. People sitting around listening to Soul records - one or two people dancing. But Queens was wild and sweaty - it more than made up for not going out Saturday night.

JERRY ZMUDA
>After a couple of months, I realized that in my Converse boots I was dressing like what was being commonly termed an "Acid Ted." I perceived that some people were smirking – giving me glances of derision, or was I being paranoid? I hurriedly bought myself some

FELTHAM MADE ME   212

Kickers, and threw the Converse away. But within weeks I found out that Kickers in some circles was now regarded as Acid Ted wear. Bah!

DERMOTT COLLINS

Don't get your kickers in a twist. So Jerry's gets himself in a Tiswas about what to wear - what a Mug! I followed no fashion but my own - and besides when it all kicked off I liked a bit of bare backing. Leaving a do, freezing cold outside and me trying to find my soaking t-shirt. Amazing I never died of pneumonia.

PETER WYATT

Queens was where I got talking to a lot of people, and I always got hired for a ride home.

OLIVER MACINTOSH

So Peter the cabbie started popping up at all these different things I'm going to. But when I saw him at Queens – I knew he must be alright. He introduced me to his buddies - Jerry who seemed like a nice guy and this other chap Dermott - he was a bit weird. He was wearing a herring bone jacket and a deer-stalker. Saying stuff like – "Have you seen le renard?" Basically a show off.

DERMOTT COLLINS

I'm at the bar at Queens, and this older guy - lean, muscular, tanned, about 30 - taps me on the shoulder. He goes - "Show us yer tattoo."
I reply – "Get knotted."
He says "You've got a Cobra tattoo on your chest - let me see it."
This geezer's looking serious, so eventually I pull up my shirt and he says "You must be Dermott. Please to meet you, they call me Lord William." "Good Lord," I said.

OLIVER MACINTOSH

Another thing about Dermott was that he didn't know his rhyming slang. We were on the balcony of Queens and there this was this one guy who had actually got himself a burger and chips - hardly anybody ever ate at Queens, but anyway Dermott says to him - "You should lay off the chips mate - you'll turn Mutton Geoff." I put him right - no Mutton Geoff doesn't mean putting on weight - it means deaf, it's rhyming slang. He goes to me - "Hark at Him – The Pearly King of Ealing." But I was right and Dermott was a suburban fraud.

BAN THIS EVIL ACID HOUSE CRAZE

PETER WYATT
>For all the exciting things that were happening, I always kept my priorities. I never forgot I had a wife and a three year old daughter to provide for. But I wanted Sarah to experience something of this new scene.

SARAH WYATT
>Peter started acting strange - like happy and excited all the time. It was weirding me out. Then after dinner I'd put Abby to bed, he said – "I've got something I want you to hear." Then he played me some 12 inches he'd bought.

PETER WYATT
>I selected the more soulful end of house - *Reachin'*, *Someday*, *Runaway Girl*. Stuff I'd thought she'd like. How can you not like music like that? She went - "Yeah great - I think Eastenders is on in a bit."

SARAH WYATT
>It was like me and Terry, but the roles were reversed. He was talking about going out, new records, and I was like - you're 24 it's time to grow up.

JERRY ZMUDA
>I'll be totally honest. I was thrilled - thrilled - when I saw a builder on the train reading a copy of The Sun, carrying some hysterical headline about this "evil acid house craze." I was like Rick in the Young Ones when he discovered he hadn't got a TV licence. I'm an outlaw - a desperado.

SARAH WYATT
>I don't normally read the papers. But I took Abby over to my parents one Sunday morning and saw this headline that went something like - BAN THIS EVIL ACID HOUSE CRAZE. With the pictures of the smileys melting. I read it - it's all about drug and sex orgies where

people went mad. I panicked - what the hell had Peter got himself into?

PETER WYATT

I said to her – "Who do you believe? The newspapers? Or your husband who's standing right in front of you? I don't go to drug and sex orgies. It's a happy scene - where everybody is happy."

SARAH WYATT

Yes happy on drugs.

PETER WYATT

OK - but they're still happy. I wanted her to try it. I said to her - "Go out one night, try it with Jerry and Dermott. I'll stay in looking after Abby."

SARAH WYATT

"Are you fucking joking? I wouldn't be caught dead going out with those two clowns – let alone take mind-bending drugs with them." I told him flat – "I don't like you doing drugs, I don't like you going to these things - and I don't like you hanging about with those two losers."

JERRY ZMUDA

Throughout '88 it seemed as if every week the national newspaper had a new hysterical slant on this "evil acid house craze." After the initial thrill, it now meant at work I had to be ultra-secretive. My colleagues would ask me what I did at the week-end and I'd clam up. They were starting to think I was weird. Now they were obsessed, curious as to what I got up to every week-end and why I wouldn't talk about it. So every Monday morning without fail the inevitable question –
"How was your week-end? What did you do? Where did you go?"
And I'd always be ultra-cagey - "Not much - not much, just a quiet drink. "
How could I tell them the truth? I took mind altering substances jumped around on a podium for six hours - then got in a mini with 7 other chaps I'd never met before - and ended up in Maidenhead.

MEETING LORD WILLIAM

DERMOTT COLLINS

> Lord William, this guy was the don. My hero. This is who I wanted to be when I grow up. He wasn't all mouth like Cobra - he knew the meaning of the word discreet and he did things proper. That's why Cobra was inside and Lord William was sunning it on the balcony at Queens. He didn't speak posh - he spoke normal like us. The Lord William name was to give him authority. But he had that anyway.

JERRY ZMUDA

> I saw Dermott go off in a corner with this mean looking sun-tanned gent - a bit older than all of us - perhaps in his thirties. I realized that Dermott was getting into serious drug dealing. I warned him - be careful. There are so many pitfalls - not just getting arrested, you have to worry about rival firms. Dermott was all – yeah, I know.

FRANK COLLINS (Dermott's father)

> I should have sensed something was up when Dermott asked to borrow two grand - promising to pay it all back after the week-end.

DERMOTT COLLINS

> With the Lord I could buy pukka Es for a lady godiva! But I had to buy in bulk.
> With two grand - I bought 400 Es. Take 6 out for personal use. Sell 394 at fifteens - return £5910.
> Profit £3910. That's more fucking like it. Paid my old man back in sweaty used notes.

FRANK COLLINS

> Then when he paid me back. "Why are these grubby notes soaking wet?" I asked. He said - "That's good honest sweat Dad. I worked hard for that money."

DERMOTT COLLINS

> Lord William told me the way he worked - he only dealt in top grade stuff - and never, never, never gave tick. Big discounts if you buy in bulk - but only cash in advance. That's so if someone got busted and had to flush it all down the toilet - he didn't have to come over like

FELTHAM MADE ME   216

Harry the Bastard. I looked at him - well dressed, easy smile - this geezer had it all sussed.

JERRY ZMUDA

So a few months in from our emotional re-union on the podium at The Trip, I found myself going out with Dermott regular - pretty much every week. It now seemed right. After all, we had been through so much together. But never at this stage did we ever talk about Botley or Septimus Grundy. We bypassed all of that, and if we ever talked about the past, we talked about Feltham School.

DERMOTT COLLINS

So we're in the toilet in Queens trying to work out what Frogspawn's assembly on acid house would be, "Why should people get on one – when they can listen to Bing?" - when this guy butts in. "I did bird at Feltham."

JERRY ZMUDA

We'd just seen *Withnail & I* on video and so Dermott says in his Basil Brush posh voice - "Ah! You went to the other place." I felt proud that this off-the-wall deranged fellow was my friend. Like I used to. Embarrassingly I told him this when I came up a few hours later.

A HAIRY EXPERIENCE

JERRY ZMUDA

This scene fired me with a sense of purpose. It gave me drive - to learn how to drive. I needed wheels to go to these warehouse parties in the bowels of deepest London, and then out to Queens and Valbonnes in the sticks afterwards. So I bought a rusty second hand car and I starting taking driving lessons - a crash course. I ripped up those L plates in September '88. That week-end the guys who did the Trip were doing a warehouse party in Wembley called Hair - the scene was still borrowing a lot hippie imagery in '88. We were going to celebrate my new mobility.

DERMOTT COLLINS

I was going to clean up at Hair. So I called Lord William on his hot-line and said – "Oi! Sort me out."

FELTHAM MADE ME   217

He said "Meet in a car park in Slough this evening at 9."
Slough how the fuck am I going to get to Slough? Peter was on missus duty. So there was nothing for else for it - I had to call Mr ripped up L Plates.

JERRY ZMUDA

I wasn't exactly thrilled that my first ever non L plate drive was a drugs deal to a desolate car park in Slough.

DERMOTT COLLINS

We do the deal - all top secret, professional stuff. Lord William is so well connected - he's not even there, he's got his henchmen to represent him. We do the deal, and I walk away with a sports bag with 400 calis - and Jerksky stalls the car. Get me fuckin' home - sharpish. "Sorry mate haven't got the hang of these gears yet."

JERRY ZMUDA

The fact that I was the driver in a drug deal was making me nervous. So I was forgetting the basics, like indicating and gear changes. Dermott was having kittens. When I finally dropped him off at home, he said - "No offence mate - but next time I'll get a cab."

DERMOTT COLLINS

On the night of Hair, I got a taxi. Jerry was driving Peter and that Oliver Mac geezer. I said – "Good luck - see you on the other side - if you ever get there."

PETER WYATT

I had to go to this party. I told Sarah I was out taking fairs - but I drove my cab to Jerry's bedsit in Willesden and went to the party from there. Did I feel guilty? A little. At Hair - Dermott slipped me a free E. I was naturally delighted. Then I see him dealing. I didn't know what to think. I didn't approve, but I didn't condemn it either. But he should have told me - he's supposed to trust me.

JERRY ZMUDA

'88 was the time of the friendly dealer with the smiling face. That was Dermott. Drug dealers you like. People bought from him because they thought him as one of us. He was more popular than the DJ. This wasn't going to last of course - but for a brief time he was.

DERMOTT COLLINS

The night was great - the music - the crowd - one of the best parties of the summer of '88. No messing with this one – we hit 3 am, and went straight on going till the morning sunshine poked through skylight.

I had six grand in my sky rocket, and Jerry says to me - "Do you fancy a lift home?" "Sure," I said, happily off me head and forgetting about earlier in the week - what could possibly go wrong?

JERRY ZMUDA

I didn't know how to work the air conditioning in my car and the windows were all steamed up, I was driving ultra slow. Of course, the drugs I'd taken weren't helping.

PETER WYATT

The inevitable happened - we get tugged by the Old Bill. Jerry gets out the car, his pupils the size of dinner plates. I know it's bad when I hear one of them say - "Look at him - it's a space cadet."

JERRY ZMUDA

The policeman says to me - "Excuse me sir - you're driving is not very good is it?"

"I only passed my test a few days ago, " I said trying to smile without gurning.
"You've been taking drugs – Sir."
I haven't had a cunt all night drugstable. I nearly said, but just smiled and shook my head instead.
"Yes - you have, I can tell by your eyes."

DERMOTT COLLINS

What the fuck do I do? The police start searching Jerry, what if they decide to search all of us?

JERRY ZMUDA

The policeman starts going through my trousers - and they are dripping wet, literally soaking wet with sweat.

"What the hell have you been doing tonight sir?"

"Dancing - it's sweat."

"I really hope it is sweat, Sir."

DERMOTT COLLINS

That's it - I'm off. I just ran and ran, faster than Ben Johnson on a ton of steroids. I hurdled over a fence, a dog barked. I jumped over another fence, nearly tripped, but kept on running until I came across a builders caff. Went in to catch me breath but I was making myself mighty conspicuous, so I dashed out of there and got a train home.

PETER WYATT

The two officers were so disgusted and distracted by Jerry's soaking trousers they didn't notice Dermott shooting off. I walked up to them - trying to act all clean and sober and said - "Excuse me gentleman, I'm a licensed cab driver - I am prepared to drive us all home." And they went for it.

DERMOTT COLLINS

Moral of the story? If you want to be a big time drug dealer don't hire Jerry Zmuda as your chauffeur.

WATCH OUT FOR THOSE LIFE STORY MERCHANTS

JERRY ZMUDA

I was dreading it - dreading it, but I knew he'd do it eventually. Peter brought up Botley. He collared me while I was dancing and he said - "I wish Botley had stayed around. He would have loved this scene." He was right. E had brought me out of my shell - and made life rosier, I'm sure it would have done the same for Botley. Then the DJ played the Waterboys - *Whole of the Moon* - and I burst into tears.

DERMOTT COLLINS

One of the big hazards of the house scene was them life story merchants. I saw Jerry chewing some guy's ear - and all of a sudden the geezer slaps him on the head - pushes him away. "Fuck off - I don't want to hear your life story."

JERRY ZMUDA

> That never happened. Another one of Dermott's fantasies. I was never a life story merchant. I was lost in the music, just wanted to dance. I was into the purity of it. I remember thinking to myself - why did I never think of doing this before? You just go out - not worried about pulling - and you just dance.

DERMOTT COLLINS

> He couldn't dance either. Flapping around like an epileptic chicken. Peter he was alright - but after a few beans he'd always end up doing this punching-the-air like he's breaking down cardboard boxes. Me on the other hand - I moved my hips like a snake on heat. That's why they called me the Balearic Travolta

JERRY ZMUDA

> Life was beautiful - the only thing that was missing was a girlfriend. Should I phone my ex Lydia? I pondered over this many times as I was dancing. I shut my eyes and imagined she was with me.

SHOOM SHOOM SHOOM ON A WEDNESDAY NIGHT

DERMOTT COLLINS

> To get our regular dose of thrills and partying we travelled all over the place - but my best times were down the Dungeons, Leabridge Road RIP. All dark and moody - you just lost yourself for hours.

PETER WYATT

> Thanks to the current bun and all that, you couldn't call the scene acid house no more. But another thing - within a few months of going out, they were legions of people walking around telling you that the scene had gone down the pan.

DERMOTT COLLINS

> When they meant it was going shit, they meant more people are getting into it. I didn't care - the more people raving - the more people to sell drugs to.

JERRY ZMUDA
Shoom was starting up again - on a Wednesday night at Busbys. I had to go. Shoom was supposed to be legendary. We smiled our way in and I wasn't disappointed.

PETER WYATT
Rampling was made of the same stuff as Weller, the same energy. Swinging the records over his head - chanting into the microphone - as crazy as the craziest person on the dance floor. I wasn't on the cabs until tomorrow afternoon - I thought fuck it, I'll get on one.

JERRY ZMUDA
So we became Shoom regulars. A lot of the crowd were a bit older like us - early 20s - and I felt at home. I got myself on Jenny's mailing list, and I felt like one of the chosen people.

DERMOTT COLLINS
I'd walk out of Shoom and you'd be surrounded by people putting flyers in yer mitts - all colors of the rainbow, all shapes and sizes. But the one that really got my attention was this crappy scrap of a photocopy - with a rat drawn on it - really badly. It was "Ratpack presents Trip City". I said to Jerry - this is the one we are going to.

JERRY ZMUDA
Trip City? Ted City more like.

DERMOTT COLLINS
A few months on the scene and he's already giving it the I-know-the score-seen-it-all-before act. "Don't be a Lionel" I said to him. "We are going to Trip City."

JERRY ZMUDA
I said "OK - let's check it out - but don't let Danny and Jenny find out." A few days later I told Danny all jokingly - like I've got a confession to make - and we laughed.

DERMOTT COLLINS
One night down Shoom I made the mistake of taking my T-shirt off. Bare-backing, showing off my tattoos. Jenny taps me on the shoulder

and I go all sheepish and put my soaking T-shirt back on. In the next Shoom newsletter it reads - *no bare-backing (Sorry Dermott)*.

I laughed it off - because Shoomers were the happy people. So I ended up having to go to Unit 4 - you know the score - for some guilty pleasures. Where I can bare-back with my brothers and not get told off.

JERRY ZMUDA

It was down Shoom that I bought a copy of Boys Own. It was funny - adding a healthy amount of cynicism to this scene. This I think was needed to put all this love and peace in context. I identified with it immediately.

DERMOTT COLLINS

"Can you feel it? Yes - but you'll never understand it." What is there to understand? You pop a pill - you get excited and you dance for hours. That's it. You don't need to read Adolf Huxley to get it. People Like Jerry are always trying to complicate things.

JERRY ZMUDA

There's the song by Inner City where the lyrics go -

Once you've had that Good Life feeling,
Let me tell you no-one can ever take it away.

And it's so true - taking Ecstasy had filled me with a whole new feeling of gregarious bonhomie that was to stay with me for the rest of my life. But there's a flip side to every coin. In downtime, returning to my crummy Willesden Green bedsit I found myself, like Raskolnikov, dashing up the stairs to avoid speaking to my landlady. Not because I owed her rent - but because she liked to talk and talk and talk. Going on about her son's imminent wedding, trying to lock me into eye contact. It was hard to take when I could barely keep my eyes open. Then that lot at work - their forced upbeat jollity was really grating. Little things like saying Hokey instead OK. Why? Why? Then talking in stupid Inspector Closeau cartoon French accent - for no reason. It got too much for me one Thursday afternoon – "SHUT LE FUCK UP!" I bellowed at the top of my lungs and stormed out.

But I came back Friday morning acting like nothing happened.

PETER WYATT

Jerry came to me with a problem. He wasn't fitting in at work. He had trouble talking to them. His supervisor would talk endlessly about her three year-old daughter and he'd just grin awkwardly not knowing what to say. I gave him a small-talk coaching session - you don't have to say anything clever, witty or original - just say something like - "Uh! They're really nice when they're that age."

DERMOTT COLLINS

I said to him when your work-mates ask you what you got up to at the week-end just throw them off the scent with some hilarious jape. Say - "I'm going to score some pussy at the week-end." They'll be stunned for a second and then follow up with - "Yeah I'm a judge at a cat show." You can't fail with jokes like that.

JERRY ZMUDA

Peter's conversational gambit totally back-fired. The "Uh! They're really nice when they're that age." Was perceived at having the most sinister connotations. As for the scoring pussy gag. I got the same reaction as if I'd sodomised a cat right in front of them. No-one spoke to me at work for weeks after that. With Wednesday now being such a big night, I was running out of Thursday morning excuses at work. Flu, ear infection - death in family - car accident. They were getting suspicious. I was now officially THE OFFICE WEIRDO.

THE END OF THE GREATEST YEAR EVER

PETER WYATT

New Years was coming up. The end of the greatest year ever and I was determined that Sarah was going to enjoy the celebrations with me. I said to her – "Get a baby-sitter I don't care how much she costs - we are going to the best ever Balearic Party in Fulham Studios."

SARAH WYATT

I hadn't been out for ages - it was New Years Eve, so I said OK. I wasn't bothered either way.

DERMOTT COLLINS

Shame that the first ever rave Sarah went to was a total dud. The sound system blew up and the promoter had done a bunk. He was in Tenerife with the rest of the villains. It was Mary Shitehouse.

OLIVER MACINTOSH

Even my amp at home was louder than this. I said to the DJ – "Do you want me to go home and get it?" He said - "I don't care, I'm off in a minute."

SARAH WYATT

I came up on my pill just before midnight - the music was a distant thud in the background, I couldn't dance, so I just talked - and talked - and talked. I told Jerry how fanciable he was. God! I even told Dermott he was a good laugh.

JERRY ZMUDA

To be honest I was embarrassed. Sarah started going on about Septimus Grundy and how good we were. This is something we had NEVER mentioned at this point since our re-unification.

PETER WYATT

"Fuck this," I said, "let's take this party somewhere else."

DERMOTT COLLINS

I thought about me old man's building yard.

OLIVER MACINTOSH

I said great – "I'll go and get me decks, amp and records."

JERRY ZMUDA

I told a few people we were going to a party in a builders yard in Sunbury on Thames, and about fifteen people showed.

PETER WYATT

So we had a party there - from about 3 am till 9 am. We had to stop when Dermott's old man came in to do some work - he didn't mind too much.

DERMOTT COLLINS
Somebody asked us what the night was called. Like we were actually party organizers. So I made something up - *Donkey Planet* after the instrumental Septimus Grundy track.

SARAH WYATT
I was saying to the boys – "Come around anytime you want - I'll cook dinner for you. Next time you come out I'll come with you."

It wasn't to be though. A couple of days later I found out I was pregnant - so I was saved.

PETER WYATT
I was thrilled to hear the news. I secretly hoped it was a boy, because I had a name planned.

DONKEY PLANET IS BORN

OLIVER MACINTOSH
I said to the boys – "We should do this Donkey Planet regular."

PETER WYATT
I said - "I know - but Dermott's dad wouldn't let us use his yard." Then Oliver said "No - I mean us put on a do somewhere else - with me as the resident DJ and give the night a name, something better than Donkey Planet."

JERRY ZMUDA
I loved the idea - let's do it.

DERMOTT COLLINS
There's gold in them thar hills. Let's show the world how to put on the best acid house party - our way.

PETER WYATT
I said – "Great - we'll meet later on in the week and have a full-on strategy meeting."

OLIVER MACINTOSH

What started off as a shit New Year had turned out to be the best ever. I ended up DJing to an up-for-it crowd, and now I was promoting nights. Taking control of my own career. I called Peter a few days later to confirm the meeting, all raring to go - and he said - "Can we make it next week? I'm getting into watching the arrows on the telly."

PETER WYATT

It's traditional, every January, first week after New Year - I watch the World Championship of Darts. Donkey Planet can wait.

OLIVER MACINTOSH

And we ain't calling it Donkey Planet. I was gutted. I was a young gun raring to go, and I was having to wait on Peter watching the darts.
So once the darts was over, I finally got my meeting with Peter and the other two about doing the parties. I suggested meeting at the pub in Ealing that I was regularly DJing at. I felt 1989 was going to be my year. Dermott shows up to the meeting grinning stupidly and tells us that Ray Allan and Lord Charles were in the saloon bar next door. Why I don't know — because they weren't - but this pathetically amused Jerry no end.

DERMOTT COLLINS

I couldn't help it - the more seriously Oliver was taking it, the more I had to take the piss. I laid down my Tony Montana strategy - first we get the money - then we get the power - then we get the women. Olly was not laughing.

OLIVER MACINTOSH

I tried to get a proper discussion going.
The most important thing, I said, is the venue. Find somewhere that was safe, that the police wouldn't bother raiding. Be discreet. I had ruled out doing a massive warehouse - that's when Dermott said that would be "Cannon and Ball — Too Risky." Jerry goes - "Why Cannon & Ball?"
"It's their catchphrase."
"No it's not — it's Rock on Tommy"
"They had more than one catchphrase."

I had to listen to them argue about Cannon & Ball catchphrases. That was it - that's when I cracked.

PETER WYATT
He slammed his bottle of Bud on the table and said – "Listen you mugs I want to go places with us. You either take it seriously, or I fuck off now and I do this with another bunch of people." That's when the landlord asked us to leave.

DERMOTT COLLINS
Olly made such a show of us, these geezers came over, giving it the - "Don't come into our manor - acting the hard man. We won't stand for it." Peter talks to them - I nearly said to them don't involve us - it's Olly.

JERRY ZMUDA
As you know I am not a fighter. But I would take a bullet for Peter, or a glass in the face. I saw this Marble denim clad type, tighten his jaw and grip his pint glass like he was ready to push it into Peter's face. I could not stand by. A split second's hesitance would be too late. I jumped the guy and pushed him into the ground. If you're going to glass anyone - glass me.
His mate starting kicking me, and then it seemed like the whole pub got involved.

DERMOTT COLLINS
In all the fracas I couldn't help noticing they were wearing marble denim. MARBLE DENIM!

PETER WYATT
I got hit a few times. The police arrived just as Dermott was picking up a chair. They grabbed him.

DERMOTT COLLINS
As soon as the Old Bill showed, my heart did a wobbly. I had two red and black capsules on me. They turfed me in the van - along with a couple of the Marb Denim crew.

JERRY ZMUDA

> With Dermott carted off to the police station, Peter and I went there under our own volition to make sure he was OK.

OLIVER MACINTOSH

> Fucking excellent. I come out for a meeting to further my career and instead I get myself banned from the pub I had a residency at.

DERMOTT COLLINS

> See I always knew that geezer Olly was a wrong 'un. HE was the one who slammed his bottle down drawing attention. He was blaming me for it all. And I was the one on the way to the nick with two bits of CLASS A in me sky rocket. I tried to drop them in the van, but I figured they'd find them. I had to think fast. I had to be like Lord William.

PETER WYATT

> I felt bad about the meeting not happening. Oliver wasn't working the next day, so I suggested coming round my house in the morning - without Dermott.

DERMOTT COLLINS

> So I'm told to empty my pockets at Ealing nick. The two red and blacks come out. The rozzer goes - "What's this?"
> I said all casual like - "It's for me Ear Infection, I have to take one in the morning, one in the afternoon."
> And he puts them away. Then he took my statement and threw me in the cell.

JERRY ZMUDA

> They took statements from me and Peter. We intended to wait for Dermott's release, but the police told us that Dermott was going to "cool off" and enjoy their overnight hospitality, so we went home.

DERMOTT COLLINS

> So I spend a night in the cells, I don't recommend it. I wanted to have a wank, release the tension, but the blanket was plastic and see through. Anyway up with the lark, comes the policeman - he's got a

glass of water and my red and black capsule. "How's the ear infection? Time to take your tablet."

OLIVER MACINTOSH

Can I ever escape him? I was round Peter's talking about our plan for the next party, and Dermott shows up, rushing off his nut, with this fucking story about the police making him take his red and black capsule.

DONKEY PLANET AT THE FULHAM FOOTBALL CLUB

DERMOTT COLLINS

A lot of parties were getting raided at this time. You had the Sunrise and the Genesis but they were massive operations – and we couldn't compete with that yet.

So I hatch meself a plan. They were doing regular dos in the function room of Chelsea Football Club, which we often went to. It was good – not amazing – but still good. So I figured with my Sherlock Holmes deerstalker on - if Chelsea have a got a function room you can hire, what about the other Football Clubs?

JERRY ZMUDA

Like it. Like it. So while I am at work, supposed to be teleselling, I phone up all the football clubs in London - Crystal Palace, Charlton, Millwall, Brentford. Telling them that my friend is a life long supporter and I want to hire their function room for his birthday party.

The chap at Fulham called me back and said – "What date do you want?"

"February 10th."

"Can't do that date - booked up."

"What other dates have you got?"

"Nothing till March 10th."

"We'll take it."

"Hang about. I thought you said this was a birthday party."

"He's a life long Fulham fan and an easy-going fellow, he won't mind his birthday party being a month late."

PETER WYATT

So we checked out the venue, it's alright. Just a normal function room - nice view of the river. Licensed till 2 am. I said – "How much to let it go on later?" He said - "Are you offering me a bribe to break my licence?" I said yes.

"Let's see how it goes on the night eh?" Then he goes to us - "Its not one of them acid house parties is it?"

JERRY ZMUDA

We signed the contract book, he gives me a photocopy. Our party career was beginning, I was ultra-excited. But it was on the tube home my worrying chip went into over-drive.

What have we let ourselves in for? In my training at work they told me to make a list of the things that were troubling me, and deal with them one by one. So I rolled out all the things that could go wrong -

1. Hardly anybody turns up - we lose loads of money.

2. Too many people turn up - but they're all dodgy.

3. Loads of people turn up but they think it's rubbish and want refunds.

4. The police raid it.

5. Nobody has any drugs.

6. The PA doesn't turn up.

7. The PA doesn't work.

8. A local criminal firm burst in with CS gas and steal all our money.

9. Our security firm is secretly a criminal firm and they attack us and steal all your money.

10. We're double booked with another night.

11. An enemy of Dermott turns up and starts trouble.

12. Somebody calls the police with a hoax bomb scare.

By the time I had got home I'd thought of dozens more worst case scenarios.
What the hell was I letting myself into? I called Peter to tell them we shouldn't do it.

PETER WYATT
Too late mate. The wheels are in motion. The Djs have been booked – so has the PA and security - the flyers have been designed and ordered. Donkey Planet is up and running.

OLIVER MACINTOSH
Donkey Planet? I thought we were calling the night 3000 AD, which was a reference to the track by Sterling Void *Its Alright*. 'The Year 3000 may still come to pass.'

DERMOTT COLLINS
I told Lord William we were doing a night. He was chuffed for me. He said - "As soon as I saw you down Queens I knew you were going places." It's like the nicest thing anybody ever said to me.

OLIVER MACINTOSH
I said - "OK this what we do. This scene is getting too big too quickly and there are lot of dodge people around. We don't blitz everywhere with flyers – we're selective. Tell the right people. Build up a mailing list."
That's how the Ramplings do Shoom. Get a sensible crowd.

DERMOTT COLLINS
Sensible crowd? Are we organizing a conference for accountants? It's a fucking rave! Let's get as many unsensible people in as possible and make a shed load of money. So I was boshing out the flyers all over the shop.

PETER WYATT
In them days it was easy to get a crowd. Our problem was the other way around - too many showed.

DERMOTT COLLINS
> A right horror show of a crowd an' all. Some of them were even wearing Marble Denim! MARBLE DENIM!

JERRY ZMUDA
> At the end of the night, we split the money - about four hundred each as I recall. It wasn't a total disaster but none of us considered it to be a roaring success. The crowd was too random - Oliver was right. We panicked about filling the place and blitzed flyers everywhere when we should have been discreet.

DERMOTT COLLINS
> I would have been around about this time that I started to get really into my Dogtanian.

THE RAY OF SUNSHINE BASSLINE

PETER WYATT
> There's this song by Wham about waking up in the morning and hearing a bass-line. And that kept happening to me. The sun rays poking through the curtains, I look over at my beautiful wife and a brand new bassline is running through my head. I strapped on my bass and tried to recreate it.

THE BIG LOG
> I was delighted to get a call from Peter. So glad they hadn't given up music. Their second demo was still among the best things I'd ever produced. The boys turned up and I was excited – yes, I admit, actually excited. They bring their equipment in and I said to Dermott - "Where's your guitar?"

DERMOTT COLLINS
> Gathering dust in the attic. Hadn't picked it up since Septimus Grundy split.

THE BIG LOG
> I said to – "Peter what about a drum kit?" And he brings out a battered grey box – he says "That's our drum machine." I said – "I hope you know what you're doing."

OLIVER MACINTOSH

I didn't turn up that day. Just couldn't handle Dermott.

PETER WYATT

I laid it on the Logster – "We are going to build a track based on this bassline."

THE BIG LOG

I said – "Let's hear it then." He straps on his bass – full of confidence – big grin and starts plucking. After a couple of minutes I said "That's great, great bass line. Except it's the same bass line, note for note, as the theme tune from GhostBusters."

PETER WYATT

I looked down at my bass, my stupid fat fingers, I stopped playing. I felt sick to my stomach. Dermott starts cackling manically which didn't help.

DERMOTT COLLINS

It was a killer bass line and no mistake – just a shame that Ray Parker Junior got there first. *'I ain't scared of no ghosts.'*

JERRY ZMUDA

I said – "Come on we're in the studio now, we may as well use the time productively and make up a track spontaneously." Then Dermott said he had some ideas.

DERMOTT COLLINS

That's right I surely did. I wanted to build a track around this drum pattern – quite slow pounding 98 bpm – building to this totally mad sound.

THE BIG LOG

So now I knew what the boys from Septimus Grundy had been doing in the last few years – copious amounts of drugs. I said to the boys – "Look I don't know what you're trying to achieve. I don't understand this music, I am a rock'n'roll man. But I'll engineer this for you and you're just going have to tell me what you need."

PETER WYATT

> After a couple of hours - the track was complete. We also recorded the Ghostbusters bass line with the drum machine and decided we'd put it on the b-side.

JERRY ZMUDA

> We played it back - it sounded odd, unconventional, like a drain laughing. It had a claustrophobic feel - like a bass line trapped in a box with only a drum machine for company. We tried to be positive - maybe we've accidentally discovered a new sound with a ground breaking record.

DERMOTT COLLINS

> I was trying to recreate that big sax sound from the *Heat Is On*, but we didn't have a sax. So we recreated it on a keyboard. But it just didn't sound the same. More like an elephant farting.

JERRY ZMUDA

> We put in some house piano, only none of us could play that either. Dermott had a go and he just ended up sounding like Les Dawson.

DERMOTT COLLINS

> You couldn't compare it to nothing else.

THE BIG LOG

> You couldn't compare to anything else, because nothing else sounded as shit as this.
> I said to them – "Don't take offence lads but please don't put my name on this record."

PETER WYATT

> We pressed a hundred white labels. Calling it THE HEAT IS PUT ON CIRCUIT by DONKEY PLANET. The B Side was called I AIN'T SCARED OF NO BASS-LINES.

JERRY ZMUDA

> We had a strategy - the track was too off the wall and dark for Rampling - but there was a young DJ on the scene - getting influential who liked the darker side - his name was Andrew Weatherall. With

my E fuelled confident outlook, I collared him at Valbonne in Maidnehead one Sunday night. I handed him a white label and launched into a big spiel, and he seemed very receptive. If Weatherall made it part of his set - we'd be hip - and quite literally laughing.

PETER WYATT

In the week me and Dermott took a batch of white labels down to a record store. Bluebird I think it was. I said - "Wait till you hear this - this is the future of dance music." The guy puts it on, and after about a minute he starts laughing uncontrollably. When he managed to finally speak he said - "I should have known this was a wind up - coming from him." And he's pointing at Dermott.

DERMOTT COLLINS

We were so ashamed we had to pretend that the record really was a wind up.

JERRY ZMUDA

Two days later I get a call from Weatherall. He says - "It's a bit fucking early for April fools." We had become the Ed Wood of the dance music scene.

DERMOTT COLLINS

The first time ever I didn't like people laughing. We put the rest of the white labels in a box in Peter's attic and they never saw the light of day again. I stuck to what I was good at that – the friendly neighbourhood E dealer – serving up the pukka gear. Lord William was putting top grade stuff my way at a time when some of the stuff going around was real moody.

OLIVER MACINTOSH

I am a very proud owner of the very limited white label THE HEAT IS PUT ON CIRCUIT by DONKEY PLANET. I always smile when I think of that track. If they'd marketed it right – the record could have taken off. Like – play this track when you've got loads of unwanted guests round your house and you want them to leave. It was as if they deliberately wanted to sound shit. Officially the worst dance music track known to man.

JERRY ZMUDA
>
> We had to come back with a victory - do another Donkey Planet party. But this time make it exceptional. Dermott had come up with a slogan for the next one.

DERMOTT COLLINS
>
> It ain't Pony - It's a Donkey!

HIT THE NORTH

PETER WYATT
>
> Saturday afternoons was my relaxation time. Sarah takes Abby to see her folks, and I would clean the cab, listening to the half-time results on the radio, or maybe sling on me George Benson tape. No trouble and strife - no screaming kids. All peaceful. But this Saturday afternoon, I found myself driving my cab up the M1 to a place called the Hacienda.

JERRY ZMUDA
>
> For the next Donkey Planet, we needed to do some research. What are the essential elements of a good party? The Music, The Crowd, The Energy. Where does that energy come from? Just the drugs? People were talking about the Manchester scene - the Happy Monday, 808 State, A Guy Called Gerald and the club where it all happened - The Hacienda.

DERMOTT COLLINS
>
> So we went round Peter's one Saturday afternoon. I said "Come geez – you're taking us for a drive up north." Peter's wasn't up for it at first. I said – "Remember the spirit of Southampton."

PETER WYATT
>
> I got talked into it. Half up the M1, I start thinking - I shouldn't be doing this, what am I going to tell Sarah? Where the fuck is the Hacienda anyway?

DERMOTT COLLINS

I had a bagful of Es. I told him once I'd sold them, I'd wedge him in
with some cash, and he can show it to Sarah and tell her that it was
from his fairs.

PETER WYATT

We get to Manchester, driving around - roundabout after roundabout
- grey building after grey building. We stop in a pub to ask for
directions. Jerry plucks up the courage to approach some local lads
at a table.

JERRY ZMUDA

"Excuse me - do you know the way to the Hacienda?"
Prolonged tense silence. Then -
"What was that you southern gobshite?"
"Errr, I was asking directions to the Hacienda."
The man stands up. "Why the fuck would a southern gobshite want
to go there?"
I stammered something pathetic like – "I hear it's quite good."
He reached over and grabbed my lapels.
"You turn left out of here. Follow the signs for Manchester City
Centre and Deansgate. You join Deansgate from the south, turn left
into Whitworth Street and proceed straight on. You can't miss it."
He beams at me and sent us on our way.

PETER WYATT

At the Hac, as soon as you get past the moody bouncers, the energy
of the place hits you. It was ten o'clock, and people were already going
mental on the stage. So we immediately all got on one and joined
them.

JERRY ZMUDA

I loved the Factory Records décor, the warehouse feel, the steel
girders neatly painted in stripes. Normally clubs this size were owned
by Mecca and turned into meat markets, playing nothing but chart
fodder. But this was how a club should be. Underground, dangerous
and wild.

FELTHAM MADE ME   238

DERMOTT COLLINS

> The only time I'd ever been up north before was to see The Jam play in Leeds. Then everybody hated you as soon as you opened your mouth. You'd go to the bar order a Sherbert – and everyone's behind muttering "He's a Cockney London bastard – we hate him." But here at the Hac nobody hated us. When they heard my accent, they were actually made up that we'd come all the way from London to visit their club.

PETER WYATT

> I told Dermott not to sell the Es until he knows it's safe. We didn't want to tackle any rival firms so far away from home.

JERRY ZMUDA

> The scene was just over a year old in London, and already people were declaring it to be over, and that there were too many 'teds' about. It made you self-conscious about enjoying yourself. But here in Manchester everyone was going for it.

PETER WYATT

> The music was loud - loud - loud but throughout you could hear the crowd underneath - shouting -screaming - laughing - cheering. Beautiful. At one point the DJ turned the music right down so you could barely hear it, and he let the sound of the crowd fill the hall. The DJ stood there with his arms in the air. Beautiful - just beautiful.

DERMOTT COLLINS

> Those air-horns blaring away. Like a European football match. If you tried that in London – you'd get branded an instant Ted.

PETER WYATT

> That night down the Hac was pukka – but a familiar problem – it all finished at 2. Some geezer we got talking to - I think his name was Bleo - or Blacko or something like that, saw the disappointment on our faces when the music stopped. He goes to us - "Don't worry sunshine - there's a party in Moss Side, that won't be stopping till Sunday."

DERMOTT COLLINS
Bleo gave me his air horn as a souvenir of the night.

JERRY ZMUDA
Apparently the party was being organized by the 808 State people.
We simply had to go. Peter didn't need much persuading. So we get
in the car and off we go to Moss Side. Outside it's starting to show
all the signs of a run-down decaying inner city, unsightly tower blocks,
vandalised phone boxes, but we had no feeling of foreboding - to us
everything was bathed with a peachy pleasant glimmer. Then Peter
has to stop his cab. We're at a traffic light, it's green but the car in
front is reversing. Peter had to reverse his cab to avoid getting hit.

PETER WYATT
Suddenly this geezer appears, running towards my cab. I see a mad
look in his eye and he slings open the passenger door. Quick as flash
I mount the curb and drive off. But I'm on the pavement. The other
car that was in front is now moving and trying to stop me from getting
back on the road. The geezer who opened my car door is chasing
after my cab. I think about reversing into him, but instead I drive off
on the pavement into this precinct. This other car is chasing me - then
I hear this loud bang.

DERMOTT COLLINS
It couldn't have been a gun. Could it?

PETER WYATT
As I drove away, and managed to finally get back on the road, I said
jokingly - "Do you think - he wanted a lift to the rave?" Five minutes
later it sunk in what had just happened - my heart starting pounding.
They were trying to ambush us. I said to the other two – "Fuck this,
we're in a strange town. Far from home, we've had a great night. Let's
quit while we're ahead."

JERRY ZMUDA
We saw the best and worst of Manchester that night.

DERMOTT COLLINS
I said – "But I've still got a bag of Es to sell."

PETER WYATT
"Never mind that, you can sell them down Queens. If we start the journey now, we'll be fresh by the time Queens opens."
So we headed down south. It was long drive, but pleasant - hardly another car in the road.

JERRY ZMUDA
We got to Queens two hours early, waiting in the boating house, drinking water, getting stared at by the boating people. Dermott was trying to be funny saying stuff like – "he's got a really nasty boat that geezer."
By this time the Queens organizers were well used to us being among the first ones in. In fact they were probably bloody sick of the sight of us - with our dumb E humour. Nevertheless they always gave us a friendly welcoming smile.

DERMOTT COLLINS
Peter was feeling guilty about leaving his three year old daughter and five month pregnant wife for the week-end, so I popped him another pill.
Queens normally went into top gear an hour before the end. That was my moment. I took out Bleo's air horn out and starting blaring it out. It was deafening - drowning out the music. I haven't seen so many open jaws since my Jesus/Kung Fu school assembly. Literally stopped the show.
The next day, nursing my come-down, I get dozens of phone calls, congratulating me on the air horn. I was a club hero for fifteen minutes.

DONKEY PLANET IN THE CLINK

JERRY ZMUDA
For the next Donkey Planet we needed to find a proper underground venue. Not a function room normally used for Wedding receptions. I went into over-drive and started compiling a file of different venues.

This time I was looking for warehouses, rehearsal studios, photographic studios.

DERMOTT COLLINS
I told Jerry to check out Clink Street where RIP was in '88.

JERRY ZMUDA
The basement where RIP used to be, the original Clink Street prison, that wasn't available anymore. I think the police had injucted them, and they were now turning it into a museum. But on the third floor there was this rehearsal studio - dinghy - dirty - dilapidated. It was perfect - and the fellow was up for it. For £600 he was happy to let the party go on till 6 am. We were in business!

OLIVER MACINTOSH
I told the boys – "This time, learn your lesson – DON'T GIVE OUT FLYERS ALL OVER THE SHOP TO EVERY TED AND HIS DOG!"

DERMOTT COLLINS
Yes Oliver we get it. Be selective. Be objective. Be an asset to the collective. He was starting to wind me up that geezer. I feel a top wind up coming on.

OLIVER MACINTOSH
The week-end before this Donkey Planet was the May Bank Holiday, and there was some proper parties on that we could go to and put the word about – discreetly.

DERMOTT COLLINS
Saturday night Shoom were doing a Joy party in Southwark. Sunday night was a coach trip to Valbonne's in Maidenhead, Rampers was playing that one too, and the Bank holiday Monday was an all dayer down Queens. So we set the promotion in motion.

OLIVER MACINTOSH
I told them – "Don't go to a Shoom party and bosh out the flyers. You put the word about on the QT, mentioning it in conversation as a by-the-way."

JERRY ZMUDA

There was a thick air of expectation as we walked down the steps to this underground Shoom/Joy party. It was low ceilinged and arched - like some ancient catacombs. The place would have been dark and moody, but hang up half a dozen luminous Shoom love hearts, play some joyful tunes and add a happy crowd - and the place had an electric ambience all of its own. Of all people, it was Peter who spoilt the atmosphere.

DERMOTT COLLINS

I was down the back by the wind- machines, which were chopping out stale air – but at least it was doing something. Anyway I point the wind machine at this geezer, and he goes - "Leave it out – you're ruining my buzz," in this really stupid croaky voice. So I did it again so that Peter could hear him and we could share a laugh. Anyway when Peter hears his voice, he turns into the Incredible Hulk and he grabs a hold of him. I said –"Wait up Peter this is a Shoom party, you can't be doing that here."

PETER WYATT

It was him. I swear it was him - the herbert who stole that box of Toblerone out of my petrol station.

DERMOTT COLLINS

He was going on about some box of Toblerone. "What drugs are you on Peter? You're losing it."

PETER WYATT

The geezer was denying it, saying he'd never been to Feltham in his life. Never even heard of the place. I said – "Don't give me that - I'd recognize that voice anywhere."

JERRY ZMUDA

I had to dash in and pull Peter away from him. I think Peter was in a dark place - I mean mentally - at the time. Despite all the happiness around him, I think he felt guilty about going out and taking drugs while his pregnant wife was sat at home. He was talking it out on this poor chap - contriving this whole box of Toblerone affair. Peter was always one for heart to heart talks. This was my turn. I said "Peter maybe you should lay off the drugs for a bit."

PETER WYATT
"Fuck off Jerry - it's got nothing to do with drugs. THAT CUNT STOLE MY BOX OF TOBLERONE."

DERMOTT COLLINS
I tried to get a joint going to calm Peter down – I couldn't get a light going because there was no oxygen in that place.

JERRY ZMUDA
The next day on Sunday, Shoom had organized two coaches to Maidenhead where Danny was playing at Studio Valbonne. As it turned out everyone piled in on one coach - and us - the Unholy Trinity got a whole coach to ourselves. Had the box of Toblerone incident made us Shoom pariahs? And would anybody come to our party next week-end? When we got to the other end - I was desperate for people to like us - so I told Oliver Mac that he could do the last set - the centrepiece 4 till 6.

OLIVER MACINTOSH
I was super-delighted. Until then I had only ever played warm-ups. So to come on after a big name DJ was a big deal for me.

JERRY ZMUDA
Box of Toblerone incident notwithstanding. That week-end is etched in my memory as one of my best week-ends ever. The drugs were working, the music was uplifting, the crowd were happy and cheerful. I was 25 years of age and it felt liberating to give my youth a second wind. My teens and early 20s had been racked with worry and pressure - this was my release. At Valbonne Danny got on the mic, as he was want to do when the party was going off. He passed the mic around to some of the Shoomers. I got my turn - I chanted something about how much I love my friends from Feltham School. Then I did my Feltham Is Mine, Feltham Is Mine bit from Feltham Made Me. Before they told me to shut up.
The next day, the Bank Holiday Monday down Queens was a more sedate affair - something of an anti-climax. It had to be after what we'd

done the previous two nights. I finally got down to promoting Donkey Planet. People seemed up for it - but you couldn't be sure until you opened those doors.

DERMOTT COLLINS

So Olly Mac was going to do the last set. Good for him. Nobody deserves it more than him. But I had to play a trick on him. I just had to.
When I wasn't serving up in clubs – or sleeping – I'd spend my time watching Dogtanian videos or hanging out down charity shops. Oxfam where selling a whole bunch of Val Doonican albums – this threw a log into my plan-hatching furnace.

JERRY ZMUDA

So the big day of the Clink Street party came. An hour before the doors opened on the second Donkey Planet - it was clear it wasn't going to be any problem filling the place. There were several hundred milling about outside on the ancient cobbled streets around Clink Street. Martin our camel hair coated security man turned up with his team and instantly began getting everyone to form an orderly queue. Then at the end of the street I saw a flashing police-car light. I felt a sudden stab of panic.

DERMOTT COLLINS

The Old Bill were at the door, telling security they wanted to speak to the organizer. "Let me handle this," I said and walked up to them. There's a strong tug on my jacket. Peter had pulled me back.

JERRY ZMUDA

"This is an unlicensed and illegal party and we are going to shut you down." Said the stoney-faced policeman. The bottom fell out of my trousers and I was preparing to make a dash for it. But while I stood trembling in the shadows, Peter with a big disarming smile went into charm over-drive - "It's just a party, we're playing soul and dance music - Barry White."
"Do you know all these people Sir?"
"Not all of them - but I know a lot of them. This is our crowd."

DERMOTT COLLINS

I was reaching into my pocket to bring out a wedge to pay the coppers off, but I see that Peter is turning on the Wyatt charm. The coppers were lapping it up – soul music club, nice people, no drunks and certainly no drugs. He was selling it so well, at one point I thought the coppers were going to stay for the party.

PETER WYATT

I was smiling the Old Bill into submission but then I fucked up. The police asked about fire exits and I took them upstairs onto the roof - instead of the staircase at the back. There was long awful silence - with me not sure whether to say anything. I heard a squawking voice on the police radio. Then one of the copper goes - "Look here Peter - you seem like a nice bloke. If you promise you don't overfill the place - we'll let it go ahead. We'll come back and check on you in a couple of hours." I could have kissed them.

DERMOTT COLLINS

The party was on, and Peter was our hero. Free drugs for him - well he was going to get them anyway.

DONNA HARVEY (Donkey Planet attendee)

The first time I saw Dermott he was rushing off his nut in the stairwell in Clink Street, his jaw was shaking all over the shop. I said to him – "That looks scrummy."
And he gave me one - a pill that is. My mates didn't see what I saw in him, but when they found out he was a top dealer, then they thought he was alright.

OLIVER MACINTOSH

This party in Clink Street was proper, much more like it. It was heaving with people, I carried my records through the crowd and Dermott was sitting next to the coat-check girl and called me over. He offered to look after my records in the cloak-room. I should have known.

PETER WYATT

The party had a pukha underground feel and was going right off. Totally forgot about the Old Bill coming back to pay me a visit. I'd dropped a couple of beans and was looking pretty fucked.

The boys in blue returned, showing up at around 2 am. The money was all in. But we didn't want to get raided. They barged past the doormen and rush up the stairs and the copper shouts over the music "I am looking for a Peter Wyatt. Where is he?" I hid, crouching behind the bar.

DERMOTT COLLINS

I said – "I am Peter Wyatt."

JERRY ZMUDA

Then I stepped up before them and declared that I am Peter Wyatt. Then some fellow behind shouted "I am Peter Wyatt." Then someone else "I am Peter Wyatt." Dozens of us came forward - with a chorus of "I am Peter Wyatt." It was like that scene from Spartacus, but with an MDMA twist. The policeman shook his head and walked out into the night.

OLIVER MACINTOSH

I had planned out my set meticulously - every record, every mix - to the second, timing the bpms - everything. My first record was going to be Roberta Flack, the big record of May '89. I collected my record box from the cloak room - getting all excited. I get behind the decks - open up the box and the blood drains from my face - it's full of Val Doonican LPs. My heart goes wobbly, how can I put together a set from this? Then I work out there could be only one person behind this. I dash back to the cloakroom, Dermott gave me back my records with a cheeky grin saying "one-nil." But I did not find this funny at all.

DERMOTT COLLINS

Jerry was saying – "We need to give them something they've never seen before." So I said – "What about a bloke dressed like Dogtanian?"

DONNA HARVEY

I was talking to Dermott. Then he said "I'd better go, I need to get changed." Then I don't see him again for hours. I found out later it was him dancing, dressed like a dog.

OLIVER MACINTOSH

I thought the bloke dancing in the dog suit was class – until I found out it was Dermott. When we divied the money out afterwards I found out the costume hire was coming out of the party's expenses. I fucking hit the roof.

DERMOTT COLLINS

The dog suit wasn't due till Monday so I got to wear it for the whole week-end.

OLIVER MACINTOSH

I finish my set off with a classic from '88 - *Musical Freedom*. Everyone's cheering as the record fades out, I'm beaming with pride. Then Dermott comes up to me, puts his hand out into a bowl shape and says - "Please Oliver can we have some more?" Very fucking funny. Then the whole place starts doing it. For the next five years afterwards I had people coming up to me while I'm DJing going - "Please Oliver can we have some more?"

SARAH WYATT

Peter was going out a lot at this time. In truth I honestly didn't mind that much. I knew that once my second child was born he wouldn't get much time for any of that. So these last few months was his final fling. But I used it as ammunition when it suited me - when we had rows.

DERMOTT COLLINS

The plan was to make a bunch of money from Donkey Planet 2 – everyone would like us, and then the next week-end we'd hit Ibiza – no sleep till Pasha. I'd bought Peter his flight – but Peter had other ideas.

PETER WYATT

> After the Manchester trip and Clink Street, Ibiza was a bridge too far. I had a pregnant wife and three year old daughter - I had to sit this one out.

JERRY ZMUDA

> Ibiza was OK - but it wasn't the same without Peter the Rock. Highlights included - dancing like teapots at some early morning affair at a café-stroke-restaurant, meeting an elderly white-bearded chap at Pasha called Nino - the Balearic Father Christmas, and at the Café Del Mar hooking up with Bleo and his mates from the Hac.

DERMOTT COLLINS

> Some posh fucker teaching me to play Backgammon at the Cafe Del Mar. He taught me to play badly on purpose, so he could beat me and show off to the ladies. I told him to FUCK RIGHT OFF.

JERRY ZMUDA

> And Dermott shouting at some posh fellow, piercing the Café Del Mar's legendary sunset magic hour serenity.
> I had told everyone at work that I was going for a short relaxing holiday in sunny Ibiza. I return to work to find the Sun's headline **Ecstasy Island**. My cover was blown.

FEAR OF A DONKEY PLANET

JERRY ZMUDA

> Months and months of hard slog had paid off. Driving around London, thumbing through directories - phone call after phone call - I HAD FINALLY FOUND THE DREAM VENUE. It was a large photographic studio in Farringdon. Nobody had ever used it before. It was spacious and clean. This is the one that would give Donkey Planet the top Donkey prize. We would become dance scene legends after pulling this one off.

OLIVER MACINTOOSH

> Jerry was right, this venue was the nuts. This was our big chance. I told the boys – "this time we go up a gear." With the help of my girlfriend we'd gathered up a mailing list – with phone numbers. No

walk-up on the door – we sell ALL the tickets in advance. We do this one properly.

JERRY ZMUDA

My contact at the venue was a chap named Howard - he was my age and knew exactly what we were up to. I didn't have to pretend about anything. He wanted two thousand pounds in advance for the hire. I did my maths and we could still make a profit on that. Hike the ticket price up by about £2 - easily worth it for this spectacular venue. Plus we'd still make a handsome profit on all the drinks we'd sell.

DERMOTT COLLINS

So the party was set for the last week-end in July. Me and Jerry turn up at Beggars Banquet – this record shop in Kingston what was selling our tickets, and turns out we've got competition. This soppy looking kid with a poodle haircut was doing a rave in his old man's barn in Cobham on the same night. I said to him – "Poodle! Let the battle of the parties commence." He looked well frit.

PETER WYATT

Dermott was as usual being all cocky and arrogant. But he had reason this time - we had a super-cool venue in the heart of London. Poodle's real name was Simon. I said to him – "Take no notice of Dermott, none of us ever do. This scene's massive, there's more than enough people to go around. I'm sure we'll both have successful parties."

JERRY ZMUDA

I felt supremely confident about this party. Oliver and his girlfriend had the foresight to collect phone numbers as well as addresses for our mailing list, so not only did we do a mailing, we called them up as well.

PETER WYATT

We'd booked a great line up of DJs, tickets were selling and people were talking about Donkey Planet #3. But my mind was elsewhere. Sarah was getting close to dropping her sprog. My sprog. I was a father and a husband first, and everything came after that.

FELTHAM MADE ME   250

DERMOTT COLLINS
>Remember kids this is in the days before the noncey internet. We had to PROMOTE this mother-fucker. This meant going out and actually telling people about it.

JERRY ZMUDA
>Promoting Donkey Planet #3 was a blast. Going to clubs with Dermott - I'd look over at him, it was like he was back in the playground of Feltham School. He'd come home. By now he had a reputation for being London's premier pill supplier, so people were flocking around him. Finally, this time, Dermott had found his true calling.

PETER WYATT
>I said – "Look boys - you lot doing are all the 'Donkey' work on this one. I can't take 25 percent of the profits. Split everything three ways and count me out."
>Jerry and Dermott were really sweet. "No way" said Dermott - "we are the MuskeHounds, all for one and one for all. You get 25% and like it. Buy a nice present for Sarah and the kids." I had the best mates in the world.

OLIVER MACINTOSH
>I don't get it. How the fuck are we supposed to make any money, if we wedge in people who are doing fuck all? No disrespect to Peter, he's a smashing bloke and that. But it's all very well Dermott coming over like the Godfather, he makes his money from pills. I wanted to make a living from music. And I said to Dermott straight – "if you want to hire any dog suits, this time it's coming out of your own bleeding pocket."

DERMOTT COLLINS
>So I show up at Beggars Friday afternoon, the geezer goes to me. "Got a problem boys – we'd sold all our Donkey Planet tickets. Got any more?" So I arranged to get another hundred printed pronto. So people will get a little squashed. They love it, and we'd make another grand on top. Lovely.

JERRY ZMUDA

We'd cracked it. We'd sold six hundred tickets in advance. Dermott got a few beers from the supermarket and we spent a lovely afternoon hanging around Beggars lording it up, watching the world go by.

Simon aka Poodle came in, and it turned out he'd only sold eighteen tickets. He looked sick. Dermott of course really took the mickey.

DERMOTT COLLINS

Poodle was giving it all the – the scene isn't about that. I said – "So what is the scene all about then? Eighteen people freezing to death in a big empty barn?" He stormed off and we were laughing.

JERRY ZMUDA

So the plan for the day of the party was this - I go round Peter's in the afternoon, and we drive down to the venue together and get everything set up.

SARAH WYATT

My water broke Saturday morning and Peter took me to the hospital. Mum came with us and looked after Abby.

JERRY ZMUDA

I get to Peter's house and nobody's home. I realized it must have something to do with Sarah's pregnancy, but she wasn't due for two weeks. We'd set the date for the party specially so it wouldn't clash. I started having palpatations. I can't do this without Peter, I thought. But it was clear I had no choice.

DERMOTT COLLINS

I was still in bed. My plan for the day was not to get up until about 10 pm and get a lift up there. That way I'd be fresh as a daisy for the whole of the night through till morning.

JERRY ZMUDA

I turned up at the venue and a balding middle-aged guy who'd I never seen before was in Howard's office - sat at his desk.
"Hullo. Where's Howard?"
"Howard's gone."

FELTHAM MADE ME   252

"What do you mean gone?"

"He doesn't work here any more."

"Did he mention anything about a party?"

"What party?"

Turned out Howard had gone travelling - Friday was his last day. And he never really was the owner - he just did admin on the bookings. The sickening penny dropped, I had been conned.

The guy was about to go, and in a fit desperation I told him everything and pleaded with him to let the party go ahead. He politely told me that his was a working photographic studio and he couldn't allow a party to take place there. He ushered me out of there, locked up and walked away. Then the PA van showed up. What the hell was I going to do?

PETER WYATT

Sarah gave birth to a strapping baby boy at 4.07 pm. I was there for all of it - the screaming - the shouting - the cursing - being called all names under the sun. It was my second time, but it was still beautiful. Donkey Planet #3 was so far in the back of my mind. There was no way I was going to leave Sarah and my new born baby. I had a name for him and Sarah agreed. He was going to be called Carl after my dear lost friend Botley.

JERRY ZMUDA

I chased the studio owner down the road and pleaded some more. I was a man whose pride had been wiped away by desperation, and promised him money and anything else that came into my hysterical head. This time he laughed as he got into his car and drove off. I was desolate. Then the PA guy caught up with me and demanded to know what the hell was going on.

DERMOTT COLLINS

I had no idea about any of this. I got woken up at around 4 pm when me old man was watching the racing.

PETER WYATT

They can talk all the crap they want about Ecstasy - the greatest feeling in the world is child birth. Obviously I haven't experienced the actual giving birth. But to be there when it happens. The beginning of a new life - that you made. To see a set of eyes focus on the world for the first time. I just felt nothing but total joy and happiness, and it wasn't chemical.

SARAH WYATT
This was my second birth, so I knew the score - I wanted as many epidurals and pain killers I could down my neck. I don't know what was worse - knowing what was to come, or not knowing.

JERRY ZMUDA
I quickly mumbled something to the PA guy that we may have to change venues, and I'll keep him posted - I then made a dash to the nearest pub I could find open, and with a stack of 10ps made camp around their pay-phone.

DERMOTT COLLINS
Jerry called me, stuttering he was. Something about losing the venue. I said to him – "Listen, you ain't going to solve nothing by getting in a flap."

JERRY ZMUDA
"That's easy for you to say, you swine! You're tucked away at home. I'm here in Farringdon, with a PA crew breathing down my neck, the lighting is on it's way - and security as well." I hung up on Dermott, got loads more change off the barman and started dialling all the venues in my book - Diorama, Clink Street, King Bee, Cobden Working Man's Club, Ewer Street Skate Park, Hersham British Legion - in the vain hope that one of them might have their venue free for the night.

DONNA HARVEY (Donkey Planet attendee)
I had a thing for Dermott. We had kissed, but he always seemed to disappear at the wrong time. I was determined to make something happen at the next Donkey Planet.
I had made a Donkey Planet T-Shirt, and I was going to show it to him, and try and get involved with Donkey Planet by doing their merchandise. I thought if I got there early enough, I could talk to him properly, before it all went mental.

JERRY ZMUDA

On the pay phone I was drawing a blank and in a blind terror. I had around two grand in cash on me - all in envelopes to pay the different people working on the party. I was seriously thinking about just dashing off to Heathrow Airport. Get the next flight, and join Smike in Goa. Start a new life, with a new identity.

PETER WYATT

Sarah and the baby were sleeping - so peaceful, so serene, I showed Abby her new brother. It had occurred to me to go and see the boys. But I figured there's three other blokes in Donkey Planet - they didn't need me - and my place was here, watching over my wife and the newest addition to my family.

JERRY ZMUDA

Then this clubber type girl came in and spotted me.

DONNA HARVEY

I spotted his plummy mate in the boozer, and I said "Hullo do you want see my Donkey Planet T-Shirt? By the way, where's Dermott?" He did a moody one on me.

JERRY ZMUDA

I sneaked out the back door and tried to find another pub with a pay phone.

OLIVER MACINTOSH

Jerry is a fucking mug. I thought something was fishy about the guy insisting on all the money up front, and then not getting anything in writing.

JERRY ZMUDA

I did have something in writing but when I showed the contract to the owner, he just laughed in my face. It wasn't worth anything. It was easy for Oliver to give it - "I just play the music man." All he does is play loads of records that Oakenfold, Rampling, and Weatherall made popular. He wants to try finding a venue, that's really hard in this twilight legal world. Anyway the hours passed - phone call after phone call after phone call. Nothing. It was now 9 o'clock and doors open was an hour away. The lighting guy was now looking for me, and the security team were due any minute.

I went back to the venue and cased the joint. There was nothing else for it. I was going to have to break in. Deal with the repercussions later. If I climbed up a drain-pipe, got on a ledge, smashed a window, climbed in, and then smashed another window - I might be able to get access to the venue. Damn! What about the burglar alarm?

DONNA HARVEY

So afterwards I went straight to the venue, and I saw Dermott's mate climbing up a drainpipe.

JERRY ZMUDA

I was lost in a crisis without Peter. I kept asking myself - what would Peter do?

I was half way up the drain pipe when Martin the head of security showed up in his Bentley. Dressed immaculately as ever in his camel hair coat, he exuded an aura of total confidence - like he was the Don of London.

"Alright Jerry - what's going on up there?" He says to me as I jump down.

"Martin - I've got a bit of a problem."

"I should say - but Dermott's sorted it."

"How has he sorted it then?"

"You'd better call your mate."

He handed me this large black thing - the size and weight of a brick. It was a mobile phone, I'd never held one before.

"He's found another venue - a barn in Cobham."

"Dermott - what have you done?"

"Just got us out of this fucking mess. I called up Poodle. He drove a hard bargain. He laid down a number of conditions - he says the first one is - you can start by not calling me Poodle – ever again."

"But 600 people are coming here - what do I tell them? What's the address? They're not going to take kindly to having to go to Cobham." I was spluttering.

"Easy fellah! I've got the list here. I've been calling some of them from here. You'll still get several hundred show up, but you'll just have to give them directions."

"But what are the directions?"

FELTHAM MADE ME   256

"Martin's photocopied loads of sheets with the directions on it."
And he had - God bless him.

DERMOTT COLLINS

I said to Jerry – "It's a better venue. It's a large barn with loads of space, not some dirty sweat-box. You'll be able to see the sunrise over the rolling green hills. If anybody gives it the – 'where the fuck is Cobham?' Just say 'there you go, tonight you will go somewhere you've never been before.' Dress it up good – you're a salesman Jerry – I don't need to tell you..."

JERRY ZMUDA

It was still a mess - several hundred people showed up, and me and Martin gave out the photocopies. Most were quite put out but ultimately fine about it - this how it goes in the world of warehouse parties - but a significant minority were mightily annoyed. Saying stuff like "What's this magical mystery tour?"
Dermott said I could promise free Es to anyone who was especially unhappy. The list was growing. One chap was especially disgruntled and wanted to be refunded his petrol money. I tried reasoning with him, explaining our situation - we are just a bunch of guys putting on parties - we don't have much money behind us. In the end I told him to see Dermott at the other side and he'll "sort him out." He stormed off in a rage.

OLIVER MACINTOSH

What a fucking mess. All my lot were well pissed off about having to go all the way to Cobham at the last minute. They were having a go at me about it and I said – "Listen I just play the music."

JERRY ZMUDA

I left Farringdon at around 1 AM - leaving Martin the trooper there with a handful of photocopies. But by now most people had showed up and got re-directed to Cobham.
My car was full of random people, gabbing away, but I was in no mood to chat. After an hour's drive I finally got to the party in the barn. The place was rocking, the strobe was flashing, limbs were flailing - and Dermott was there. My hours of anxiety melted and gave way to joy and relief. We had pulled it off.

DERMOTT COLLINS
Yes we had pulled it off. All thanks to me – Mr. Fix-it Dermott. But
we weren't going to make any money out of this one. God knows
how many Es I had to give away.

JERRY ZMUDA
At around 5 am, me, Poodle I mean Simon, and Dermott were
supping cider in this shed we'd commandeered as our office - when
that miserable so and so showed up whinging about his petrol money.

DERMOTT COLLINS
I tossed him a score. "Go – git awt – you're not welcome at the
Donkey no more. Here's another twenty for your dry cleaning bill."
"What dry cleaning bill?"
Poured some cider over his jacket. The geezer was ready to punch
me, when Lord William showed up and grabbed hold of him. "Don't
you dare - ever swing a punch at my friend. Understand?" The geezer
turned white as a sheet and left. I had some serious connections.

JERRY ZMUDA
It's the spirit of acid house, you lose your venue - you pull out all the
stops to find another venue. You don't whinge about petrol money.

OLIVER MACINTOSH
I'll always remember that party because the sun came up and shone
into the barn while I was DJing. I was playing Voodoo Ray – and the
crowd gasped – it was a religious moment. Then Dermott got on the
mic and thanked everyone for their patience and congratulated their
absent friend Peter whose missus had just had a baby.

JERRY ZMUDA
The mist rising over the lagoon. The bird's singing - nature's call.
Mother Nature was putting on the most spellbinding show. This is
what Piper at the Gates of Dawn, that chapter in The Wind of the Willows
was all about. Suddenly I understood it all - the beauty behind our
existence, just waiting to be seen, if only we took the trouble to look.

Why did it take something like the drug scene for me to experience what I could see anytime if I got up early enough? In my transcendental state, my thoughts turned to Lydia.

PETER WYATT

It felt weird turning up at the barn at Cobham at 8 am - everyone off their head, and me straight as a die. I was seeing things from the other side - and from there it didn't seem especially happy or care-free - just insane. That barn was a loony bin. I had something to tell the guys.

JERRY ZMUDA

Peter came to tell me he was dropping out the scene and he couldn't be involved in Donkey Planet anymore. I gave him a smile and a hug, but I was devastated. It wouldn't be the same without Peter. Nothing is ever the same without him.

HULLO LYDIA - REMEMBER ME

LYDIA DANCEY (Jerry's ex-girlfriend)

My first job on leaving Polytechnic was as a researcher for the BBC on their Woman's Hour programme. I loved it. After a year, I was writing copy. I got to travel and interview people. Of course I knew about this whole dance music thing, we even talked about doing something about it on the programme. But we concluded that it had all been covered extensively elsewhere, and our core listeners - middle aged women - wouldn't be especially interested.

JERRY ZMUDA

I phoned Lydia's parents who told me she was living in London and working for the BBC, but they refused to give me her number. Hah! I'll just get it from the Beeb. I have to admit, I was ultra nervous about phoning Lydia after all these years. I was so uneasy I took the afternoon off work to do it. For a few years now I had been harbouring thoughts that Lydia was THE ONE.

I'd always planned on getting in touch. I think I was waiting for some kind of achievement, something positive happening in my life before I called, so she wouldn't write me off as a deadbeat again. In my stupid thinking I thought Donkey Planet was that achievement. I certainly felt I'd pulled off something special with Donkey Planet #3.

I was pacing around my room, rehearsing my opening sentence – "Hullo Lydia. Remember me? It's Jerry." I was trying to sound all masterful and confident but there was a distinct tremor in my voice. I went to the off licence and bought a bottle of Pils. And tried again. Better. Now or never. I made a dive for the phone.

LYDIA DANCEY

It was weird getting a call from Jerry at work. I had been thinking about him earlier that day because I had driven through Battersea, and the spot where he stood for fifteen minutes after he stormed out, and was waiting for me to call him back. Strange, he acted like an arsehole, but the memory made me smile. He sounded strange on the phone. He was breathing strangely, like he was constipated. He wanted to meet up. I said Ok. His parting shot was - "Be warned - I am very different." I was intrigued.

JERRY ZMUDA

The call had gone well. She sounded cagey, but she said Yes - she wanted to meet up. I wanted to take her to a club and show her the scene I was a part of. But instead she wanted to meet at the BBC Club off Great Portland Street. That sounded good to me - having a drink with the showbiz people. I now had to make the necessary preparations.

LYDIA DANCEY

I found myself dressing up and putting on some extra make up before meeting up with Jerry. But I told myself in the mirror – "Don't let him get you drunk."

JERRY ZMUDA

I'd got Dermott to sort me out with some of his best pills. I wanted to make this a date to remember.

LYDIA DANCEY

Apart from the fact he was wearing Kickers, and his hair was a bit longer, Jerry didn't seem so different. But I have to admit I felt my heart flutter when I saw him for the first time in years.

He started off as the same old whinging Jerry, going on about his boring office job. But then he changed gear, and his face light up as he started going on about "the scene." He was full of evangelical zeal - how it had opened him up to new experiences, new people. I was indifferent, but I said – "Well I'm glad you've found something you really believe in." Then he started pressing me about doing a piece on "the scene" for woman's hour. I explained our demographic, but he was unrelenting.

JERRY ZMUDA

She looked even more beautiful than the picture I kept stored in my cobwebbed memory vault. Damn! How could I have ever let her go? Now I had a mission with Lydia. I had to turn her onto to what was happening. I couldn't believe that she had got through the Summer of 88 and 89 without experiencing it in some way. I said to her – "Come to a club with me." She said No. I said – "Try these pills I've got - Dermott sez their pukka!"

LYDIA DANCEY

I couldn't believe he'd try and peddle me some drugs, right there in the BBC Club.

JERRY ZMUDA

"I'm not peddling drugs. I'm giving them to you." Had I made a faux pas? Lydia was not impressed. She gave me a peck, a useless distant peck on my cheek and told me to stop whinging about my dreary sales day job - and follow my dream - whatever it may be. That's easy for her to say, not when you've got to pay the rent on a bed sit.

LYDIA DANCEY

I had toyed with the idea of getting back with Jerry. There is always a special place in your heart for your first love. But I couldn't be doing with this - "get on one" "mental" rave new world that Jerry was in.

JERRY ZMUDA

When I offered Lydia the drugs, I immediately felt this sudden distance between us - we weren't going to get back together. But I had read *Radiate Sunshine* the novel she wrote as a teenager. Something was happening in Britain now that echoed the crazy days of Warhol and his Factory. Back then Lydia wanted a crazy whirlwind lifestyle, but her career and education had turned her into a stiff corporate person.

JERRY DOES HIS CAINE FROM KUNG FU BIT

JERRY ZMUDA
> Shoom announced their last ever night in November 1989. Everyone was geared up for one wild celebratory party, and it did not disappoint. People were going round hugging each other saying – "Keep the Faith." Whatever that meant. It was still very moving. Jenny Rampling did sour it somewhat with her speech at the end. She was standing up on a platform and started spewing vitriol and bile, decrying all her "jealous" critics - saying "I CAN ONLY PITY YOU" - as she glared down into the audience. Which was urinating on our happy-happy-happy mood from a great height.

DERMOTT COLLINS
> Jerry's such a slobbering weasel, he was shouting back "I never slagged you off Jenny – I'm one of the nice ones."

JERRY ZMUDA
> I had to go into work the next morning, like four hours later - no sleep. I worked in a groggy sleepless haze but I also felt a strange hollowness. Was this the end of an era? Was the best over?
> I endured the monotony of work virtually in a trance and got home and turned on my TV, and there it was, one of the most momentous events in history - the Berlin Wall coming down.
> Throngs of people clambering all over the wall, this symbol of repression was being broken into pieces. The flummoxed guards putting their rifles down, just looking on. This was some party.
> I was born in the mid-sixties, a cold war kid, conditioning into thinking that the wall was always going to be there. I always used to wonder about the people living on the other side - and there they were, tearing the wall that divided us down.

LYDIA DANCEY
> It was exciting working at the Beeb when things like this happen. You got to hear it first. I had mixed feelings about it though. Did this mean

FELTHAM MADE ME   262

that capitalism was going to take over the world unchallenged? How soon before we see a MacDonalds in East Berlin?

JERRY ZMUDA

We were living in remarkable times. Lydia's words to me were resonating in my head. "Follow your dream." I felt an impulse to go to Berlin - see history in the making and be a part of it. I decided to sleep on it and see how I felt in the morning. The next day - I woke still feeling this strong calling to go to Berlin. So I packed a few toiletries and underwear - took my credit cards and headed for Heathrow Airport. From the airport I phoned work. "I'm not coming in, ever. I resign - I'm off to Berlin, See Ya!"

DERMOTT COLLINS

Fucking nice! So Peter's settled down and Jerry now going to Berlin to find himself. What about me? I was left to serving up and having to deal with the news that Cobra was due out soon - on my own.

JERRY ZMUDA

By the time I got to Berlin the wall had been flattened and I was in sore head city. The height of the party may have been over, but there was still an electricity in the air. There was loads of badly dressed East Germans visiting the West for the first time. Walking in goggle-eyed into supermarkets, into department stores and into burger bars. It was weird. I wanted to talk to them, but I couldn't speak any German and I felt self-conscious being on my own. I decided to hit a bar and get drunk and hopefully get talking to someone. I passed this basement dive, playing the Birthday Party really loud. I took a peep inside. Bukowski types propping up the bars, huddles of people in alcoves, it was a gloriously seedy cavern - my kind of place.

LYDIA DANCEY

Jerry called me from a pay-phone in a bar in Berlin, ranting about being part of history. I said – "Jerry are you on drugs?" He kept blabbering on, then the pips ran out.

JERRY ZMUDA

After a couple of beers, I thought - to hell with it. I'm going to start talking to people whether they want to talk to me or not.

FELTHAM MADE ME   263

"I've come all the way from London - you know."
I chose this seedy bloke who looked like the godfather of Heroin chic.
He spoke good English and before long we were getting on like a
house on fire. Poland had yanked off the yoke of communism earlier
that year. They'd had their first free elections, and I had meant to visit
Poland then. But when Grandad died, I'd lost contact with any of my
Poland based relatives. Baron Von Smack says to me - "You must visit
Poland. It is your heritage, your spiritual home."
After several beers I slammed my fist down onto the bar and declared
– "Damn! you're right. I WILL GO TO POLAND."
"But you need visa," he said. "I can fix it for you, not cost much."

DERMOTT COLLINS
While Jerry was doing his Caine from Kung Fu bit, walking the streets
of Eastern Europe on a quest to find himself, I got a call from Brixton
Prison. Cobra's voice was on the end - "Get the party streamers
ready. I'm coming out in a couple of weeks."
Fuck!

JERRY ZMUDA
The train journey from Berlin through to the Polish border was
spectacularly grim. I was in awe, to be actually in Eastern Europe - the
other side. I felt I was going on a pilgrimage. To find what? I didn't
know. I suddenly got nervous at the check-point. I had paid 600 Marks
for my visa. It was a forgery but I was assured that it would work, and
that it would take two years to get one through the proper channels.
I opened my passport on the page with the stamp on it as the border
guard approached.
The stamp was very convincing – an eagle over a shield with the word
VISA in Germanic type.
The uniformed officer looked at the stamp, he was silent for a second.
"Wait there," and he returned my passport. What the hell was going
on?
He returned minutes later with a stern looking man in a massive
peaked cap.
"Can I see the passport please?" I showed him the VISA, he took a
look and cracked into a big laugh.
"Please sir - what is this?"
"It's my VISA." I replied feebly.

FELTHAM MADE ME   264

"We opened our borders in June. You just need to show your passport. You do not need Visa to visit Poland for holiday."
"Oh!"
"How much did you pay for this drawing of an eagle?"
I told him and he laughed again.
"Welcome to Poland and look out for those con-men."
I felt sick, stupid. But all that was rubbed out as the train lurched closer to Warsaw. I was finally in Poland - a land I had spent all my childhood wondering about. I stared at every building, every telegraph pole – taking in every detail.

NATALIE ZMUDA

I was alarmed to get a phone call from Jerry in Poland. "What on earth are you doing there? What about your job?" He wanted the contact details of our relatives who lived in Slominiki - a village outside Krakow. I said to him – "Why do you want to get in touch with them? I am certain they have no interest in meeting you."

JERRY ZMUDA

I was on a pilgrimage to find myself. Poland the land of my ancestors, maybe I would fit in here, maybe I could feel at home. Be happy - at last.
Armed with a clutch of Polish phrases I started exploring Warsaw, walking around, anywhere, street to street, park bench to park bench. After several hours I found myself in a somewhat bleak and run down district - a place not unlike Feltham.
Then I thought I'd get the train to Krakow. Now I was roaming around Krakow, which at least was more picturesque.
But I hadn't had a proper conversation with another human being for several days now. I felt wretched, I caught my reflection in a shop window. I looked wretched. Yes! I had truly discovered myself here in Poland.
I go to the toilet in one bar and to my distress I become aware that the burly tattooed man urinating next to me is looking straight at me.
"English eh?" He said at last.
"Errrr yes."
"England I like."
"Yes I like too."
"The punk rock? Do you like?"`

"Errrr yes some of it."

"The punk rock. I love. The Hundred club? Do you know it?"

"Yeah I've been there, a jazz club on Oxford Street."

"No the Hundred club is a punk club, the Sex Pistols play there."

"Yes the Sex Pistols played there many years ago- but now it's a jazz club."

"To play there. It is my dream for my punk band."

"Oh right. Good for you."

"Pleased to meet you, my name is Cockney....."

The man raised his un-washed hand for a shake.

I was horrified but shook it anyway.

"Your name is what?"

"Cockney."

"Cockney?"

"Yes Cockney!"

Then he showed me his bulldog union jack tattoo on his fore-arm with the words COCKNEY in large scrawling blue ink. I felt like recoiling, then laughing. But I did neither - I needed a friend.

By the end of it I found myself promising my new anglophile friend that I would fix it for his punk band to play the 100 club.

Talk about the grass is always greener. We were both around the same age, and both of us had spent all our lives building up a fascination with a far off land. I indulged Cockney and let him carry on thinking that London was this wonderful mad place where punk rock still ruled. What was the point in telling him the truth – that London's music scene had been hijacked by a bunch of corporate careerists. What was the point in both of us being disillusioned?

Two weeks later I was back in London and unemployed. Like a man with not a shred of dignity, I called my previous employers about getting my job back. They just laughed down the phone. But I found another crappy sales job easy enough. Those sales jobs were ten a penny in those days. On the plus side - all those excuses for days off sick I had used in my previous job, I could use them all again now.

DERMOTT COLLINS
  I wanted to talk to Jerry about doing Donkey Planet full-time, like
  once a week in a licensed night-club, make some regular legal money.
  But Jerry didn't seem that interested.

COBRA COMES OUT

DERMOTT COLLINS
  When Cobra went inside he was THE MAN, I wanted to be just like
  him. Five years later, and a lot had changed - Lord William is my idol
  now.
  C-Day - the day I had been dreading was getting near. I told Lord
  William about Cobra coming out, and he's shaking his head - "Don't
  get me wrong I like him and that, but keep him away from me. I've
  got everything going sweet right now. The guy's a head-banger and I
  don't want him messing it up."
  You and me both, Lord William. Except it weren't so easy for me to
  keep Cobra away. I didn't have me hide-away cottage in the
  countryside like him. I was living in the same house I was living in
  when Cobra went inside. He knew exactly where to find me.

PETER WYATT
  I told Dermott to be careful of Cobra. After a couple of years in stir,
  there's every chance he's going to be madder than ever.

DERMOTT COLLINS
  The big day came. I meet him outside Brixton prison. I was the only
  one there. Where the fuck where all his other mates? His Family?
  He gives me his usual steel-vice hug and I ask him – "So Cob what's
  the first place you want to visit now you're outside? A boozer? A
  football match? Strip-joint?"
  He says - "The sweet-shop round the corner." He explains - his Old
  Girl used to take him there after they'd visited his Old Man. We're in
  the shop and he's looking around the counter. "Where are the
  Penguin bars?"
  The Asian shop-keeper gives him a blank look. "No more Penguin -
  sorry." I said – "Never mind Cob lots of other chocolate bars to
  choose from."

FELTHAM MADE ME   267

Suddenly Cobra starts wailing - "I want to pppppppick up a penguin - pppppppick up a penguin!"
"I call the police," said the twitching Asian shop-keeper, reaching for something under the counter. I marshal Cobra out of the shop and sit him on the kerb.

JERRY ZMUDA

I always found Dermott's relationship with Cobra a curious one. With everyone else Dermott is the agent of madness, and they play the straight man to his lunacy. But Cobra's is so out there, Dermott suddenly becomes the straight man.

DERMOTT COLLINS

I don't like being the sensible one. Trying to comfort a crying Cobra, getting him to calm down. He says while I'm drying his eyes "You don't understand Derm - a whole part of my life has gone while I was inside."

PETER WYATT

Of course they hadn't really stopped doing the Penguin bars - it's just that this corner shop in Brixton didn't have them in stock. All that wailing for nothing.

FRANK COLLINS (Dermott's father)

Dermott comes home all hot and bothered. I said – "What's up?" He said - "If that Cobra ever phones for me, tell him - I'm not in EVER!"

DONNA HARVEY

I was getting upset with Dermott, I was always doing the getting in touch, phoning up. When Cobra came out you could tell he was really tense about it. He was never at home, didn't see him down Full Circle, he virtually went into hiding.

PETER WYATT

Dermott comes round asking if he can stay round mine for a bit. I said – "not really, Sarah and that." He said "Just a couple of months, I need to keep away from Cobra, just enough time for him to find a new friend."

DERMOTT COLLINS

Cobra had phoned dozens of times, each time Dad was "Oh! I don't see Dermott so much these days - here there and everywhere that lad." Cobra bought it - I think. But one Sunday morning I'm in bed smoking a tab, and there's a knock on me window. I got the shock of my life to see Cobra's ugly mug pressed against the glass. "Let's go out," he says. I'm putting my clothes on saying – "OK how about Full Circle?"

"I don't like that scene. Drugs have killed the criminal world."

PETER WYATT

Cobra was one of those people who thought that drug dealing was not what proper criminals did. He saw it when he was inside - with drugs anybody can think they're a gangster. People who should never be criminals. "Snotty nosed types like Jerry" he described them. He had to get a dig in at Jerry.

DERMOTT COLLINS

Five years on I didn't care about being a proper gangster no more. Drug dealing for me was a nice easy way of making exciting amounts of cash. Anyway Cobra invites me to go to Sandown Park for the racing. I felt I had to go.

PETER WYATT

Dermott's plan was to go to the racing with Cobra, but he took with him about 100 Es and five hundred pounds in float - neat crisp fivers. So around mid-afternoon, he can say to Cobra - "gotta go, I'm going serving at some club," and he's got the drugs and money on him to back up his story.

DERMOTT COLLINS

So we're in the VIP enclosure at Sandown, feeling out a place.
Cobra then tells me he's got his eye on doing some big racing score - armed robbery. Did I want in? I said – "Not really Cob, I don't fancy going to prison."
Then Cobra said - "Prison ain't so bad. I got myself a dream. You and me sharing a cell, and we run the place. All the scams, it all goes through us. But the best bit is - we're together."
He looked deep into my eyes.

FELTHAM MADE ME   269

"You've always been special to me."
"What do you mean?" He places his hand on my chest. Right where my Cobra tattoo is.
"I love you Dermott Collins."
I gulped – "You have changed in prison." Trying my best at a joke.
"Nothing to do with prison Dermott. I've loved you since the first moment I laid eyes on you. When you used to come round my house with the stuff you've nicked.
I knew then."
Then he grabbed hold of my hand and squeezed it, in front of everyone at Sandown. I froze to the spot as he looked at me like a lost puppy. Cobra love-sick - over me.

JERRY ZMUDA

Cobra gay? I am worldly now and I would have spotted it a mile off. But when I first met him as a fourteen year old, I took him at face value. All that hard man stuff - calling me a poof because I didn't want to play William Tell. All this cult of masculinity was a smokescreen. All along Cobra really loved men - and Dermott in particular.

DERMOTT COLLINS

He were still staring deep into my eyes - waiting for my response.
I said – "I'd gotta go to the khazi."
In the cubicle I couldn't face going back. I panicked, thinking he was going to be coming in after me, so I climbed out of the tiny window. It was a ten foot drop down onto the grass. I let myself down to find myself surrounded by a couple of coppers. I thought fuck. What about my 100 Es and my 500 pounds in float? I was arrested and searched. The copper holds up the bag of one hundred Es and says - "So what's this then?"
I said "Ear Infection?"

Chapter 7
Dermott's Countdown to Porridge

DERMOTT'S COUNTDOWN TO PORRIDGE

FRANK COLLINS

It is the most heart-breaking moment for any parent to get a call from the police telling you that they have arrested your son. Dermott was 25 at this point, but the police needed to verify his address. I went down the station and I felt sick when I found out what the charge was.

DERMOTT COLLINS

This was my moment to show 'em all that I could hold my nerve. If I played it smart I could get off this charge. My story was that I bought the Es, but I wasn't going to sell them - I was going to give them away so people will like me.

The Old Bill weren't having it - the amount of pills and money on me points to me being a dealer.

The geezer in charge of the case was Sergeant Badcock of the drug squad, a dead ringer for Mr. Dunne of Feltham. So much so, when I first clamped eyes on him, I thought – sweet, Mr. Dunne - I can talk my way out of this one.

But this Sgt. Badcock has got a face like a sack of rocks and he tells me that from their undercover operations they already had a record on me being a dealer. Were they bluffing? Probably. I had to sweat it out and deny it all.

Mr. Dunne, I mean Sgt. Badcock, then tells me that I was going to get done for possession and intent to supply in any case. I was looking at some porridge - whatever. All my brief could do was damage limitation. The war of nerves had begun. When I got let out on bail, Cobra was there waiting for me, telling me "Prison is alright really. As long as you got respect."

FRANK COLLINS

Cobra comes out and Dermott immediately gets himself involved in serious crime. This was no coincidence. That man is an evil influence on my son. I was going to get the best lawyer I could afford, and get my son off this horrible charge.

DONNA HARVEY

After Dermott gets lets out, he calls me. He never called before. I wondered - what brought this on, all of a sudden? But I was glad.

DERMOTT COLLINS

With Cobra coming out of the closet I needed to get myself a girlfriend sharpish, to keep old lover-boy away. Donna seemed like a nice girl and quite keen. I then called Cobra – "Look Cobra – thanks I'm flattered I really am. But I ain't that way, I've got a girlfriend." I also said – "Whatever you told me – I won't breathe it to another soul."

"You can tell whoever you want," he replies. "I am a man who loves other men - and I don't care who knows it. I'm not living a lie any more."

FRANK COLLINS

Dermott never knew his mother, that had to count as mitigating circumstances. I was determined to keep my son out of jail. I knew Peter would also help.

PETER WYATT

I met with Frank and suggested pooling some money together for a decent brief. I thought about organizing a fund raiser and I needed Jerry to help me. This was a time for friends to pull together.

SARAH WYATT

Using up our savings for a solicitor for Dermott? Oh no you fucking don't.

JERRY ZMUDA

There was no point in throwing money at this - Frank and Peter's hope was a cul-de-sac.

In this hysterical antidrug climate, every class A drug conviction from trafficking, dealing, down to intent to supply nearly always carried a custodial sentence. Dermott was going down - there was no way out of it. Peter was telling me to help. What the hell could I do? Change the law? Dermott got into big time dealing and it was only a matter of time before he got caught. That's just the law of averages.

DONNA HARVEY

After Dermott's arrest he was cooler than ever before. Everyone wanted to talk to him, show their support. I felt proud to be his girl-friend. The only trouble was, it couldn't last - because he was going inside soon. Plus he wasn't serving up anymore, so I never got the freebies.

DERMOTT COLLINS

I was released on bail facing trial in a couple of months. It looked set to be a Crown Court job. But those months before the trial were ace. I've never ever been so popular. Even my wind-up victims were talking to me and buying me beers.

Sgt. get down boy Badcock - called me in to tell me that if I grassed up Lord William I would get off the charge – he could arrange it for me to walk. I told him – "No way – I ain't no fucking rat. If I go down, I go down. But I ain't taking no-one with me."

Listen to me. What a hero! I _am_ Jimmy Cagney.

SARAH WYATT

I was sad when I heard about Dermott. If I'm honest I did think it serves him right, but I did feel sorry for him.

DONNA HARVEY

Dermott's Countdown to Porridge was one non-stop party. He was making the most of his liberty while he still had it.

PETER WYATT

Dermott was trying to show the world what a man he was. That he wasn't scared of going to jail. But I knew him better than most, I could see that behind that big fuck-off grin was a look of fear.

JERRY ZMUDA

During this time Peter was always insisting - "Talk to Dermott , talk to Dermott."

So after one Full Circle while we were waiting for our lift I said - "Look Dermott, I know what you're going through. I know you must be really terrified about prison. But me and Peter - we'll be here to support you." He just looked back at me with this goofy I've-done-five-Es smile.

FRANK COLLINS

I met with the brief, and I said – "Look at this poor lad, never knew his mother. Has lived with the unfounded guilt that it was his fault that she's gone - this has got to get my boy off. At the very least a suspended sentence."
The brief shook his head - "This can only cut down the sentence. He will go to prison, I can guarantee you that."

DONNA HARVEY

I said to him – "I'll wait for you." Not because I meant it, but it sounded good.

PETER WYATT

A week before the trial, Sunday night, the kids are sleeping. I'm watching telly and there's a knock on the door. It's Dermott, he's looking all wide-eyed and troubled, so I take him into the kitchen and make him a cup of tea. He bursts into tears - "Help me Peter - help me, I don't want to go to jail - it'll destroy me."
My only advice was - let's buy some time, try and get the trial delayed and think of something. He was going "I want to watch the Darts World Championship on the telly with you, not in some horrible cell."
I said – "I doubt you'll get a telly in your cell." This made him feel worse.

DERMOTT COLLINS

Inside the doubts started creeping in about jail. How would I cope? You're supposed to show you're a hard nut on the first day - start on someone. But I'm a joker, not a fighter. I'm the sort of bloke who happily takes the piss out of people, but usually with someone like Cobra and Peter to back me up. I wasn't cut out for the criminal life - what the fuck had I got myself into it? But I never showed it. I felt like balling my eyes out but I never cried once.

FELTHAM MADE ME   274

FRANK COLLINS

The brief managed to get the case adjourned pending psychiatric reports. It would mean at least he got to spend Christmas at home. But we were still stumped to find a way of beating the custodial sentence. Maybe if they kept adjourning, eventually the law will change - will soften - and he'll just get probation. We were clutching at straws really.

DERMOTT COLLINS

I bumped into a Cobra a few times during this waiting for the trial bit. He didn't seem as guilty as I thought he might be. He seemed to think that prison would be good for me – "an education" is what he described it.

I thought about the showers. People like Cobra waiting to jump me. I thought however long the sentence is, even it's five years, I won't take a shower - not once.

JERRY ZMUDA

As the Crown Court trial date drew closer I started getting really upset for Dermott. Prison changes people - it can decimate people. I would hate to be in that situation myself. In fact I think it must be the nightmare of every man - unless you're someone like Cobra.

DERMOTT COLLINS

The weekend before the big Crown Court case, I get a telegram, a fucking telegram from Lord William. Requesting the pleasure of my company, a car will come and pick me up and I may bring a couple of friends. So I invited Peter and Donna along.

DONNA HARVEY

Lord William knew how to throw party. It was in his smart house in the middle of the countryside. It was like a celebrity's house.

DERMOTT COLLINS

So Lord William had thrown a party for me. It was a thank-you-for-not-grassing-me-up party in his swanky cottage near High Wycombe. He put his arm around me and squeezed me tight - "You won't regret this me old china. When you get out - you'll be made - do you hear me? Made."

FELTHAM MADE ME   275

Then he goes over to Donna and starts chatting her up. My Donna. And I thought to myself I'm going to lose several years of my life getting buggered in the shower - all for this smug oily git.

FRANK COLLINS

So the day of the big trial came, a cloudy dismal day in early January. Peter and Jerry showed up - no Cobra. Dermott looked respectable but unfamiliar in the suit I'd lent him. I was now resigned to the fact that my youngest son was going to jail.

JERRY ZMUDA

The case lasted a couple of hours, he was found guilty. Then the judge came to pass the sentence. I had to look down, I couldn't bear to look at Dermott in the dock.

PETER WYATT

I was praying - just 6 months - just 6 months - I looked straight at the judge. Tried to send positive thought waves over to him - "He's a good lad. Go easy on my friend."

JERRY ZMUDA

Looking down, there was nothing but the judge's voice.
"The supplying of Class A drugs has become an epidemic in recent years. The tide must be stemmed, and punishments must be meted out to those responsible. So I have decided to sentence you to two years in prison." (HORRIFIED GASP)
"But In the light of the mitigating circumstances, and the lack of concrete evidence to show that you have been dealing before, I have decided it should be suspended for two years."
We all let out a big relieved howl.

PETER WYATT

I nearly jumped over and hugged the judge. Once we had all quietened down, the judge looked at Dermott very hard. He said - "This is very exceptional. If you are caught dealing or even in possession again you will be dealt with most severely. Do you understand?" Dermott was saying – "yes - yes -yes." But I looked at him as if to say - be sure that you do.

FELTHAM MADE ME   276

DERMOTT COLLINS

So I got let off.

I watched the World Championship Darts from Frimley Green round Peter's cosy house and not while being buggered by Cobra Number 2 in a grey-walled prison cell. But I wasn't too relaxed, I had paid a terrible price.

Two months later I was in Crown Court again, this time testifying against Lord William. Though I never knew his real name I was able to point him out to the court. He looked back at me - full of hate. I knew he would get back at me for this. But what could I do? Turns out his real name was Clive McKnight and the police knew of his smuggling and dealing activities. They knew his antique business was a front for it all. But they needed somebody like me to grass him up and to build a case.

That film *Good Fellas* came out over Christmas and I went to see it with Peter. I thought - if it's OK for that Ray Lee Otter geezer to be a grass - why not Dermott Collins? Other people didn't see it that way. Cobra for instance. He came to find me at home with tears in his eyes - "Tell me it ain't true - tell me you ain't a grass."

I said – "Sorry, Cobra I'm a grass," and he walked away. That was one way of getting him off me back.

PETER WYATT

Dermott never actually told me that he had done a deal with the cops to get him off his charge, that he had turned informant. But it was obvious. Of course this was a whole new can of worms - people who get sent down want revenge.

DERMOTT COLLINS

So Lord William alias Clive McKnight got sent down for a couple of years, and I said to Sgt Rockface – "What happens now? Do I get a new identity like that Harry Hill in *Good Fellas?*"

He said - "Don't be silly - we haven't got the money for any of that."

I said – "So what do you suppose I do? Just get killed?"

He said – "Just lie low - don't move in those circles."

I didn't feel like going out at all ever. But I sneaked out to a low key Sunday evening thing in a pub in Windsor, dancing in a dark corner, keeping it down, lost in my thoughts when one of the bouncers came up to me. He said "A message from Lord William - dance all you can while you can. When he gets out you won't be able to. He wants the pleasure of doing it to you himself - he'll find you wherever you are." I felt sick after that and went home.

Chapter 8
Whatever Happened To
The Unholy Trinity?

FAST FORWARD TO 1994

JERRY ZMUDA

A friend from school moved to Miami when he was a child. The very first weekend, his Father takes him to Disneyland. Going on all the rides, watching the parade under the magnificent spired castle, singing *When You Wish Upon A Star* as he went home. It's the most amazing experience of this young child's life. He says to his father - "Thank you Daddy for bringing me to this wonderful place."

So Daddy takes him to Disneyland the next week-end and it's still great - and the next week-end, and the next weekend and so and so on - and the kid is happy that he is building up an intimate knowledge of this unique, magical place.

Four years later his Father is still taking him to Disneyland every weekend. Suddenly my friend says to his Dad - "Enough! The rides aren't thrilling anymore, the parade under the castle has lost its magic. Singing When You Wish Upon A Star has become a dirge! I AM BORED WITH DISNEYLAND." The father looks back at him with a blank face - "But son, I can't think of anywhere else to take you." And that's what happened to me with the Ecstasy scene.

PETER WYATT

Jerry was in the habit of phoning me up at weird times, just wanting a chat. Saying stuff like - "Have you heard Nirvana ? All that whispering stuff and then shouting - all quiet and then loud. We were doing all that ten years ago." That's right, we were, we should have stuck with it. But we didn't - and now we're all going to be 30 in a couple of months.

JERRY ZMUDA

Me a 30 year old? How did this happen? I found the very thought deeply traumatizing. How did I achieve so little in such a large amount

FELTHAM MADE ME   279

of time? I was still clubbing it, putting on the occasional half arsed event. I kept on telling myself it was great that I was still "having it" at my age, when I presumed that everyone else from school would be at home working out their mortgage re-payments. I told myself this, but I would sometimes catch my reflection in a mirror in a night-club - my filled out face, my weather-beaten features. Should I <u>really</u> still be doing this at my age?

DERMOTT COLLINS

Me Old Man came to the rescue, sorted me out a job doing landscape gardening. Liked it, all peaceful, listening to Cds all day and grafting away. A nice feeling at the end of the working day looking over what I'd done and compare it to how it looked when I started that morning. Mind you, you didn't want to work too fast. Not when you're on a daily rate.

I liked being close to nature - the birds singing, a breeze in my face, all that bollocks. After the Lord William bit I stayed well away from drugs and drug dealing. Well, now and then the boys I worked with needed some Ganja sorting - so I acted as a middle man. So apart from boshing out the occasional pill in the boozer, and the odd wrap here and there, I'd given up drug dealing totally.

JERRY ZMUDA

When you first take ecstasy, it's a catalyst. Your mind starts thinking in a new way, it opens you up to meeting new people, it really does broaden your mind. But after months of repeated use, you begin to stagnate. Now you're saying the same old stuff over and over again. Same old routine and it's no longer creative. Your mind isn't taking you to new places anymore.

Some of my fellow clubbers had "graduated" from E to charlie. But charlie is deceptive - you think you're holding it together, being cool. You think you know what you're talking about. But soon enough you're just another babbling idiot. It's hardly progress.

PETER WYATT

After Carl was born, Sarah started getting all moody again. This wasn't how it was supposed to be. I wanted an atmosphere of family bliss. I couldn't just blame it all on post-natal depression and PMT and other women's trouble. I could tell she was getting bored with me. I needed to do something - take charge of my life and win back the respect of the woman I love.

SARAH WYATT
I know I was being hard on Peter. He's a very caring considerate man - no woman could hope for any better. But I'm sure most women go through this when it comes to kids. You feel that you're carrying everything on your shoulders. The man of the house just thinks - oh! there's two more in the family now, that two's more plates on the table and we need a couple of spare rooms. But there's so much more to raising children than men realize.

PETER WYATT
It was very important for me to stay close to my buddies, I'm talking about Dermott and Jerry here. So I would often invite them round. It was fascinating to watch them play with the kids. They were so different - Dermott is a natural with kids and knows how to play with them - make 'em laugh. "It's Monkey Time" he would go, and Carl's face would light up with laughter. Carl would often ask "when is Uncle Dewott" - he couldn't say Dermott - "coming round?
Jerry on the other hand - all stiff and awkward. "How's it going?" And shake his hand like he's at a job interview.

SARAH WYATT
Peter was always getting Carl and Abby to call them Uncle Jerry and Uncle Dermott. I kept saying "No! No they are not your uncles. No way are those jerks related to us - in any way at all."

DERMOTT COLLINS
Carl's an amazing dustbin lid. I loved being Uncle Dewott. Going round Peter's was ace. Having all the good stuff about being a Dad - all the playing around - and none of the bad stuff - the bills, the cleaning up the mess, the trouble and strife.

JERRY ZMUDA
I envied Peter. Marriage is natural and normal. Being on your own in some crappy bedsit is not right at the age of 29. I should have been paired myself off by now. Was it too late?

SURREY'S BURNING

SARAH WYATT
> I suppose it's inevitable, but ten years into a marriage and a lot of the magic has faded. You fall into a routine and there's no heart racing over seeing your partner come through the door. But I knew things had reached a real low when Peter started breaking wind in front of me while we were watching telly.

PETER WYATT
> This became a big thing with Sarah. "I can't believe you'd break wind in front of me." Made me feel really low, I was so apologetic. "Sorry it just slipped out," but she wouldn't have it. I try not to do it in front of the old girl, but you know, I was in my own house, I'd had a hard day, I was relaxing and it just slipped out.

SARAH WYATT
> Another thing that started taking the shine out of it was hearing Peter through the wall making these loud straining noises when he sat on the toilet. That was a total turn-off.

PETER WYATT
> Cabbying was getting me down - driving drunks, swearing and puking up in your cab, or drugged up kids talking endless bollocks from Acton Vale to Upminster.
> Late one night, I was taking this yuppie couple back to their home in Chiswick. As I turned into their nice well-to-do road - we saw ahead of us this house ablaze and a big fire-engine beside it. All these firemen were running around trying to put the fire out with their hoses. I slammed the brakes and the couple dashed off screaming in the direction of the fire.
> "My House - My House!"
> I thought Oi -What about my fare? There was well over a score on the meter. I was parked there waiting for my fare but the couple had other things on their mind. I looked over at these fireman in their uniform trying to put this fire out, and I thought to myself - NOW THAT IS A PROPER JOB.

SARAH WYATT

He should have consulted me. That's what marriage is all about - sharing your life and making decisions together. And decisions don't come bigger than changing your job.

PETER WYATT

I wanted to surprise Sarah. They say romance is all about surprises. I certainly didn't want the embarrassment of telling her I was applying to join the Fire Brigade, and then get turned down. So I filled in the form and went for the interviews and physical tests. I knew they were going to be rigorous so I had been on a strict exercise programme for a couple of months before. I wouldn't have made it otherwise.

JERRY ZMUDA

Fireman, a very noble profession The polar opposite of snivelling telesales. I was phoning people up all day and trying to weasel money out of them. At the end of the working day I felt dirty, I had to clean the smarm out of my phone.

PETER WYATT

So the day I got the letter of acceptance from the Surrey Fire Brigade, I went down to the station and asked to borrow a uniform. Then I went home to see Sarah.

SARAH WYATT

I opened the door and there's Peter dressed up like a fireman. He's smiling and goes - "Anybody order a strip-o-gram?" Then he tells me he's been accepted by the fire brigade. I was furious. Totally hit the roof. Mind you, he did look sexy in that uniform.

PETER WYATT

Initially I was taking a drop in wages from cabbying to being a fire-fighter. But to offset this I did bit of moonlighting - cabbying on the side. A bit naughty I know, but I had a family to feed. Plus I was determined to raise the money to have this we're-all-thirty-now re-union party.

FELTHAM MADE ME   283

WHATEVER HAPPENED TO THE UNHOLY TRINITY?

JERRY ZMUDA

I wasn't at all keen on this joint 30th party idea. Especially as I'd been telling people on the club scene that I was 28. This party was going to blow my cover.

PETER WYATT

So we're all turning 30 - so fucking what? What are we supposed to do? Shrink away and pretend it's not happening? No! Let's have a fuck-off party and make a song and dance about it. Celebrate that we'd got this far without dieing, getting bankrupt or going to jail. Though we've scraped pretty close to all three. Invite all our old friends from the past - all the kids from Feltham, the people who used come and see The Grundy, bods from the club scene. Maybe even get The Grundy to reform and play a few tracks.

JERRY ZMUDA

This 30th party would be sad enough, but re-forming Septimus Grundy would be one drive too far down Tragic Boulevard. I became even less keen on this 30th party idea when Peter told me the venue he had booked for it - Feltham Football Club. Why not book British Steel as well?

PETER WYATT

Feltham Football Club is the ideal place for our 30th get together. Jerry - this is your roots mate. Remember your song? *FELTHAM MADE ME*.

OLIVER MACINTOSH

This is totally regrettable. I got a message on my ansafone from Peter asking me to DJ at their joint 30th party, he wanted me to play a classic '88 set. So I call back, and his nine year-old daughter Abby picks up the phone. There should be a law to stop kids answering phone calls between grown-ups.

FELTHAM MADE ME   284

PETER WYATT

I was furious when Abby gave me the message. He was saying he doesn't play the '88 stuff anymore, and in any case he now charges £300 a night and he's got a booking that night at Checkpoint Charlie in Reading. I called him back and left a message on his ansafone. My message - "Stick your Moody DJ attitude and your box of boring records that all sound the same up your arse!"

OLIVER MACINTOSH

Peter totally got the wrong end of the stick. The message I left with Abby was I was happy to play the party - I normally charge £300 a night but I don't want any money for the party. I've got a booking that night in Reading but I'll get it moved to play the later set, so I can play in Feltham earlier. I tried phoning back to explain and got Abby again. Kids who'd have 'em? A month or two later, I write Peter a letter, just to say I wanted to do the party for free - as a way of saying thank you. Them Donkey Planet parties were insane and chaotic, but that's what gave me my first break in DJing. I am not the Moody DJ - not just yet.

PETER WYATT

In the event, tracking everyone down that I wanted to invite turned out to be a fucking nightmare. Remember this is the days before the internet - emails and what have you.

DERMOTT COLLINS

Dead set on inviting Mr. Heyward - teacher from primary school. Sort of wanted to say sorry, laugh about it all. Phoned the old school - they tell me that he's packed in teaching in - he's a bus driver. So I phoned London Transport, someone was going to leave a message in his pigeon hole.

MR. HEYWARD (Bus Driver)

I got the message – 'Dermott Collins and Jerry Zmuda are having a re-union party at Feltham Football Club. Fancy coming?' It was obviously a trap. I decided I was going to beat them at their own game. I was going to turn up early and turn the tables on them.

FELTHAM MADE ME   285

SANJEEV SRIDHARAN (Feltham School - left 1980)
It had been a seriously shit time for poor old Sanjeev. After doing
rather nicely in the boom time of the late eighties I bought a large
house on the edge of Bedfont and moved in with my wife. Things
were going great. Then the business started faltering, I fell into
negative equity, nearly went bankrupt and the biggest heart-break of
all, I got my house repossessed. I had some builders booked into to
do about three months of renovation work and I had to cancel them
at short notice. I was dreading having to tell them, but fortunately the
guy was very understanding, a chap called Frank Collins who turned
out to be Dermottitus's Dad. I explained everything to them and at
the end Dermott invites me to their 30th re-union party. Loads of
old faces from Feltham will be there. Sounds great, I said, I could do
with some fucking cheering up.

PETER WYATT
The invites had a picture of us three, grinning like cheshire cats -
fourteen years of age. It read WHATEVER HAPPENED TO THE
UNHOLY TRINITY? Find out at their 30th birthday re-union party.
There was buffet layed on, but they had to pay for their own booze.
Everyone had to be there by seven o'clock, because I wanted to show
them a slide show.

JERRY ZMUDA
But once you got beyond the words Feltham Football club, there was
nothing foreboding about the place once you were inside. It was basic
function room, bar to the side, stage at the end with a tinsel cloth
behind. To help perfect the family party ambience Peter had done the
place up with balloons and streamers. All we needed now was the
bad dancing from your Aunties & Uncles.

MR. HEYWARD
The invite said get there by seven, So I got there for six. So I can
observe my plan unfold.

JERRY ZMUDA
I arrived early as instructed; there was about eight people in.
As I made my way to the bar I felt these mad eyes burning into me
from across the hall. They belonged to a bearded man - it was Mr.

Heyward. I went over to him and said – "Hullo Mr. Heyward. How has life treated you?"
"Not bad. I've changed my career. How about you? Badly I hope."

"Why Badly?"
"No reason - I just want bad things to happen to you. I don't know why."
This fazed me, I was trying to frame a reply when this really smelly tramp walked in, wearing boots made out of carrier bags.

DERMOTT COLLINS
Thought it would be a top fucking cackle to show up dressed like some tramp. Walked in wearing rags, loads of carrier bags with cans of Special Brew in them.

JERRY ZMUDA
The handful of people there gasped and just stared - no-one said hello, though they all eventually recognized Dermott. Then he took his coat off and underneath he was wearing a smartish suit. He then went to the toilet for a shave. It was actually rather amusing.

SARAH WYATT
Yeah that's funny. Funny and true at the same time. Dermott was turning into a bit of Special Brew type. The sort you see coming out of the bookies and grabbing all the special offers down the offie. Jerry on the other hand was starting to look quite dapper.

PETER WYATT
Before the booze starts flowing I see Jerry sat at a table talking to Sarah. He's looking all miserable and forlorn. I said – "What's up?" He says - "I just feel down, I really wanted to have made it by the time I was 30."

JERRY ZMUDA
He said to me - "Fuck Fame and Success - it's Friends what Matter!" But that's hardly any consolation when your friends are people like Dermott.

FELTHAM MADE ME   287

SARAH WYATT
> It was nice to see Jerry. Jerry had grown up - he'd matured. He wasn't putting on his tortured artist act, like he used to. We sat down and we had a proper heart to heart. Something we'd never done before.

JERRY ZMUDA
> I told Sarah I felt I should have been paired off and married by now, and she agreed with me. Peter was a very lucky man to be married to the beautiful and intelligent Sarah.

SARAH WYATT
> I tried to comfort Jerry. I said to him at least you're ageing better than Dermott. He looks like a drunken slob. He's getting fat, but he's also losing it. He's not sharp anymore, there's long gaps before he thinks of something to say. And when he does, it's something boring and tired like "isn't that the geezer that stole your box of Toblerone?"

PETER WYATT
> The place is filling up, slowly. Too slowly for my liking. I'd planned on showing a slide show of old photographs, which is why I wanted everyone there early. But I needed more people in, so I put it off till later. I'm getting anxious behind the decks playing soul music to get the few people there in the mood. Then this sour faced geezer with frizzy hair comes up to me and in a thick Glasgow accent asks to see Dermott Collins or Jerry Zmuda. He tells me he's the children's entertainer and he's got his clown suit in a dry cleaner bag.

JERRY ZMUDA
> I explained to the gruff Glaswegian that it was certainly not me that booked the children's entertainer. But it's the sort of thing Dermott might have done.
> Dermott strolls over. Apparently he hadn't booked the clown either.

DERMOTT COLLINS
> Scottish geezer not happy - saying he's turned down two bookings when he took this one. Wants his money. Out of the creepy shadows up pops Mr. Heyward. About to say Hullo - glad you can make it, when he's shouting at us "PAY THE CLOWN, PAY THE CLOWN" over and over. Gets a bit much, so after a while, Jerry the soft touch

says to the clown "OK - I'll pay you half the money as a cancellation fee."

MR. HEYWARD

Just as I planned it. The children's entertainer won't accept the cancellation fee. He wants all the money - They Must Pay The Clown.

JERRY ZMUDA

Eventually I succumbed. I'll write you out a cheque for one hundred fifty - now please go. But Dermott has other ideas.

DERMOTT COLLINS

Hang on. If we're paying a tonne and a half, I want to see our money's worth. You have to do your act. Clown bleating that it's an act for eight year olds. Don't fucking care, I know my bleedin' rights - if I'm paying for a clown act, I bloody well should get to see my clown. If not - I'm going to Watchdog.

JERRY ZMUDA

"But there are no kids!" Shouts the clown. "I can't do my act without any kids." I could see Mr. Heyward was really enjoying this heated discussion. The clown then suggested a compromise - he had been working on a stand up routine aimed at adults, this could be his debut. Dermott said yes - "but an extra nifty says you did it in your clown outfit." The clown gave an exasperated howl. He obviously needed the money.

PETER WYATT

So I have to stop the disco to let this clown in his full outfit get on the mic and do his stand-up routine. He remained deadpan throughout this routine, which was quite amusing. But apart from that, he barely raised a titter. People were just staring with puzzled looks.

JERRY ZMUDA

"Do you know what makes my blood boil? Temperatures of over one hundred degrees - that normally does it." That was his opener. "My Dad's black - well he is now we cremated him." Came next.

"I've got the body of a man half my age. I keep it in a chest underneath my bed, it's starting to smell."

The clown does his ten minutes, hands the mic back to Peter and I give him his cheque. As the clown went to the toilet to take off his outfit, Mr. Heyward re-appears and says - 'THAT'S RIGHT - YOU PLAY THE CLOWN - NOW YOU HAVE TO PAY THE CLOWN!' Laughing like a maniac. Then I twigged - Mr. Heyward had booked the clown as some sort of revenge. I mention this to the clown as he comes out of his costume and he explodes with rage.

PETER WYATT

So I'm back DJing trying to lift the mood of the party, trying to get the crowd dancing. Then I see the clown head-butting the mad bloke with the beard. I dive over to break it up. The doorman pulls the clown out. I said to Jerry - "What the fuck is all that about?" "That's Karma," he replied.

MR. HEYWARD

My work was done. I left the hall with a broken nose, but I had given those two something to think about. They, after all, were the ones who had to pay the clown.

JERRY ZMUDA

After the clown got ejected I noticed that Dermott was never far from the bar. He was juggling the pints, one in his right hand, one in his left hand, one in mid-air. Barely coming up for breath.

MR. DUNNE (Feltham School teacher)

Curiosity. Closure. I'm not sure what it was. But I felt compelled to go along to this re-union party. No-one had made a crack about me sounding like a sea-lion for well over a decade. Maybe it was that, that I was missing.

JERRY ZMUDA

Suddenly a whole bunch of kids appeared at the door, people I hadn't seen since the last day of Feltham.

It was weird seeing these old faces again. These faces now filled out and jowly. The ravages of time had really taken some of them to task.

It was extraordinary how Dermott remembered all the old wind-ups and catchphrases in minute detail. Feltham Football Club, turned into Fetham School Playground and Dermott was once again back in his element.

MR. DUNNE

I was getting loads of cracks about sounding like a sea-lion. Stuff about Fish. Stuff about my party piece being balancing a ball on my nose. It was re-assuring.

JERRY ZMUDA

I was delighted to see Sanjeev come through the door. Dermott told me that he had just moved into a spectacular new home. Dermott says to me - "Ask him about it - he just loves to talk about it." So I did.

SANJEEV SRIDHARAN

I couldn't believe what Jerry was saying to me. Did he think he was being funny? Well as far as I'm concerned he was just being nasty and pathetic. I didn't need that shit - I bailed straight after.

JERRY ZMUDA

This trip down memory lane was making me feel quite odd, I headed for the bar.

PETER WYATT

This party wasn't going as I'd hoped. There was a strange atmosphere hanging over the hall. I needed to lift the mood. I played Barry White's *Ecstasy When You Lay Down Next To Me* - nothing doing. This is a job for Frank Collins.

FRANK COLLINS

Peter insisted on me doing *Mule Train*. I staunchly refused. I was sixty odd for pity' sake - leave me with some feckin' dignity. But Peter plied me with drinks and then handed me the beer tray. I ended up doing it.

PETER WYATT

MULE TRAIN! CLIPPETY CLOP! Franky boy rocked the house crashing that tea tray against his nut. Cheered everybody right up. Dermott's tugs at my shoulder he wants a go on the decks. But before he puts a record on, he grabs the mic.

DERMOTT COLLINS

I did a little speech, it went something like this.

"I'd like to thank Peter Wyatt who you all know, for organizing tonight. A top night well done. Peter's the sort of bloke who's always got a kind word for you, so considerate, so understanding. (Big Pause.) It gets on your bloody nerves sometimes. DON"T YOU JUST HATE PEOPLE WHO ARE ALWAYS SO BLEEDING NICE? Why can't he be a bastard like the rest of us once in a while?"

That got a bit of a laugh. Then I moved onto - "Jerry - my oldest friend. He became my friend because he laughed at all my jokes even the shit ones - not laughing so much now is he? He's very shy - especially when it comes to standing his round. He's the sort of bloke that when he buys you a pint - he'll take a sip out of yours before he gives it to you."

That got a laugh. "Did I mention that he piped on the last day of school? And that he likes ELO?"

JERRY ZMUDA

Dermott's cheeky chappie act was all well and good for a young kid or a teenager, but for a 30 year old it was just too tragic boulevard. As we sat there listening to his little speech, laughing along, I made a big decision. Whatever lay in the future for me, Dermott was not going to be in it. I was going to cut him out of my life.

PETER WYATT

After the speech. The first record Dermott puts on is the 12" of the Real Thing's *Can You Feel The Force*. Excellent choice. The space travel intro really got the audience hooked. They're fidgeting around waiting for the record to kick in - and then just as it's about to go off...

JERRY ZMUDA

> Dermott puts on the *Birdie Song*. This was met more with bemusement than amusement.

PETER WYATT

> The Molesey Boys didn't find this too funny, they start chanting at Dermott - "Are you looking for a slap because you're giving it some of that." Then this plastic chair flies through the air and hits Dermott's square on the bonce.

JERRY ZMUDA

> Now that got a laugh. Dermott meanwhile is on the floor and his head is bleeding. He's not unconscious, but unsteady on his feet. All the time the *Birdie Song* is playing along its merry tune.

PETER WYATT

> Dermott gets up with a big smile and puts on Chicory Tip and we danced like teapots, just like we used to. We started singing along going 'Feltham Is Mine, Feltham Is Mine, Feltham Is Mine.' Blood was pouring out Dermott's head and people were saying we'd better get you to Casualty, and Dermott was saying - "Yeah after the party."

JERRY ZMUDA

> Sarah had enough, and she left to get a taxi home. I told Peter, but he didn't seem to mind. He said something like -"Now I can break wind without worrying." There was nothing else for it but to get steaming drunk and pretty soon I was singing 'Feltham Is Mine' with everyone else.

PETER WYATT

> After all the crap - the strange atmosphere at the start, the head-butting clown, the chair in the air - it was all worth it. It gave me a warm feeling to see all my friends together after all this time. Here's to another thirty years.

DERMOTT COLLINS

> At the end - everyone dancing - me on the table - shaking people's hands. Done a bean. Thinking we should do this regular. Jump down from the table and head off to the khazi. There's a geezer loitering in

the shadows - cropped hair - craggy features. **Stone me - it's fucking Cobra.** Don't remember seeing his name on the invite list. Hope he's not going to try and ambush me in the toilets. He's looking desperate and grabs me arm - "You'd better get ready - Lord William is out."

HIGH NOON IN HIGH WYCOMBE

FRANK COLLINS

Dermott was 30 and still living under my roof. But I don't see anything wrong with that if you get on with your Old Man, as Dermott did with me. What's so great about renting out some grot hole and lining the pockets of some sleazy landlord, or crippling yourself with a mortgage and getting into the black hole of negative equity? Nightmare.

Anyway one day I'm playing back the ansafone messages and in amongst all the usual hellos from friends I got this -

Lord William – "Still living with your dad – you loser. How old are you now? 30? We have some business to catch up on. Looking forward to it."

I play the message back to Dermott and he turns as white as a sheet.

DERMOTT COLLINS

The hairs all over my body went Ping! Bricking it I was. There was no point going to the Old Bill - they'll only get involved when the deed's been done - and my cracked knee caps are somewhere over Shepperton rubbish dump. They wouldn't give me any protection. Only one person I can turn to in a moment like this.

PETER WYATT

Dermott came round my house and played me back Lord William's message. The guy was in big trouble and he knew it. He was even more scared than when he was facing prison. He was pacing around going - "let me hide here, let me hide here."

SARAH WYATT

No way. No fucking way. We have a nine year old daughter and a four year old son living here. I am not having Lord Harry the Bastard and his henchmen turning up and torturing Dermott in front of them.

I'm quite happy to have Dermott tortured, just make it well away from this house and my kids.

PETER WYATT

Dermott was saying - "I'll hide in the attic, he'll never find me there. I'll just stay up there until this all dies down." I said - Dermott - you can't live up there like the bleedin' Diary of Anne Frank. He said — "Why not Anne Frank did?"
"Yeah but she got caught in the end."
Eventually I agreed. Sarah was not happy - I lost my conjugal rights for a couple of months after that.

DERMOTT COLLINS

So I started living in Peter's attic, only ever coming down to use the toilet. Nice and cosy - had a portable TV and Peter would bring me sandwiches. Sarah refused to cook for me. I kept on getting woken up in the middle in the night by the starlings on the roof, then couldn't go back to kip for worrying about Lord William and his torture rack. Was I going to have to stay up in this attic forever?

FRANK COLLINS

I was worried out my wits, then a few days later this Lord William bloke comes a calling. He barged in demanding to know where Dermott is.

PETER WYATT

It was about a week later when Lord William came round.
He looked calm and business like but Lord William had a tight menacing smile.
"Hullo Peter - I wondered if you knew where Dermott is."
I said No and immediately felt a twitch in my face. Did Lord William spot it?
"Listen Peter, he's run away from home and I know he's your closest friend. So I have every reason to believe you know where he is."
"No No I don't."
He tugs at my collar and pulls me towards him. We're face to face, breathing all over me - "Where is he?"
"I don't know, I don't know. I've got a wife and two kids here." I pleaded with him. Eventually he releases his grip. "Just tell him, he

can't hide forever, and when I do track him down...." And he left it at that. Let my imagination think the worst. The door slammed shut and we were all too scared to do anything for hours.

DERMOTT COLLINS

I'd seen Lord William turn up in the drive and I made a dive up to the attic. I stayed up there for ages after he'd gone in case he came back any minute. It were about midnight when Peter put his nut through the attic trap door.

PETER WYATT

I felt horrible, violated after the visit. It reminded me of those men who came round looking for Dad and threatened Mum. Why do people do that sort of thing? I hate them for it. Then Cobra phoned. I told him I had no idea where Dermott was. Cobra is going - "Lord William ain't the Lord no more. He kept his house, but the law took all his dough. He ain't got the money to pay for any muscle. HE'S GO NO BACK-UP." This planted a seed - let's turn the table on this cunt.

SARAH WYATT

I had no idea that Peter was planning on visiting Lord William with Dermott. Dermott should go alone. What is the point of Peter putting himself in danger like that? There's being a friend, but this is insanity.

PETER WYATT

I remembered where Lord William lived in High Wycombe from that thank-you-for-not-grassing party. Ironic or what? So we drove over there on a sunny Saturday Afternoon. Dermott was swigging from this bottle of brandy to calm his nerves and dull any expected pain. He goes - "Peter what the fuck is going to happen when we get there?"
I tell him my plan - we get our point across, very firmly. We put the frighteners on Lord William - he's just one bloke. We explain to him that you grassed, not just to save your own skin, but the police were going to put your old man inside as well - fit him up. This is a lie of course, but just to explain that in the end Dermott had no choice but to grass.
Dermott starts squealing - "Let me out of the car, let me out the car."

DERMOTT COLLINS

It was amazing we were driving to god-knows-what in High Wycombe. And we were both really calm - scared but really calm. I started - singing 'Do Not Foresake Me, Oh my darling' - you know the theme tune to *High Noon*. The tension was unbearable as we drove up his drive way - I remembered it from his 'thank-you-for-not-grassing' party. I immediately started imagining the pain I was going to feel - would it be worse than my Daffy Duck tattoo? I took another swig of my bottle of brandy and I nearly passed out then and there.

PETER WYATT

Something was strange. The gate was open. I drove up the gravel driveway up to the house, a real beautiful country cottage, like something out of Horse and Hound magazine. His Black Merc was outside. We get out and waited for someone to come out. I looked at each window, nobody seemed to be looking at us. I walked to the front door.

DERMOTT COLLINS

Got out the car and shouted "**Clive McKnight** - we're here - let's get this sorted out!" Been practising what I was going to say in the car, - "They were going to put me old man in stir - I had no choice." The front door was open and Peter walks in. I thought it's a trap, they are going to jump him.

PETER WYATT

I walked into the living room, very plush, very expensively furnished. Classic furniture - that was his front, wasn't it? Antique furniture. And there was Lord William sat on his couch - sprawled out - not moving a muscle.

DERMOTT COLLINS

Peter came out, with a puzzled look on his face. He looks at me and starts laughing, but it's not a happy Monkey Time laugh. It's a nervous not-happy laugh. What? What? What is it?
"He's dead." I walked in all shaky and saw his leg and then quickly looked up at his face – all run amok with claret.

PETER WYATT

It was really freaky seeing a dead body. For about ten minutes all I
could do was laugh. What do we do now? We were going to go, and
leave it at that. But someone might see us leave and think we did it.
So I figured the right thing to do was to call the Old Bill. I went into
the spare room and picked up the receiver by the edges, cos the killer
might have left his prints on it. And I did it – I called the Old Bill.

DERMOTT COLLINS

As we were waiting for the Old Bill to come along I went back into
the living room cos I never seen a real-life murder scene before, and
I looked at the corpse and in Lord William's forehead was a big black
bolt sticking out. **A big black bolt exactly like the type you
would find on a cross-bow.**

PETER WYATT

I was so shaken, I drunk the other half of the bottle of brandy that
Dermott had. By the time the police showed I was too drunk to drive,
but I was able to give a statement. And I just told them everything -
that Dermott was a grass, and that we had come to deal with it. I
didn't say anything about who I thought might have done it.

DERMOTT COLLINS

The police took our statements but the car had to stay where it was
for forensics and that. We walked into the village and got drunk as
Lords.
I hate to say it, but we were happy he was dead. Am I going to hell?
Not yet, not yet.
I did a couple of toasts for Cobra and start singing 'The Things We
Do For Love.'

PETER WYATT

So we spent Saturday night getting pissed up in a country pub outside
High Wycombe. The barmaid asked why were celebrating and I told
him the story about Lord William and how he had just been
murdered, and Dermott here had got a let off. She didn't believe us
at first but then she got upset because she knew who Lord William
was, and thought he was a good bloke.

DERMOTT COLLINS

Cobra saved me from God knows what. While I knew it was him, I would have never grassed him up. But the forensic trail had lead to him. He'd left his dabs all over the cross-bow bolt. Doh!

JERRY ZMUDA

I was genuinely moved by what Cobra did for Dermott, he had truly shown his love for him. Peter would always say to me - "You're Dermott's greatest friend," but I would never have killed a notorious gangster and served a life sentence for him.

DERMOTT COLLINS

So I go and visit Cobra on remand. I felt it was the least I could do. He's done a guilty plea so he's likely to be away for some time. Fingers crossed. Seeing him sat there - different - all peaceful.
Talking about how he did it, and he was proud of it, excited about what he done.
Acting it out for me. I was laughing along with him. He was gutted because he remembered to take out the CCTV, to wear gloves, but totally forgotten about the prints he left on the bolts when he was loading at home. "Shame" - he said "I would like to have been a hit man full time. The cross bow could have been my thing."
There was a silence and then I asked him why he did it. "He was going to cut you up badly - scar your face for life. I couldn't let that happen." Another silence and then he goes. "I love you Dermott - I will always love you."
I told him I loved him back. Had to, I mean he's looking at 20 years of bird because of something he did for me, least I could do was make him feel good about it.
Just hope they weren't going to grant him any of them conjugal visits.

EXPRESS YOURSELF - DON'T REPRESS YOURSELF

PETER WYATT

So the unholy trinity are past 30, and I'm the only one out of us three that's married. Now most people are married by the time they're 30. So why hadn't Dermott and Jerry? In fact neither of them had even had girlfriends for a while. It got me thinking.

FELTHAM MADE ME

JERRY ZMUDA

So I'm talking to Peter on the phone. I'm my usual introspective whingeing self, which I have to confess had become my trademark in those days.

Then Peter says to me - "You know if you and Dermott were to come out..."

"Come out what do you mean?"

"Come out - you know if you two were gay. I'd be alright about it."

"Well thanks Peter - but I'm straight."

"You know maybe that's why - you're like - you know - a bit off with him - because..."

"Because?"

"Because you haven't come to terms with..."

"Come to terms with what?"

"That you love each other."

I laughed so much I ached.

PETER WYATT

I wanted him and Dermott to know that if they are gay, I was totally fine about it. In fact I'd rather they came out in the open, than keep it repressed.

JERRY ZMUDA

I am an open-minded guy, I hate homophobia but I am not gay. Being the reflective type I've mulled over my sexuality - but I know what gets my blood flowing. I know what I fantasize about. What I see inside my head when I have my regular-like clockwork early morning erections. And it's all female. I can't speak for Dermott though...

PETER WYATT

Of course yer worries don't end when you get married. A whole new gateway of stress opens up. I tried to win over Sarah with flowers, which ain't easy for me because I'm allergic to them. She smiles, while I sneeze my head off, but she's still off with me.

What troubled me about our marriage was that I couldn't be myself with her. I couldn't tell her about the trauma of seeing my first corpse as a fireman. Lord William was the first corpse I ever saw. I thought – good, this would prepare for my first corpse as a fireman - now I wouldn't find it so upsetting.

But I was wrong. Seeing my first corpse as a fireman was one the most upsetting things ever in my life. This time there was no nervous laughter - I just felt destroyed by it. To see a human body, charred and disfigured, their face coming away from their skull, to see the positioning of the body showing how they tried to escape. To die in a fire must be one of the worst ways to die. I cried - I admit I cried. And even after I cried, I was still upset. Part of it was because I felt I had let them down. I was a fireman and I am supposed to stop this from happening. Of course there was nothing me or the other firemen could have done. The house was fully ablaze by the time we got there , but you still felt that sense of failure.

I was still shaken from it when I finished my shift. I thought I can't let Sarah see me like this - she'll think I'm weak and pathetic. But I had to talk to someone, the other guys on the shift were shooting off. So I called Dermott and Jerry - and met them in a pub.

JERRY ZMUDA

This time it was Peter's turn to call me out of the blue. It was a Monday afternoon, he insisted we meet up for a drink.

I'd never seen Peter so shaken up before. He talked about it, and when he finished he talked about it again. I felt privileged that he chose me as a close enough friend he could talk to.

DERMOTT COLLINS

Thought a joke was in order. I said – "You need to relax - have a cup of char" - you know char as in burn.

But Peter was having none of it.

JERRY ZMUDA

Dermott jokes through trauma therapy was not working. Peter just wanted someone to listen.

But what I found alarming was that Peter felt he couldn't talk to his wife about it. If I had met THE ONE - the love of my life, I would hope that I could talk about something that was distressing me like this.

PETER WYATT

I used to think that all these precautions, all these drills, all these rules and regulations, were just something you did - like for the sake of it. Now I realized they were vital, it was to stop this from happening.

FELTHAM MADE ME   301

SARAH WYATT

Peter would often come in from his shift with nothing to say to me. He never talked much about his job at the fire brigade. I once said jokingly that all he did all day was play snooker with the lads and this really annoyed him.

PETER WYATT

That is a fucking myth. FIREMEN DO NOT SPEND ALL DAY DOWN THE STATION PLAYING SNOOKER. There's a darts board as well. No - seriously. Firemen do loads of things while they're on stand-by. Checking and double checking the equipment, doing drills, keeping fit. It's like being a top class goalkeeper - you go for ages with nothing to do, but when you're called into action you've got to be like a tightly coiled spring.

CALVIN BETTERIDGE (Surrey Fireman)

I never once encountered full blown racism in the fire brigade. Just sometimes it was - you know - patronizing - stupid comments about smoking ganja - or silly Chalkie voices. It got worse when they had a couple of drinks down the pub - and that's why I stopped going with them after a while. But Peter was different, he just talked openly about stuff. He talked to me like I was person, not like he was thinking at the back of his mind he was talking to a black person. We talked a lot about sport, music, pretty soon we were lending each other CDs, joking about our family life, getting on like a house on fire - if you'll pardon the expression. He was someone I would happily go for a drink with.

PETER WYATT

Calvin or Betty or Black Betty became my buddy at the fire station. He became the guy I could talk about things. And I really needed that.

CALVIN BETTERIDGE

After a shift Peter wanted to have a chat, we go to a place where none of the others would go - and Peter opens up to me about the problems he's having at home.

PETER WYATT

I told him Sarah has lost any respect for me, she doesn't take any interest in me. I try and chat to her - try and cheer her up, and I get nothing but a cold shoulder.

CALVIN BETTERIDGE

Look - are you still having regular sex? "Yes." With each other? "Yes." YOU DO NOT HAVE ANY MARITAL PROBLEMS. You've described every marriage that's normal. I tell him that there's nothing wrong. Every marriage goes through something like this. He says - "I want us to be happier than this."

PETER WYATT

I wanted our marriage to be special. I can't go on like this. I have to do something to win her back.

WHITE CHRISTMAS

JERRY ZMUDA

In an attempt to lift my spirits I put up Christmas decorations in my squalid bedsit. Instead the whole exercise had actually made me feel worse. Then Mother phones, asking me what my plans were for Christmas. I said not much - she said "Well OK then, I suppose you may as well spend it with us." Thanks Mother - that makes me feel very welcome.

I had always wanted to go home as the local boy made good. But instead I was the local boy made mediocre.

So it was Christmas Eve night - and I was sitting in my old bedroom, looking at that stained carpet, giving me unpleasant flash-backs. So I called Peter for one of my chats. He was busy preparing for Christmas Day for his kids. It rubbed in how empty things were for me.

PETER WYATT

I said – "Well you should call Dermott. He'll be out on Christmas Eve, in one of the pubs round Sunbury or Walton. You'll catch him if you call now."

JERRY ZMUDA

A night alone feeling sorry for myself seemed preferable than a night of predictable and tired wind-ups from Dermott. But in a bout of desperation I found myself picking up the phone and calling him – "fancy a beer?"

I arrange to meet Dermott in a pub. It's one by the river where a loads of young ones hang out. Waiting for Dermott I get talking to a guy named Ferdy who was a Donkey Planet regular. "No you can't have a refund!" I said to him, and we both laughed.

Anyway Dermott's now fifteen minutes late and I ask Ferdy if he knows anybody who can sort me out with some charlie. Just to stop me from drinking too much - only reason. I was worried about getting a beer gut. Ferdy says he will put the call out and goes to the pay phone.

"The dealer is on his way." I get talking to some more people and eventually the door swings open, the howling wind blows in and with it struts Dermott. He gives me a manly hug and my misgivings melted. Very soon we start chatting away. Ferdy walks past and I say to him –

"Has your man showed up yet?"

"You're talking to him."

DERMOTT COLLINS

So what's with a bit of dealing? It was only to people I knew in pubs. Jerry was all taken aback that the dealer he was waiting for turned out to be me.

JERRY ZMUDA

Dermott had given us all his word that he had stopped dealing. To the judge, to Peter, to me, to his father, everybody. Cobra had saved his skin, and now he was at it again, dealing out wraps in a pub in Sunbury. I was disgusted - disgusted.

And the quality of the cocaine wasn't good either - more speed than charlie. I got terrible shrinkage afterwards.

DERMOTT COLLINS

So the award for BIGGEST HYPOCRITE OF THE YEAR goes to - Jerry Zmuda - regaining his crown. If people like him didn't buy drugs there'd be no drug dealers. And the quality of my charlie is safe. By

FELTHAM MADE ME

the time it reaches the pub in Sunbury it's just stepped on a few more times than when you buy it up the West End. And I never got shrinkage from my stuff. Mind you, when you've got one as big as mine, you're not going to miss an inch or two.

JERRY ZMUDA
I didn't start a scene, I didn't make a big deal out of it. I expressed my concern at the time. The night progressed and I saw Dermott get more and more out of it.
You can tell a lot about a man by what they choose to talk about when they've knocked back several pints. With Dermott it was – Man About The House, St. Petersburg, Don't be A Lionel - the same old catchphrases, same old digs at me - and still knocking out drugs. I remembered my statement to myself at the 30th party. This time I decided firmly that I was going to cut him out of my life. I didn't want to see Dermott any more, because when I do, I see my own inertia, my own failure.

SMIKE - NO STRAIGHT JACKET REQUIRED

JERRY ZMUDA
1995 became a watershed year for me. Why? Because I spent more money on books than on drugs. The first book I read in seven years was by Charles Dickens, his most popular and personal favourite - *David Copperfield*. I gulped when I picked up the book and felt it's thickness. But I was determined to get stuck in. I found it difficult at first, reading slowly, reaching for the dictionary every couple of paragraphs. But it was rewarding. After a couple of weeks of devoted reading - turning off the TV - no other distractions, I felt a satisfied enriched glow.

PETER WYATT
Smike called me out of the blue one day. What a welcome blast from the past. Smike had moved out to Thailand and had started making himself a bit of money selling bootleg CDs. He told me that Phil Collins was big in Thailand and he had made a bunch of money out of him. But some Triad gang had been closing in on Smike's CD bootlegging activities, so he had left the country for a couple of months, to wait for it to die down. But I should have noticed

something was not quite right with Smike - we'd been on the phone for nearly half an hour and all he seemed to want to talk about was Phil Collins.

JERRY ZMUDA

I needed someone I could talk to about my new-found intellectualism and Smike was always an avid reader, and someone you could talk to about the deeper things in life. He had his own unique way of seeing the world. He would talk about the counter-culture, of a different way of living. So I was delighted when I heard he was back in the country. I gave him a call and suggested meeting up over a Pizza.

PETER WYATT

I couldn't make it that night. I would have loved to have to seen it first hand. But at the same time, it was also quite heart-breaking.

JERRY ZMUDA

Smike looked different when I met him at the pub in Soho. He was wearing a suit. It didn't look right, long-haired Smike in a suit with rolled up sleeves – eighties style. He explained that he'd been to a job interview. I said how did it go? He replied with - "If I get it - it will be Against All Odds." We strolled over to the Pizza Express in Soho Square and I couldn't help noticing that Smike seem inordinately obsessed with Phil Collins. "He's a working class guy like us - made good." "He's such a versatile entertainer." I said to him jokingly - it sounds like you should start up a religion based around Phil Collins. He seemed to consider this seriously "That's not a bad idea!" Was this a prank?

PETER WYATT

Of all the things in life to get obsessed about - why choose Phil Collins? Was it because he'd made a bunch of money selling his CDs? Did he feel it coming in the air tonight? Why Phil Collins?

JERRY ZMUDA

So we sit down at the Pizza Express and I ask him if he's missing Thailand. He says of course, he can't get into the groove of Western living. I nodded empathetically just grateful we'd got off the subject of

Phil Collins. He says he can't get used to wearing trousers. So what do you wear in Thailand then? "Robes, nice loose fitting robes." "Yeah you couldn't go round London dressed in a robe." "Why not? What's this conspiracy to keep all men's genitals tightly covered in cloth? What are they scared of?" He was getting quite angry about this, and I found it all very unsettling.

PETER WYATT

This is the bit I wished I'd seen. So Smike stands up and takes off his trousers in front of everyone in the restaurant, giving a big huff of relief when he pulls them off.

JERRY ZMUDA

The Italian owner comes over - "Signore - Signore you must putta da trousers on." Smike stares back at him, with this weird look on his face, grinding his teeth –
"They were rubbing against my nuts."
"I don't care Signore aboutta your nuts you putta da trousers back on, or I calla da police."

PETER WYATT

Smike wouldn't put them back on, and then he tried to get Jerry to join his anti-trousers demonstration.

JERRY ZMUDA

I obviously was not going to take my trousers off in front of a crowd of people, my underpants were at least two days without a wash. Smike accused me of a being a Tory, which upset me a bit. It also confused me, because I thought that Phil Collins was a Tory. But still my trousers remained firmly on. The Italian manager tried to push Smike out of the restaurant. Smike pushed him away - shouting "Think Twice - This Is Not Another Day In Paradise." A policeman arrived and dragged him away. And that's the last I saw of my friend Smike.

PETER WYATT

Nobody pressed any charges against Smike, it was clear the poor chap needed help.
The next thing I heard, his parents got him sectioned under the Mental Health Act. The men in white coats came to their house and

FELTHAM MADE ME   307

dragged him away. He was shouting "NO JACKET REQUIRED" over and over again.

JERRY ZMUDA
This was a cruel break. Smike was my MCA baseball cap of hope. My long-standing friend that I could talk to about things in a mature and intelligent way. Who else could I talk to now?

PARIS MATCH – THE MATCH THAT LIGHTED MY FIRE

PETER WYATT
Of course the real reason I became a firefighter was to be a hero. To save someone's life and be appreciated. After doing it for eighteen months, I did my fair share of rescuing and playing my part. But I was I still waiting for my BIG ONE. The big rescue that marks you out as a real life-saver.

CALVIN BETTERIDGE
A toaster had caught fire at an old people's home. One of the residents made the fatal mistake of throwing water over it - ON AN ELECTRICAL FIRE! Their stupidity was rewarded by an electric shock, and the fire spread. By the time we got there the place was being eaten up by flames. A lot of those old people weren't too good on their feet and they were really slow in coming out. It was terrifying, we were dragging them out as quickly as we could. The officer in charge goes to the one of the staff - "Is that all of them?" But the man just couldn't answer. So Peter dashes back into the house of flames.

PETER WYATT
I felt no fear, I just kept thinking - this is my big chance. I checked every room, one by one, the roof is creaking above me, ready to cave in at any second. I dash into the TV room and there's an empty wheel chair. I crane my neck and next to it is a body slumped on the ground. I lift him up and make a dash to the door. I can hear the roof starting to give way.

CALVIN BETTERIDGE
And out he came, with this old man on his shoulder right then as the flames took over and the house fell apart. If Peter had been in that

house 30 seconds later he surely would have died. The man he saved must have been 80 - and he was barely conscious, but when he came to he insisted on knowing the name of the man who saved him.

PETER WYATT

The man sent me a letter. It was beautiful. The final sentence goes something like *"I may not have long left on this earth, but I appreciate life all the more now. Drop by for a cup of tea sometime. I would offer you some toast, but I don't want to take any chances!"*
NOW SARAH HAD TO SEE THIS LETTER! So I left it lying on the couch in the living room. Sarah finds it and picks up it and gives to me without reading it. So not to be beaten, I leave it on the bed-room table, right by the mirror where she does her make-up. Same thing - "Is this yours?" Not even looking at it. So next, I leave it on the dining room table - she picks it up, about to throw it in the bin. I shout at her "READ IT! FUCKING READ IT!"

SARAH WYATT

So I read the letter and said – "That's nice darling are you going to drop by for a cup of tea?" He went all red-faced and snatched the letter out of my hand.

CALVIN BETTERIDGE

I wanted to help Peter with his campaign to save his marriage. So one day at the station I was watching TV and there's this thing about the Channel Tunnel that's just opened. I said to Peter – "why not take the missus on a trip to Paris on the Eurostar!"

PETER WYATT

Genius! GENIUS! Paris - the city of romance! This will make her fall in love with me all over again. So I decided to make it a big surprise for her birthday.

SARAH WYATT

I wake up on the morning of my Birthday and Peter hands me a card with some flowers. After he stopped sneezing, I open up the card and there's two tickets in there. It was very sweet of him, but I couldn't go. I'd already arranged to have a big girl's night out in Kingston.

FELTHAM MADE ME   309

PETER WYATT

WHAT? She would rather go out on the piss in Kingston with a bunch of ropey old dogs than go to Paris with me?

SARAH WYATT

It wasn't that - it was that this had been arranged in advance - the table, the entertainment, probably a stripper. I suggested Peter still going to Paris, but with Dermott or Jerry. He didn't like this at all.

PETER WYATT

There was no point having the tickets go to waste, so I call Dermott up and ask him if he fancies going to Paris with Jerry.

DERMOTT COLLINS

Going to Paris with Jerry - and the train leaves in two hours? Not 'Arf! I hadn't been abroad since Ibiza. Let me grab my passport.

JERRY ZMUDA

Peter calls me, saying he's got two tickets to Paris on the Eurostar for today. Do I fancy going with Dermott? Sharing a honeymoon suite, sleeping in the same bed like Laurel & Hardy. I didn't have to think about that one too hard.

DERMOTT COLLINS

With Jerry refusing to go to Paris with me, Peter was asking me to call Jerry up and sweet talk him into it. Then me old man walked in.

FRANK COLLINS

So in the end it was me and Dermott that went to Paris on the Eurostar. We had a great time. And it was nice to spend some time away with my youngest son. We went to see Paris St. Germain and saw David Ginola play a blinder - I tipped him to do well. Then we did a bistro crawl and knocked back beacoup du vin and one or two Courvosiers. The next morning - the hotel served us breakfast in bed with a glass of champagne and a bouquet of flowers. That made me feel sad, sad for the two people that this week-end was supposed to be for. Why weren't they having this romantic week-end together?

JERRY, IT WAS REALLY NOTHING

JERRY ZMUDA

Peter says nothing happens unless you make it happen. But that's not always the case.

LYDIA DANCEY

Right! I know you're going to ring out the square alert, but I took my first ecstasy tablet sometime in the mid 90s - and yes it was at a dinner party held by a colleague at the BBC. By now most people in Britain had tried it and I was at the tail end. In my trancey state I started thinking sweet thoughts about Jerry. He was right about all of this after all.

JERRY ZMUDA

I was sitting, or more like wallowing in my bedsit one Saturday afternoon, making myself listen to Radio 4 when the landlady told me there was call for me. It was Lydia - "Fancy meeting up?" This I could not have predicted.

LYDIA DANCEY

It's not that I'd been playing the field or anything, but I'd been with arrogant men, shallow men, boring men, inadequate men - and, I had reached the conclusion that Jerry was not that bad. He was sweet - rather immature, too self-conscious, but generally a good spirit. And, like I said before, there is always a special place in your heart for your first love. I found that my memories of him were now tinged with fondness.

JERRY ZMUDA

Lydia just wants to meet up. Don't read anything into it. I wanted to come across successful and going places - but of course I wasn't. But I wasn't going to lie or put on some act. This is me - take it or leave it.

LYDIA DANCEY

We met at the Coal Hole on the Strand, and Jerry seemed much more relaxed and easy going than before.

JERRY ZMUDA

I was expecting any moment for Lydia to say to me - "Well it's been so nice to see you again, I've got to go." Peck on the cheek, and off into the night. But she kept ordering more wine, and I had to stand my round. I told her about my ambition to move out of sales and into journalism. Which, to be honest, was an ambition I made up on the spot, but she seemed to approve of this.

LYDIA DANCEY

We then went onto a pub that had a jukebox and Jerry was dancing around. That's what I liked about him, none of my recent boyfriends ever danced. They just sat there like lumps and droned on about themselves.

JERRY ZMUDA

So the eleven o'clock bell came too soon. Chucking out time. Lydia was heading to Raynes Park via Waterloo - and me, I had my trip up to bedsit land on the Jubilee Line. Lydia kisses me on the lips - and says to me - "Follow your Dream."

LYDIA DANCEY

I begin my walk over Waterloo Bridge and Jerry is walking behind me. I say to him "What are you doing - your tube station is that way." "I'm following my dream - You!"
So we walk over Waterloo Bridge hand in hand, taking in the glimmering city lights shining at us. It was the perfect moment to kiss me - and he did. We looked out over the bridge and London wasn't a cold and lonely place anymore.

JERRY ZMUDA

I was so drunk, I told Lydia as we walked over the bridge that I often masturbated over her. How I used to re-enact our finest moments in my mind. She blushed and clamped her hands over my mouth - "Too much information." I found myself getting the train back with her. Before long we were re-enacting our finest moments for real.
I woke up the next morning in Lydia's flat. It was tastefully furnished, not all studenty and bedsitty like my humble abode. I said to her - "You realise you're place is so nice, I couldn't possibly invite you back to mine."

FELTHAM MADE ME   312

LYDIA DANCEY

From there Jerry was round mine pretty much most of the time. I introduced him to all my friends, and there was no friction, no resentment, none of the bitterness I associated with the Jerry of old. I was tired of being alone, sick of nights out, getting drunk with my female friends and waiting for some drunken fool to chat me up.

JERRY ZMUDA

I started thinking - Could Lydia be THE ONE? I come up with my five point criteria of who THE ONE would be -

- Someone I can have fun with

- Someone I can feel relaxed with

- Someone I can share my innermost feelings with

- Someone I look forward to seeing every time

- Someone I want to spend my future with

LYDIA DANCEY

London is an expensive place to live, it might even be <u>the</u> most expensive place to live. It occurred to me that if Jerry moved in, contributed to the mortgage, the bills, the groceries - this would take a lot of financial pressure off of me.

JERRY ZMUDA

Within a month or so of our get together. Lydia suggested moving in. My initial thoughts where - Hey! Wait a minute. But then it made perfect sense. Moving out my bedsit was a liberating experience. Not in the least dampened by the landlady stiffing me on my deposit. Raskolnikov was right! Kill your landlady! No remorse. I threw out my stash of porno mags and gave all my videos to Oxfam. I was delighted when moving the sofa, a white cali dropped out. Lydia and I went half's, and we had blissful first night of living together.

The next day she threw a "Welcome to Jerry" party for all her friends. She suggested I invited my friends - but I didn't. I didn't want this spoilt, I was in a New World.

LYDIA DANCEY

These were wonderful times, all of a sudden my bank balance looked much healthier with Jerry's contribution. I now had a much bigger disposable income - a nice feeling. Then Jerry tells me he's bought two tickets on the Eurostar to Paris - he's paying. This was almost too good to be true.

JERRY ZMUDA

And it was in a restaurant in Montmartre that I popped the question. I was just going with the flow - it seemed like the right thing to do.

LYDIA DANCEY

I said Yes - and I came back to work dancing on air. The girls at work asked to see the ring.
What ring?
The engagement ring.
I felt that I'd been conned. Nina explained that the man is supposed to spend a month and a half of his salary on an engagement ring.

JERRY ZMUDA

A month and a half? Are you joking? Am I supposed to live on nothing but unconditional love for six weeks?

LYDIA DANCEY

It was a work colleague who said that month and a half salary rule thing - not me. I just wanted an engagement ring.

PETER WYATT

Jerry calls to tell me he's got engaged. I gave a loud cheer and shouted over to tell Sarah, then I said –
"How's Dermott taken it?"
"Nothing. I haven't told him, and I won't be telling him either."
"Isn't he going to be your best man?"
Jerry just laughed.

JERRY ZMUDA

I hadn't spoken to Dermott since the Christmas drug incident. Somehow he had got my number at Lydia's, Peter must have given it

to him, and he kept calling again and again - leaving messages. "What
are you up to?" "I'm up in London this week-end - fancy going to this
or that? "
But I never picked up the phone and I never called back. This is was
all part of my cutting Dermott out of my life. Now I was with Lydia I
didn't want to go back - to that "who's holding?' "Sort me out with a
parcel" world. It wasn't me any more - it never really was.

PETER WYATT

So Dermott's phones me up one evening, he's very upset. Jerry has
spent all year blanking him, never calling him back, ever since
Christmas. I said to him "let me speak to this rascal."

JERRY ZMUDA

Then I get an ansafone message from Peter, he sounded very serious
and he demanded I call him back immediately, I thought something
terrible had happened. As I dialled I was thinking which of my suits
was most suitable for a funeral.
Peter was very stern saying - "What's going on? Why are you blanking
your oldest friend? Who do you think you are?" I tried to explain my
position. I wasn't trying to be superior - I just wanted to move on.
Lydia was in my life now, and I didn't want Dermott coming round,
getting drunk and making snidey comments about her looking like a
horse. I said to him – "You did the same when you married Sarah."

PETER WYATT

I fucking didn't. When I married Sarah, when I had my kids - I still
found time for my friends. Even if Sarah didn't approve, I still always
stayed in constant contact with them two.

JERRY ZMUDA

It wasn't even personal against Dermott. I just needed to stay well
away from the alcohol and drugs - and criminal types.

PETER WYATT

I said to him - don't you understand? DERMOTT NEEDS YOU TO
KEEP HIM AWAY FROM THE ALCOHOL, DRUGS AND
CRIMINAL TYPES. You're just about the only one who can do it. He
listens to you, he respects you.

JERRY ZMUDA

Don't be silly - he doesn't respect me. Our friendship is a classic example of familiarity breeds contempt. He would never, I mean never take any advice from me.

PETER WYATT

We were on the phone for hours - eventually he said he had to go because Lydia had come in. He put the phone down and I was in the foulest mood I'd been in for years.

Chapter 9
Monkey Time Revisited

YEAH RIGHT WHATEVER

PETER WYATT
>As everybody knows when you're a fireman you have to stay fit. You can't be turning up to a fire panting and straining as you climb up the ladder. I used to do me regular exercises at home, but got sick of the girls taking the piss and making snidey comments. So I started going to a gym.

CALVIN BETTERIDGE
>I told Peter I had a tip on the 3.15 at Chepstow. His eyes go all glassy and he gives this look of terror like I was offering him crack. I thought any minute he was going to howl NNNNNNNNN000000000. I said to him –
>"Take it easy will yer - it's a harmless flutter - take it or leave it, get a grip."
>He told me his Dad fucked his family's life through his gambling. I thought fair enough - I won't offer you any more racing tips.

PETER WYATT
>I was paranoid that I'd end up like my Dad. But right before my eyes it was all happening. The distance between me and my wife and my own kid turning against me.
>I got used to seeing Sarah all sour-faced scowling at me, but seeing the exact same expression on Abby my daughter was a real shock to the system. Had Sarah poisoned my daughter against me? I wanted to be the best parent in the world. Where did I go wrong?

SARAH WYATT
>I don't blame Peter for this, but he related far more to Carl than he ever did with Abby. He took time to talk to him - explain things to him. Take him to places. It's only natural I guess that as a father you feel closer to your son than your daughter.

PETER WYATT

> I showed Abby the cover of the *Abbey Road* album and told her we'd named her after it. I thought she'd be interested, maybe listen to the album - instead she just goes - "Yeah right whatever."
> Every time I asked Abby to do something and even tried to make conversation with her, Abby would pull a face or make a loud tut. It broke my heart.

CALVIN BETTERIDGE

> Again Peter was blaming himself for something every family man goes through. Every man has trouble with their teenage daughter, that's just how it is. In fact you'd be weird if you didn't.

JERRY ZMUDA

> I'd visit Peter at home once in a while and Abby had shot up real quick. I'm not really comfortable around kids, but I'm even worse around teenagers. I found it alarming that Abby knew nothing about the sort of music we liked, and wasn't even remotely interested. Carl was sweet kid though.

PETER WYATT

> The biggest blow came with Abby's birthday party. I helped with all the preparations, hiring the hall, the entertainment, sending out the invites, and then Sarah dropped the bombshell.

SARAH WYATT

> Abby asked if Peter didn't come along. It wasn't anything personal, it was just a girlies party, and she didn't want him "showing her up."

PETER WYATT

> Why didn't she want her own father at her birthday party? She wouldn't even explain it to me, and neither would Sarah. It's was just "like - you know that's how it is." Learn to fucking speak will yer?

ANGELA KNOWLES - A NEW LIFE

DERMOTT COLLINS

> So Peter had Sarah, Jerry was getting hitched to the horse, and poor old Titus was left on his jack. Things were looking bleak for yours

truly. Jack Daniels and Jim Bean had become my closest friends. All my brothers had moved out, so I lived with just me and Dad. I passed my week-ends watching the football in pubs and having the odd flutter. I'd knock back a couple of headfuls of JD and starting thinking about my Angela.

JORDI KNOWLES
Dermott hadn't phoned asking about Angela in well over a decade. But when he called I recognized his voice straight away. "What's Angela up to?" The guy's is persistent I give him that.
There had been some quite amazing developments in the world of Angela.

JERRY ZMUDA
What a story this is!
So Angela had dropped her punk look and become a high class prostitute, making money by the sackful. She deliberately got herself pregnant from one of her customers, apparently a Spanish aristocrat, who had no idea he had an illegitimate son.

JORDI KNOWLES
Angela called her son Salvador, and he really was her salvation. Life seemed great for Angela, once you got over the moral stumbling block of what she did for a living, which as her younger brother I could never do. But she had a nice flat in Kensington - had just two or three clients a week, and could afford a nanny to look after young Salvador while she was working. Despite my misgivings, I had to acknowledge that Angela was the happiest I've ever known her. Salvador had made all the difference, the brooding anger had gone - and replaced by doting attention and love for her son.
But this wasn't to last. Somebody reported her to the Vice Squad. They investigated the claim that Angela was raising a child on immoral earnings. They raided her house and Angela was charged and sent to prison for three years. Thankfully Isabella, my mother, stepped in and agreed to give custody to Salvador, who was only two. But Angela's world was in ruins.

JERRY ZMUDA

Work had sent me to some dreary conference up in Harrogate - boring, boring, and still more boring. You could spend literally years in this line of work before you meet anyone remotely interesting. I was facing a parade of dull people, and in amongst them all I see a familiar face. It's very familiar. It's Angela Knowles from Feltham School - WHAT THE HELL ARE YOU DOING HERE?

JORDI KNOWLES

When Angela got out of prison, she had just one thing on her mind - to win back the custody of Salvador. Mother refused, Salvador was now five, and was settled living with her, and calling her Mummy. Isabella wanted to protect him from any psychological damaging traumas.

Angela might be allowed to introduce herself to Salvador as her mother, but only when he's old enough to handle this sort of emotional bombshell. What age would that be? 12, 15, 21 never? This decision was painful for Angela but she understood, and this is why she went straight. Once she was out of prison she gave up prostitution and got herself a job in media sales, using her negotiation and man manipulation skills she's homed to perfection in her previous "career."

She wanted me to give her a fraudulent reference to set her on her way, which I agreed to without a moment's hesitation. It worked, and in a short time she had talked herself into a job as a manageress of a publishing telesales team. So Angela transformed herself into a target-smashing high-powered sales manager.

JERRY ZMUDA

Angela hated the conference even more than I did, saying to me –
"I feel more of a whore now, than I ever did as a call girl. At least I got paid properly, and treated with respect. This is Hell!"
"It's not that bad," I joked "Hell's not this bad."
She told me that not a day at the office goes by without her going to the toilet cubicle and having a cry. Hey! Me too! I shared her pain, I too was losing my soul to dreary corporate culture.
She told me that the most worrying thing for her was spending her whole day immersed and becoming tainted by it. Before long you'll

become part of it - start thinking like that, behaving like that. Your spark of life and humanity is snuffed out. Death by corporate culture. We escaped our work colleagues and we went for a drink. For all her pain and regular crying sessions she looked as stunning as ever.

DERMOTT COLLINS

Quaking in me boots I was, but I chomped the bullet and made the call. Whatever Angie was doing now, I weren't going to judge her. Just wanted to be a friend, and talk about the good times in that old house. So Jordi tells me she's out nick - with a new identity. He'll have to check with her to see if she's be willing to talk to me. So I wait.

JORDI KNOWLES

Angela was doing well at her new job, she got promoted quickly. But she told me she was regularly getting these boredom blackouts in meetings, and she was building up a strong dislike to the men she reported to. She couldn't help but grimace when they spoke, and found it difficult to look them in the eye. This posed something of a problem. I kept on saying to Angela - "Just deal with it, don't mess this up – everybody's job is boring, and remember why you are doing this."

With Angela's new veneer of respectability, Isabella allowed Angela to visit Salvador on a weekly basis, but Salvador was told that Angela was her aunt.

DERMOTT COLLINS

So Angela agreed to see me. I went to see her in her place of work in Farringdon. Weird - she had her own office and was opening the door to shout at her boys to get them on the phone. She was like a dominatrix and they were loving it. Then she turns round to me and says - "Fuck me this is boring. I've got to get out of this."

I says pathetically – "I'll help you escape." Not having a clue how. I'd work something out. I was so happy that we were friends again. Now I had a chance with her. I had plans to pour my heart out to her, but I had to choose the right time. Maybe get her drunk first.

JORDI KNOWLES

Angela had her work appraisal where she was told she had to keep her tattoos covered at all times. Angela just snapped. After re-building her life and gaining some respectability, she smashes it all to smithereens. She storms out of work and snatches Salvador from school. My mother calls the police. On the run Angela drives Salvador over on the San Sebastián ferry to take him to Spain, to meet his father. This man who had not seen or spoken to Angela since he was her client. She was planning on just showing up at his castle and say "Ola! Here's your lovely child you had no idea you had." Which was going to be something of a nasty surprise to a man who is already "happily" married with legitimate children.

DERMOTT COLLINS

The next time I go and see Angela, she's gone, run away. The boys who work there are running around like headless chickens. She'd escaped me again. I thought - fuck this, there's only so much a man can take. Turned out she'd run off to Spaghetti land to find Salvador's father. I hope he hires the Mafia to do it a hit on her. OK - not really - but I was real upset for a bit.

I preferred her when she was a punk anyway.

DERMOTT COLLINS - A DRINKING DAY IN THE LIFE

JERRY ZMUDA

I heard that Dermott was now drinking heavily. Turning into a suburban Jeffrey Bernard, only without the wheelchair, without the column in the Spectator and without any of the wit.

DERMOTT COLLINS

So Ladies & Gents let me take you through a day in the life of Dermott Collins around this time. It's a warm sunny day in May and I wake up fully clothed. To kick off the day, I knock back some Curvy-Sir hidden under the bed, nicked from me old man's drinking cabinet.

I look round the room and something's different. There's a dirty great big Casio keyboard in the middle of the room. RESULT! It must be worth a few bob. I investigate my loot - and then I feel a pang in my heart. At first I think it's the old heartburn, but it's guilt, and it's telling me DO THE RIGHT THING HERE DERMOTT.

So I lug the keyboard back to the Star and say to the landlord - "Sorry, I must have nicked this last night - just drinking high spirits." The

landlord looks at me all suspicious then laughs. Then I start hanging around, the landlord eyeballs me –
"Yes and?"
"Don't I get a drink as a reward?"
The landlord explodes - "You must be joking!"
Fair enough - but you've got to ask.
The next thing, I get down the Watermans to hook up with my drinking buddy Hoaley Goley. We get slung out after ten minutes after we get seen swigging from the bottle of Curvy I smuggled in.
So it's down the Mow next. Of course my drinking buddy Holey-Goaley weren't his real name, and I never call him this to his face. But this was his nick-name I give him on account that he isn't too fussy about the birds he had a charver with - as in any hole's a goal.
Some of them were so dog-rough, he may as well do it with a geezer, cos there was nothing feminine about them. Holey's real name was - Fuck! Can't remember - it was Oi! You're round. No it was Jamie. He was a sex addict first - and the drinking just came along so that the sex was easier to get - and he'd get less fussy. That was my take on it, but granted I ain't no shrink.
Anyway as drinking buddies goes Holey Goaley's a bit shit - because every time I'm trying to tell some funny joke, he keeps on interrupting. Now this is something Zmuda would never do. And HG keeps interrupting with stuff like "she's well up for it that one" and "I bet she takes it up the arse." Now today's the day I lose my rag with him, - "Yes we get it - you ain't a poof - you love shagging birds. Why do you have to keep going on about it?" We have a massive barney - and I storm off.
Walking the streets of Hersham I find myself in yet another boozer this time it's the Old House At Home. There's excitement in the air and a big Screen in the corner, the FA Cup Final is due to be played. Lot's of excited lads in Chelsea tops about to watch them take on the Villa.
I sit down to watch the build-up and Paul Merson who now plays for Villa is saying he is going to stay sober for the final, because he was so drunk when he won the FA cup with Arsenal he couldn't remember nothing - and this time he wants to remember it. A few hours later he lost the final - so I shout real loud – "HE SHOULD HAVE GOT PISSED - HE'S GOT A BETTER SUCCESS RATE!" The place roars with laughter, which send me onto cloud nine. I love it

when they laugh. All the Blue boys are buying me drinks - slapping me on the back. A couple of hours later I keel over and fall akip under the table.

I get woken up at round nine by none other than Holey Goaley - and he's rather pissed off. He's found out that it were me that gave him the nickname. He'd actually discovered this a few months previous, but he were so bladdered he clean forgot all about it.

He's fuming - "Who are you to judge me?"

I said – "I ain't judging you, I just think some of the girls you do it with are a bit ropey."

Then he goes - "Do you know what they call you? Grassy-Ass. Because you're a grass."

If he were trying to make feel bad, then he's pissing down the wrong alley. I had no regrets about that Lord William dead - and Cobra in nick scene. "I'd rather be Grassy-Ass than Pumped-in-the-Ass." I said. Then in a moment of self-realisation HG starts balling his eyes out. A cry of regret. "Oh my God - I'm a slag."

Aw! For fuck's sake! I think, I bought him another Nessy and sneak off home.

On the way home, I found myself compelled to visit the Legion. Down the Legion I tell a few geezers my Paul Merson wisecrack. But I'm so gone I mess it up, and it don't make no sense. No-one laughs. Time to go home. With legs like lead I walk along the street. I collapse by a bus shelter and wake up a few hours later.

Finally get home at 2 am, a few hours kip, and then to do it all again on Sunday.

PETER WYATT

Jerry would often phone me up for a chat saying stuff like that - "What's all the fuss about Oasis? We sounded like that ten years ago." Dermott also would often phone up, but I'd noticed that lately he was never sober. I was worried. So I said to him - come to the house - let's have a proper chat.

DERMOTT COLLINS

Peter invites us round one Sunday afternoon. Sarah and Abby had gone out, and there was Carl there - we were playing Planet of the Apes. Having lots of fun, then Peter says to me - "Don't take this the

wrong way Dermott, but your breath stinks of alcohol. I don't want you breathing it all over my son."
I'd just had one Sunday afternoon sherbert. Then Peter said - "Every time you phone you're drunk."
I said - "That's just my way. I sound drunk on the phone."

PETER WYATT

He was a sad sight to see, bloated, pale skin. He used to be sharp, fast-talking, bright. Now he talked slowly, his senses were dulled. It was painful hearing him speak waiting for him to say something funny, which nowadays hardly ever happened. It usually be something tired like – "isn't that the bloke who stole your box of Toblerone?"
I said – "The first important step in dealing with your problem is admitting you've got a problem."

DERMOTT COLLINS

I fucking blew a stack. I didn't swear mind. Not in front of young Carl. I told him I didn't realize when you invited me over it was going to be an AA meeting.

PETER WYATT

Then he slumped down on the couch and started sobbing. He wanted a drink. I said No - talk to me. He blurted out about how life was getting him down - there was no parties to go to, just old men in pubs to chat to. Angela had run off, and he was devastated by Jerry not wanting anything to do with him. I said to him – "I can't do nothing about Angela, but Jerry - let me have a word with him."

THE CHRISTMAS GET TOGETHER THAT NEVER WAS

DERMOTT COLLINS

I don't know what it is about Peter, he's always into having re-unions. The man's obsessed.

PETER WYATT

I said it's time we re-united the unholy trinity. Christmas was coming up and it's been ten and a half years since our landmark get-together at the Astoria.

FELTHAM MADE ME   325

JERRY ZMUDA

He wanted the three of us to get together, reluctantly I said yes. I had no desire to meet up with Mr. Drinkie again, but Peter railroaded me into it with his over-powering bonhomie. "Dermott's really looking forward to seeing you." "He's really changed - he's hardly drinking these days." "We'll have lots of fun."

DERMOTT COLLINS

Peter suggests a big get together at the same London pub we all met up in '88 before the Astoria – the setting for our emotional re-union on E. As it turned out this time there was no E, no emotional re-union and no Jerry.

PETER WYATT

I couldn't believe it. The cunt didn't show. He just didn't turn up. We were sat in the pub, round after round, Dermott was pretending he wasn't bothered - but each round showed a little bit more that he was getting really cut up by it. I kept wanting to tell Dermott to slow down on the old drinking, but instead I kept praying that Jerry would show up any second.

JERRY ZMUDA

As I was double-locking the front door I looked down at my jacket. It was a present from Lydia and the designer had been rather generous on the cloth around the collar. I had a flash-forward prediction of Dermott saying something like "when's take-off?" And not letting it go for the rest of the night.
Then I thought about all the other stuff – Don't be a Lionel, Man About the House, St. Petersburg.
I couldn't face it.
So I switched off my mobile and sat at home instead. The landline kept ringing and I never picked up. Eventually at ten past eleven Peter left a message saying he was very disappointed I didn't show up, and then Dermott shouting in the background - "Good Riddance!"

PETER WYATT

I wish I'd never fucking bothered with that Christmas re-union. This really hurt Dermott, and his drinking got worse. He was reaching the stage where he couldn't just cut down, he was going to have it give it up for good. Go cold turkey.

DUNCAN DISORDERLY

DERMOTT COLLINS
It all kicked off over Pudsey Bear. The local was doing a collection for Children In Need. They had this large stuffed yellow Pudsey sat at the bar, holding a collection box. He's got one bandage over his eye, and he's looking at me - pleading with his good eye. It was doing my head in. Got myself into a debate with the barman about cartoon characters. I was saying something like Pudsey Bear was a rubbish cartoon character compared to Daffy Duck. He was saying that Pudsey weren't no cartoon character, he's the Children In Need symbol. I wasn't having any of it.

FRANK COLLINS
Chinese whispers. It's crazy how the truth gets distorted and rumours get out of hand. I heard a story that my Dermott ripped the head off Pudsey bear. MY DERMOTT IS NOT CAPABLE OF SUCH MONSTROSITIES.

DERMOTT COLLINS
I was pretty lagged, but I do remember grabbing hold of the bear and ripping his head off. There was loud a gasp from everyone in the pub, I was even shocked myself when I looked down to see what I'd done. Then in a split second the red-faced landlord and three other geezers get a hold of me and sling me out into the street.

JERRY ZMUDA
Pathetic! Absolutely pathetic behavior for a grown man. I hear about this and then Peter wonders why I want nothing to do with him.

PETER WYATT
When Dermott sobered up, as a peace offering he went back to the pub with a brand new Pudsey Bear he'd bought off Children In Need, a large box of chocolates, and a hundred nicker to put in the fund, which he'd borrowed off his old man.

FELTHAM MADE ME   327

DERMOTT COLLINS

Walk back into the pub, everyone staring daggers like I'm the Antichrist. The Pudsey Bear I'd ripped the head off back in his place, his head sown back on. I put on a smile for the guvnor and hand over my peace offering. Get slung out on my arse - again.

PETER WYATT

With Dermott now banned from his local pub, he decides to get revenge by breaking in and stealing all their drink.

DERMOTT COLLINS

I was all ready to apologize and they boot me out. Fuck them! Now I'm hell bent on vengeance. Necked a few beers from the offie and at gone midnight climb over their garden wall and smash a glass into their storeroom. The next thing I know I'm in the bar and pouring myself an extra large Curvy. The alarm is screaming blue murder and I think to myself - just a couple of minutes to grab myself a beer barrel and roll it back home. Then the Old Bill show up - give them a big smile.

PETER WYATT

They threw Dermott in the cell with another pisshead, which was probably a good thing. It made him take a good hard look at himself. This other geezer was known as Duncan Disorderly - some out of control type who was banned from every pub in the area, always getting done by the law for petty thefts, abh, the whole pisshead scene. He was a few years older, and Dermott was basically seeing his future if he didn't change his ways.

FRANK COLLINS

Dermott had to go to court, and was sentenced to another suspended sentence and six months community service. The whole thing just highlighted what we all knew about Dermott - his drinking had got out of hand. But it took something like this to ram it home to Dermott, and make him admit it to himself. Something had to be done, or I was going to lose my youngest son to the demon drink.

A friend had been through a rehab programme in this mansion house in the countryside - it straightened him out and kept him sober. It was a Christian programme but it worked, so I was going to put my hands in my pocket and send him there. But I got a big shock when I found out the costs. I was going to have to get out a crippling loan, when Saint Peter stepped in.

PETER WYATT
I found out that Frank was struggling to raise the cash, and he only had half the money. I said – "don't worry about it. I'll put in the other half." It came well recommended, the thing is though - it was a Christian programme.

DERMOTT COLLINS
God Squad? Rather spend the rest of my life a smelly drunk than join that lot.

CANCEL THE WEDDING

JERRY ZMUDA
After a year of living together, we were now getting on each other's nerves.

LYDIA DANCEY
I would sit on the couch watching television with him, and Jerry would start pulling strange faces, making sudden weird noises for no apparent reason. Was he losing his mind?

JERRY ZMUDA
I was getting E Cringe Flashbacks. Snapshots of silly, stupid and embarrassing things I'd said or done on ecstasy appearing involuntarily on my mental landscape, and so I'd pull a cringing face or make a whoop of dread. And Believe me there was a huge archive of incidents to play back.
Lydia had only taken E twice, so she could not relate to this at all. But she had been doing something herself that was twisting my melons - talking in this affected Audrey Hepburn/Holly GoLightly voice. Trying to sound dreamy and soothing, but instead it just came across as patronizing and fake. This was especially pronounced when she spoke to new people. This I found incredibly irritating.

LYDIA DANCEY

I was <u>not</u> putting on a fake voice when I spoke to new people. Jerry was just imagining it. How can you trust the word of a man whose mind is so shot away on drugs, that he can't sit through *Eastenders* without squealing like a pig or pulling a face like he's swallowed a wasp?

JERRY ZMUDA

"Follow your dream" - was her advice to me. So this is what I was trying to do. I asked to borrow her Media Studies degree diploma for a couple of days.

LYDIA DANCEY

My diploma? What the hell for? Apparently this guy at his publishers who worked the scanner told him how easy it was to forge a diploma in Photoshop. Just get an original, scan it, and then rub out the original name and superimpose another one. This was deceitful, criminal, I wasn't going to do it, but he just went on and on, and in the end I just caved.

JERRY ZMUDA

I was sick of doing sales. All that smarminess and weaziling. I envied the guys across the floor who were journalists. I'd like to have a career like that, just spending all day writing drivel. I figured a forged diploma would allow me to quit this crummy snivelling sales job and find a new one as a journalist.

LYDIA DANCEY

But what about references? What about writing samples? He told me glibly that all those kind of things were easy to fake. It was the diploma that was tricky. This wasn't the innocent Jerry I'd met when I was giving him English lessons. He'd become a rogue - been hanging out with the likes of Dermott for too long.

JERRY ZMUDA

I explained how I'd cut Dermott out of my life for good. In fact that was one of the main reasons for us getting together - to keep him away. I shouldn't have told her that, she didn't like it.

LYDIA DANCEY

Then he started trying to pitch me ideas for TV shows, in the hope I would pitch then to my colleagues. All of his ideas were silly - every single one. But the silliest of them all, was the one he was most insistent on.

JERRY ZMUDA

It was the *Spot the Looney Sketch*. A hybrid of a game show and a comedy sketch show. This is the pitch - a team of contestants watch a batch of three sketches, two are written by normal script-writers and one is written by someone sectioned under the Mental Health. The contestant has to guess which sketch was written by the loony. It's genius. Lydia predictably didn't like the idea because it exploited the mentally ill, but it is exactly this that makes the idea so good.

LYDIA DANCEY

Our relationship wasn't working. We'd had got engaged but he didn't seem to have any real plans or direction about him. We weren't gelling as a couple. We weren't having fun. We weren't connecting.

JERRY ZMUDA

So I fraudulently carved my way into a job as a journalist. It gave me a real sense of achievement.
It was a weight off my mind to turn up to work without some crappy sales target to hit each day, no call rates to make. Of course the world of Health & Safety journalism is not a racey one of adventure - within a week I was bored sick. But hey! This was a stepping stone. To what? I wasn't quite sure yet.

LYDIA DANCEY

I decided to finish it. The idea was to shake him out of his complacency.

JERRY ZMUDA

So I come in from work one evening and she dumps me. She tells me I'm rubbish, which I knew already, and I'm a deadbeat - which of course goes without saying. To stick up for myself I explained that I had conned myself into a job as a journalist for a trade journal - so I had effectively gained promotion from Deadbeat Division 4 to Deadbeat Division 3.

LYDIA DANCEY

I needed him to come back with something re-assuring. What do you like about me? Why do you want to be with me? I wanted him to make a strong statement - not the usual Jerry drivel. If he did, I would stay with him, and if he didn't - I would let him go.

JERRY ZMUDA

I called up Peter to tell him Sorry! The wedding's off. No stag night. No best man. I was ultra sad and deflated. I was alone again - and being alone meant I was a sitting duck for Dermott.

FAMOUS FOR WHAT?

SARAH WYATT

I used to look at Abbie's glamour magazines and think to myself - with a bit of a make over I could look just as good as them. I was over 30, but still beautiful, and in the back of my mind I couldn't help feeling I could have done better than just being the wife of a fire-fighter. I could see myself in a big house with servants - and a press officer. I started day-dreaming.

PETER WYATT

Years ago at Botley's funeral my words had been "We will never forget you," and now I'd gone months without thinking about him once. I felt bad, and missed those days. So I dug out the old Grundy tapes - hadn't listened to them for years.

JERRY ZMUDA

The songs we wrote together are always in my head somewhere. A snatched riff or refrain occasionally plays back in my head. But I never, but never listened to those tapes - never.

DERMOTT COLLINS

Never kept no Grundy tapes, wouldn't mind listening to them - just to hear how shit we really were.

PETER WYATT

When I played *London After Midnight* - that bit at the end, I could see Botley bounding on stage and bashing that tambourine I'd left out for him on the drum riser. Good Times!

SARAH WYATT

The big row started over dinner, when I asked Abby what she wanted to be when she left school. And quick as a flash Abby said she wanted to be famous, just like any teenager would.

PETER WYATT

Famous for what though? She goes "just famous" - she couldn't tell us.

SARAH WYATT

This really wound Peter up.

PETER WYATT

It reminded me of me Dad. Normal people and normal life wasn't good enough for him, he wanted to gamble his way into the jet-set.

SARAH WYATT

"Leave her alone," I said, but Peter was like a dog with a bone - growling and spouting nonsense.

PETER WYATT

With Sarah and Abby, everything revolved around famous people, listening to them on talk shows dribbling on about nothing. Ignoring their own father and husband. Why are you listening to this shit? I am just as capable of dribbling on about bollocks as that useless lot.

SARAH WYATT

It was around this time that Abby was playing that record by Robbie Williams *Angels* - over and over again. Now that really wound Peter up. Then one Saturday evening Peter came back after taking Carl to see West Ham. They must have lost because he was in a stinking mood.

PETER WYATT

My daughter comes in with her friends, barely gives me a look and shuts herself in the bedroom. Then out the open window comes Robbie Williams warbling away on her CD. I wanted to kill someone.

SARAH WYATT

She comes down for dinner, her friends thankfully go home, and that's when Peter gets it out.

PETER WYATT

I say to her – "Do you want to hear some real music?" I get out our Septimus Grundy demo tape - the good one - where we sounded like Who and the Ruts. And I played it to her. Big fucking mistake. What the hell was I thinking?

SARAH WYATT

What an invitation to take the piss. Peter was telling her - "We got played on John Peel." Abby just laughed. I mean obviously she's going to laugh.

PETER WYATT

The point I was trying to make was that fame is not the be all and end all of life. People who sing, write songs, play music, act, perform, people with talent, they are everywhere - just normal people. Famous people are just normal people with more attention around them. You shouldn't look down on people just because they're normal. Abby had that mask of disrespect that she always wears whenever I speak to her.

SARAH WYATT

Abby just walked off, smirking. Went up to her room and slammed the door. Then she started playing *Angels* at very high volume. That was it. He cracked.

PETER WYATT

Who's the better person? Me. Who puts out fires and saves lives, or Robbie Williams who sings like Elton John, and prances around like a dick? It's me isn't it? What kind of a sick world do we live in - where people like Robbie Williams are treated like gods and people like me are treated like shit?

SARAH WYATT

Peter runs up the stairs, for an awful moment I thought he was going to hit her.

PETER WYATT

It was like someone else had taken control over me. I fling open the door - Abby's head bolts round. Then I find myself opening up the CD player and slinging the CD out of the open window into the neighbour's garden.

SARAH WYATT

When Peter calmed down he had to go round the neighbour's house and, all sheepish, ask for the CD back.

PETER WYATT

I felt proper stupid, real ashamed. I was making a good point, but I went about it in completely the wrong way. Instead of winning the respect of my daughter and wife - I'd lost what little I had.

SARAH WYATT

Peter had to do some major grovelling to me and Abby. Bless him! Blaming it on the pressure of work. Abby asked for the Robbie Williams Video as compensation and Peter had to swallow it and buy it for her.

JERRY ZMUDA

Your teenage daughter won't talk to you and she plays Robbie Williams over and over again. Who can blame a man for losing his temper? That's justifiable grounds for homicide.
When Peter told me the story, it made me grateful that I missed out on the joys of parenthood.

DERMOTT AT GOD SQUAD TOWERS

DERMOTT COLLINS
> Yes, I have a drink problem. But I was never an alcky. I never got them early morning cravings for a brew. Well not often anyway. I turned to drink for something to do, and it got so I was drinking all the time, and then getting into scrapes. That's what I brought me to God Squad Towers.

BIFFO (Shelby Towers staff)
> I was appointed Dermott Collins' key worker and later his counsellor at Shelby Towers. The first thing he said to me at our first face-to-face was - "You ain't turning me into no born-again Christian."

DERMOTT COLLINS
> Felt sick when the car picked me up to take me there. Kept on thinking - if only I'd kept the drinking down a bit, this needn't have happened. I was only going cos Peter and me old man wanted it, and they were footing the bill. I was scared I was going to get turned into a Stepford Dermott - spouting 'Jesus Love You' to passing strangers and the old Dermott Collins with the Basil Brush laugh, that we all know and hate would be no more.

BIFFO
> Many people coming on the programme are very wary at first. I tried my best to put Dermott at his ease. I explained that we are not trying to brain-wash him, or destroy his personality. We are going to work together to beat your addiction.

DERMOTT COLLINS
> But I haven't got an addiction - I just like a shant.

BIFFO
> And an important step in beating your addiction, is admitting you have one. And then searching within yourself the root of it – the feelings that you are trying to suppress.

DERMOTT COLLINS
> Fuck off God Botherer.

BIFFO

The first one-to-one with Dermott Collins didn't go too well. It was going to be a difficult eleven months.

DERMOTT COLLINS

But got a pleasant surprise when I finally arrived at the place. God Squad Towers was a beautiful large house in the countryside with peacocks in the gardens, like the sort of place a rock star like Keith Moon might live in. I always dreamed, if The Grundy ever took off, that I would live in a big country house like this. And now I was - for eleven months, sharing it with dozens of alckies, druggies and Jesus nuts.

PETER WYATT

On Dermott's first day on the programme, he phones me from the place, saying how beautiful the house is. Then he goes, "Is it alright if I bail and come home? Will you get your money back?"
I said – "No Fucking Way - you are seeing this one through."

BIFFO

My name is Craig Barrowman, and I have been through the programme myself, my vice was Heroin. In my first one-to-one with Dermott he decided I looked like the comic character Biffo the Bear. Within a couple of hours this had passed around the manor, and so I had myself a new nickname.

DERMOTT COLLINS

So I was stuck here for the next eleven months or incur the wrath of Peter Wyatt.

BIFFO

Here at Shelby Towers we offer the perfect peaceful environment to get your life back on track. It's a robust programme based on the values of companionship and teamwork. We need them to look at why they are addicts – look at the root causes. We also need them to live to a strict routine - eating at specific times and a rota of duties and tasks.
It's not an easy programme. But if it was easy - it wouldn't work.

The Christianity is not obligatory. We do <u>not</u> force it down people's throats. But it helps, because it's all about humility and surrendering yourself to a higher power.

DERMOTT COLLINS
I had surrendered to myself to a higher power – his name is Peter Wyatt. He ordered me to be here – so be it.
The place was a right horror show of geezers from all over the British Isles. Scouseland, Yorkshire, the East End, the Uh Ar West country, and some Jock who I couldn't understand a word of what he said. All of them with a story to tell, and boy did they like to tell it. What I found funny was that we are all in the same boat and we were all supposed to have stopped using - but there was a real strong rivalry between the alckies - who think they're funny, to the druggies - who think they're hardcore, living on the edge.

BIFFO
Dermott's big problem at the outset was that he still didn't consider himself an addict. He thought he was above the rest of them. He needed to empathise with his fellow residents.

DERMOTT COLLINS
We used to have the regular sessions where we all sit around and talk about our lives. Fuckin' stroll on. I thought 'muda the brooder was the king of self-pity – but this lot were in a different league.
"I never 'ad nothing. Going up in a puff of smoke."
I try and liven it up with a bit of Titus Humour. I say – "I never had much of a chance I was brought up in a Craic House. You see me Dad being Irish and he was always up for the Craic."
Nothing. It was tumbleweed time, the wind whistling in the background. God I hate that.

COLIN BREWER (Shelby Towers resident)
I got talking to Dermott. You could tell he was a drinker, he just had that look. I told Dermott – "It's easy for you, you're over 30 – you've done your years of gear and booze. Me I'm only 20 and I've got to pack it all in now."
But it was music that helped me through it. Shelby Towers had this little music studio, and a couple of times a week, we were allowed to

have a go. I was trying to learn the guitar from a book I'd got – and it really helped take me mind off things. Then, over a smoke, Dermott lets on that he used to play a bit. I said – "Come on then, let's hear yer."

DERMOTT COLLINS

Colin was a bundle of energy. Like Tigger the tiger bouncing about. I could see how he could easily become an addict - always so enthusiastic about everything. Biffo said to me – "Help him channel his energy into a positive direction." So we talked endlessly about music, swapping CDs.

COLIN BREWER

He's like 20 years older than me and he's going – "Do you think when we get out, it would be alright to do some MDMA powder once in a while?"
I said – "Course not – you've got to stay clean – that means CLEAN."
"But I'm an alckie not a druggie."
"No difference mate – we're all addicts, you've got to stay clean for now and the rest of your life."

DERMOTT COLLINS

I hadn't played a guitar in eighteen years. When Colin asked me, I strummed a bit, and it all came flooding back. After a couple of minutes of fiddling about, I went straight into the riff of *Feltham Made Me* then I started singing along – 'Feltham Is Mine, Feltham Is Mine.' It felt good.

COLIN BREWER

I was blown away – "What the fuck is that tune?"
"I made it up myself."
"Will you show me how to play it?"
"Yeah OK."
"So I take it you were in a band then?"
"Yeah – sort of."
"Where did you play?"

FELTHAM MADE ME   339

DERMOTT COLLINS

We headlined The Hand & Spear in Weybridge a few times, King's Head, Putney, Feltham Football - err no we pulled out of that one. The Airman in Feltham - oh no we got chased out of that one. Well we didn't do too many gigs come to think of it.

COLIN BREWER

I insisted we form a band together when we get out. But Dermott was going "Nah! I'm too old."
I said – "You're never too old mate. Not when you can come up with riffs like that."

BIFFO

Once Dermott started playing that guitar he changed. His cynicism melted away. He wasn't especially brilliant – but he played with panache. And he forged a friendship with young Colin. They were two of the most vulnerable people on the programme at the time. I was delighted.

DERMOTT COLLINS

I taught meself to play *Hibernation* by Ted Nugent. Very satisfying. Looking out onto the grounds, morning sun coming out, peacocks squawking away. I think I was finding what them ponses call inner peace.

PETER WYATT

I got a postcard from Dermott - one sentence. "Send me an electric guitar."

DERMOTT COLLINS

Christmas at Shelby Towers was going to be difficult. For me Christmas had always been one long booze up that started in early December and didn't finish until after New Year. It were traditional, passed from generation to generation.

BIFFO

I knew we'd turned the corner with Dermott when he started coming to church with us.

DERMOTT COLLINS

I started going to church for one reason and one reason only - to see a bird, any bird. I'd been at the Towers for months and the only ones I'd seen had been on the telly. So I got myself dolled up, nicked some of Cozy's aftershave and got on that mini-bus.

JERRY ZMUDA

I got Peter on the phone saying to me - "You must write to Dermott." I said "OK OK OK." I turned on my computer and stared at an empty screen. So in the end, I just sent a Christmas Card and all I could think to write was STAY FREE.

DERMOTT COLLINS

I was over-joyed - yes overjoyed when I got that Chritsmas card from Jerry. It meant a lot to me, and *Stay Free* is my favourite Clash song.
We met when we were at school,
Never took no shit from no-one - we weren't fools.
On my last day at Shelby Towers I gave the lads a little speech. I said to them – "When I came here, I was a right cocky bleeder, taking the piss out of the druggies and the Christians. But this place has taught me many things – and one of them is HUMILITY."
I left my guitar behind, it was my donation to the manor. I promised I'd stay in touch – especially with Colin.

BIFFO

I told Dermott – "You a very lucky man to have a father like yours. Many men on this programme have been deserted by their parents. Your father is a true rock."

FRANK COLLINS

When Dermott came out of rehab he was talking about moving into a flat and getting out of my way. I said – "No way. Stay with me."

DERMOTT COLLINS

I said I needed to live somewhere that doesn't have a drinks cabinet - I can't have that temptation. And it's not fair on me Old Man. I don't see why he should go without his stocked up drinks cabinet just because I got fucked up on the booze.

FRANK COLLINS
But I will. I want to. The drink cabinet goes, and you can stay.

SARAH WYATT
I had no idea that Peter had spent some of our savings on rehab for Dermott "lost cause" Collins. If I had known I would have left him.

THE CHRISTMAS GET-TOGETHER THAT NEVER WAS – NUMBER 2

JERRY ZMUDA
Time whooshes by when you hit middle age. You can't chart what you were doing by which Jam release was out at the time, or which club night you were going to. When you're middle aged all the days and week-ends merge into one unexciting cultural blandness. I had stayed in touch with Peter, mainly chatting on the phone, but I hadn't seen or spoken to Dermott for years. Life was less eventful, not as crazy without him, but I never once felt the urge to get in touch.
But I'd often get a Dermott flashback – like listening to Radio 4 one time and they mention the Labour MP Stephen Ladyman. Was this same Ladyman that me and Dermott crank-called as kids? Then on *Watchdog* I heard about some Bank Transfer email scam that used the name Jonathan Bagg. Was Dermott behind it, using our old fictional alias?

PETER WYATT
I knew it was right, with Dermott clean and sober, I was determined to get my friends together.
Jerry was carrying this whacking great chip on his shoulder about not making it when we were Septimus Grundy. But that's not what matters. What really matters is that we shared those times together and that we had a marvellous adventure. And that's why the three of us should get together - to celebrate that.
I felt sure that once Jerry set eyes on his old friend, once he heard Dermott do his Basil Brush laugh - all those memories and good times would come flooding back and - Jerry would accept him back into his life. It really mattered to me. All my life I've seen people around me flaking out on each other, not supporting each other. I was determined my closest friends wouldn't do that.

JERRY ZMUDA

When I was with Lydia I was buffered, protected. I had a good excuse for not going to any unholy trinity re-union. But now I was exposed and vulnerable. Peter assured me that Dermott was now clean and sober. I said I didn't believe it. He said "seeing is believing" - but I was adamant about not wanting to see him.

PETER WYATT

With Jerry still refusing to see Dermott, I did another one of my sneaky ones. I invited Jerry round one Saturday afternoon around Christmas. The big surprise was that Dermott was hiding in the pantry. So when Jerry comes round I loosen him up with a beer and tell him – "There's something in the pantry for you."

DERMOTT COLLINS

I'd been sat like a lemon in there for an hour with nothing but a thermos flask of tea to keep me warm.

JERRY ZMUDA

So I go in the kitchen, open the pantry door and there is sat Dermott. He jumps up and yells "SURPRISE" and started off with his manic Basil Brush cackle. I hadn't seen Dermott in so many years - and I was immediately struck with how healthy he looked. His complexion was not pasty any more, he was back to being slim and he had healthy rosy complexion.

But I just wasn't in the mood. It's not even that I made a decision to walk out. I just couldn't bring myself to stay there. I couldn't hang about with Dermott. Same old jokes, trying to wind me up. I don't want to be a prisoner of the past and I don't want to be Dermott's perpetual fall guy. So I dropped my awkward smile and stormed out of there with Dermott and Peter looking on open-mouthed.

DERMOTT COLLINS

Once a sulk. Always a sulk. Jerry thought we were going to chase after him. We should have done – to give him a good kicking.

FELTHAM MADE ME   343

JERRY ZMUDA

I called up Peter the next day to apologize. But I wasn't really sorry at all, in fact I thought Peter should apologize to me. But I felt I needed to explain my position. I'd had a lifetime's worth of Dermott. I had to move on. There's too much baggage with him - and you know what? I still blame him for the demise of Septimus Grundy.

PETER WYATT

I was fuming, proper fuming with Jerry. This could send Dermott back to the bottle and undo all the good work from the last year.
But it was important that I stayed in touch with Jerry. That way there was still hope that we might all get back together as friends. I was still hopeful that Jerry would change his mind - and I wanted to be there when it happened.

JERRY ZMUDA

I have to be honest but my thoughts at this time were - what the hell is wrong with Peter? Why is it so important to him to have these re-unions? Doesn't he understand that people change - people move on? I wanted to remain friends with Peter, and maybe one day I'd happily sit down and chat with Dermott. But I just couldn't bring myself to do it right now.

SAINT PETER

JERRY ZMUDA

I called Peter one night, I was saying something like –
"The Libertines what's all the fuss about? We were doing that sort of thing 20 years ago."
Peter was silent for a bit and then said - "Fuck off Jerry I haven't got time for this now." And he hung up.
Those were the last words he ever said to me.

CALVIN BETTERIDGE

People don't realize that one the most common reasons for the fire brigade to get called out is for road accidents. You arrive in the fire engine and cut the survivors out of the car. Then the ambulance crew take over. I used to hate it. I would turn up to my shift and think - hope we get a proper fire today.

SARAH WYATT

We were sitting down to Saturday lunch - in silence. Peter finished off his apple pie and custard, he got up and said - "I'm off - I'm doing a double shift today." And he was out of there. I didn't so much as look at him.

CALVIN BETTERIDGE

He switched shifts, he fucking switched shifts. One of the young 'uns wanted to go out Saturday night. So good old Peter stood up and said - "Go on to your stag night. I'll cover for you." How much do I wish he never said that.

Around 5 am we get a call, there's a pile up on the A3. We raced there in the engine and we got there before the ambulances. The pile up involved three cars. One hit the bank and the crash victim had gone through the windscreen, the second car is on fire but the family thankfully got out in time, the third car is overturned, petrol leaking, and inside is a trapped solitary female. Peter runs to the car, I remember clearly his words - "Don't worry Lady. We'll have you out of there in no time."

The rest of the crew get to work putting out the flames on the burning car as the ambulance crew finally arrive. In the dark we didn't see the trickle of petrol trail towards the upturned car. When it caught light it all happened so fast. Within seconds the upturned car became one big loud fireball. Peter was killed instantly.

SARAH WYATT

When I got the call. I didn't move - didn't utter a word. I just went into shock.

I then went up to our bed-room and picked up his bass guitar. I strummed a note and then it started to sink in, and I broke down and cried.

ABBY WYATT (Peter's daughter)

I heard Mum crying. No it was wailing – upstairs. So I ran up and saw her there with Dad's bass guitar strapped on. I said – "What's Dad gone and done this time?"

"He's gone and died".

FELTHAM MADE ME   345

SARAH WYATT

They gave Peter a big Fireman's funeral, never seen so many flowers, which is a bit funny really given Peter's allergy.

JERRY ZMUDA

At the funeral among all the reefs somebody lay down a box of Toblerone I looked round - who was it? Is this Dermott's idea of a joke? But then I let it go. There was a bigger picture.

CALVIN BETTERIDGE

I tried to comfort Sarah and Abby. But how can you comfort someone when something like this happens? I just touched Sarah's elbow and gave her a sorrowful smile. There was a massive turn out to his funeral. Unsurprising - everyone who ever met Peter was won over by his cheerfulness, friendliness. He was always there to help people out, show support when you needed it. He died a hero trying to save someone's life – and we will always remember him. I was going to say all this when I did the eulogy but after a couple of sentences, I broke down and cried.

FRANK COLLINS

Going to Peter's funeral with Dermott was truly the saddest thing ever. Never been to a funeral where there were so many people and so much grief. No one was in the mood for a wake afterwards, that's normally for when someone who's had a good innings and we drink to their memory. But to be cruelly taken from us like that - the mood was one of abject misery. Peter was a good influence on Dermott - a good influence on anybody that ever knew him.

DERMOTT COLLINS

At the funeral I felt like drinking so bad. My mind kept telling me just one - just one. But then I kept on thinking about Peter, looking down from the heavens, saying to me – "I didn't spend all that money on rehab just for you to blow it all at my funeral."

JERRY ZMUDA

Peter had a worthwhile life - a family, a proper job, saving lives as a firefighter. This should not be happening. It should be me in that casket. Me - a useless regurgitator of press releases, no proper friends, no real loved ones. I swear if I could have traded with God I would have done. I was in no mood to be philosophical about it. My best friend was dead - nothing was ever going to be the same again.

DERMOTT COLLINS
I saw Jerry in the church standing up praying, looking downwards. I felt my heart go a-flicker - I guess because I hadn't seen him for a long time. After the service I push my way over and say Hello. He said Hello back, smiled and walked away. I felt like pulling him back to say something like - "Peter wanted us to be friends." But he walked away real quick.

ABBY WYATT
I never once thought that the whole throwing the CD out of the window was the work of an abusive father. I mean you don't want your Dad to be happy and reasonable all the time – you've got to have an edge. It was funny – me and the girls used to laugh about it. I made him feel bad about it afterwards – so he would buy me more stuff. He was so generous, he was the best father anybody could wish for. I just wish I could have told him that before he set off to work that day.

SARAH WYATT
I found out afterwards when I went through his finances that Peter had paid for Dermott's rehab. But I wasn't angry now - instead it was just more proof of how kind and caring Peter was.

IT'S MONKEY TIME REVISITED

DERMOTT COLLINS
With Peter gone, every now again I'd think - who the fuck am I staying sober for? I liked to think he was looking down from the clouds - smiling at me. But maybe he wouldn't mind me having one drink after a hard day's graft. No. No. NO!

LYDIA DANCEY
I made my decision. If Jerry was going to make the effort to phone me - I was going to stay with him and make that big commitment. But if he didn't phone, I'd move on and forget about him. It was all down

to him. I was sick of having to be the initiator all the time - it's not very good for a girl's self esteem. All he had to do was pick up the phone. So I waited. I gave him six months.
Then I gave him another six months.

JERRY ZMUDA
I was still single and felt I needed to settle down with a woman. I was still looking for THE ONE, and reflected back on that list -

- Someone I can have fun with

- Someone I can feel relaxed with

- Someone I can share my innermost feelings with

- Someone I look forward to seeing every time

- Someone I want to spend my future with

And with that my thoughts returned to Lydia. She is all of those things - just not all of the time. I came this close to picking up the phone but started thinking about all the ill-feelings. How we'd lived together and experienced the dull ache of the magic expiring from our relationship. Then I found myself thinking about Sarah. I'd had a thing for her since primary school. She was single now after all.

SARAH WYATT
So I was a widow, the Fireman's pension and insurance meant I didn't have to go out and get a job. But with the kids getting older I thought about getting one, just to get me out of the house. Then I had the brainwave of starting up my own clothes-making business.

JERRY ZMUDA
Christmas gave me the perfect excuse to get over there. I gave Sarah a call, and after about fifteen minutes of chatting, she invites me over. So I dressed up and set off, armed with a stack of presents for Abby and Carl.

DERMOTT COLLINS

I'd been doing a job in Feltham converting these waste grounds into a park. When we were kids we used to call this place the 40 acre, where I used to sell my freshly stolen porno mags. Right nearby was the cemetery where Septimus Grundy himself is buried. The first day I worked there, the memories came flooding back, but after a couple of days it was just another place of work.

JERRY ZMUDA

I was going to cab it over to Sarah's, but then I thought I'd save some money and get the bus. I walk up to pay my fare, and the driver's glaring at me. "Get off My Bus!" He growls. I'd recognize that growl and stare of hate anywhere - it was Mr. Heyward my primary school teacher. "Get off my Bus - I mean it!" As I waited for the next bus I thought I'd call Dermott and share the moment with him. But then I realized we still weren't talking. But that put Dermott in my mind for the first time that day.

SARAH WYATT

I knew what Jerry was up to. But I actually didn't mind, I didn't want to be alone forever. It didn't feel right, but at the same time, it didn't feel wrong.

JERRY ZMUDA

When I got to Sarah's, to my dismay young Carl had a friend round and they were playing round the living room. I still wasn't comfortable around kids. I watched them playing. Could I be a step-father to him and Abby?
It wouldn't be easy, but I could adapt. I had to. They were playing Planet of the Apes and Carl was wearing his Galen mask.

SARAH WYATT

I could tell Jerry was nervous, he said something really unoriginal like - "It's good to keep the kids active and not spending too much time on the Play Station." I realized he had something else on his mind.

FELTHAM MADE ME   349

JERRY ZMUDA

I was gearing myself up to asking Sarah out on a date. I looked down on Carl, still in the ape mask playing dead - when suddenly Carl jumped up in the air and yelled "IT'S MONKEY TIME!"
Those words were the cue for someone to switch on a film projector inside my head. A sequence of shots flashed away…I was there - fighting the Kung Fu Kids - heckling the Nativity Play - phoning Mr. Ladyman - playing tricks on the Vicar - bunking off school to see The Jam. I swear all those images, all those emotions ran through my brain, triggered off by just those words - IT'S MONKEY TIME.

SARAH WYATT

Jerry had his moment. Just staring at Carl playing in the living room - and then he just got up, said his goodbye and went. I was relieved. Very relieved.

FRANK COLLINS

I got a phone call from Jerry sounding all hyper demanding to know where Dermott was working. I said – "He's not got himself into any more trouble now has he?"

DERMOTT COLLINS

So I'm working away at the 40 acre all on me jack, the winds gets icier and I'm thinking to myself - why couldn't I get an office job? Then I get a call on my mobile. The geezer sounded all bunged up. But I could tell he was trying to disguise his voice.
"I've got a job for you."
"Great."
"Pays well."
"Even better."
"But there's one special requirement."
"I'm listening."
"You have to listen to Supertramp all day."
"What the fuck is this? Fuck off you crank," and I hang up.
He calls back - "Don't you dare hang up on me…." Then I could hear the geezer talking was hiding behind the wall. I ran over and there he was - that fucker JERRY ZMUDA. My first thoughts were - what the fuck do you want? It seems he wanted to chat, about Mr. Heyward working on the buses.

FELTHAM MADE ME   350

JERRY ZMUDA

Dermott didn't seemed overjoyed to see me - in fact he seemed put out. He wasn't due to finish work for another two hours, so I made him promise to meet me at the nearby pub when he finishes off. "I'd better warn you, I don't drink no more," he says.

DERMOTT COLLINS

By the time I get to the boozer, Jerry was pretty steaming and went on some more about the old days, like we'd never been away from each other. For me this were all a bit strange - but I've had such a history with this geezer, it was impossible for me not to feel a little bit happy about seeing him again.

JERRY ZMUDA

He matched me for a lime and soda for every beer I drank. I said –
"Come on have just one beer - one beer."
Dermott politely declined - "I can't, the man upstairs man is watching." I knew immediately who he meant. I raised a glass to his memory.

DERMOTT COLLINS

Then out of the blue - out of all this blabbering about the old days, he says to me - "I'm sorry."
"About what?"
"I'm sorry I blanked you - I'm sorry I never got in touch."
"It's alright - I understand."
"You do?"
"Of course." Then he gave me a hug. I said -
"Steady on mate. The locals are staring. This ain't the done thing in a Feltham boozer."

JERRY ZMUDA

It got so I drank my fill, time to go home. Dermott ordered me a taxi and put me in it. He even paid for it. This was a different Dermott, a responsible Dermott, lime and soda drinking Dermott. Dermott giving a nod to the man upstairs.
There was me looking for THE ONE - and there he was all the time.

CARL WYATT (Peter's son)
> Dad would always call them two Uncle Jerry and Uncle Dermott, although Mum said they aren't really my uncles. Monkey Time was just something we always said when we were playing – Dad would say it and Uncle Dermott would say it as well, all my friends said it from time to time. I had no idea when I was playing in front of Uncle Jerry – by shouting "It's Monkey time," I was helping him and Uncle Dermott become friends again. I just said it because it really felt like Monkey Time.

FELTHAM MADE ME   353

FELTHAM MADE ME   354

The Puppy Mod a short story by Paolo Sedazzari

They call me the Puppy Mod. There used to be four us – the Puppy Mods. But Chris moved to Swanage, Lee became a dresser and Barry became boring overnight. Then when I found out Barry wore Clarke Commandos to school one day, he was as good as dead to me after that.

So now there's just me. I feel like the last of a tribe - an endangered species. Like the last of the Mohicans or something. Strange to feel this way when I am going to be fourteen next month.

When there were four of us, we'd try to hang about with the Sunbury Aces - that's the older lot of local Mods. They'd either ignore us or take the mick. Because we're so young (wo-ho!) - they'd say stuff like "we didn't know Mothercare did Parkas" or "come back when it's got hairs on it." I answer back by telling them I hit puberty over two years ago, but then they just laughed even more.

So from what I can gather there are two leaders to the Sunbury Aces. There's Dave the Mod - he's not got the most imaginative nickname I give you that - he does most of the talking and the other Aces are always looking to him when they are deciding where to go. He's all square jawed with big teeth, and sandy cropped hair.

But also in contention is Swade or Swadey. He was the one to start calling us the Puppy Mods - and he's about the only one out of them that properly gave us the time of day. Swadey is thin and wiry - with features all streamlined like a leopard.

When you talk to him he twitches, snorts loudly and bods his head up and down like you're sparring with a boxer.

Now Dave the Mod and Swadey may both be Mods, but they are chalk and cheese. Dave is a trainee manager at United Biscuits, so he ain't exactly a rebel. He's also got a steady girlfriend, and a car. Outside of being a Mod – he has a quiet life with his bird. Now with Swadey, there is no quiet side to him. I could never imagine him just sitting home watching TV in dead silence like me folks at home. He'd have to be cracking jokes and answering back the TV all the time. Life could never boring with him around. That's not always a good thing mind, as you will soon find out.

Swadey is a bit of a thief. Now he won't mind me saying that, he's actually proud of it. He's promised to steal me a scooter to order when I'm old enough. But he'll steal it from a showroom, not from another Mod. He's a thief with honour. Swadey's been to borstal, and he makes borstal sound like a brilliant laugh – like I was missing out for never going. He told me something about inside that warmed the cockles of my heart.

Now those horrible NF boneheads who go around terrorizing all the decent people, properly suffer in borstal. Their swastika tattoos would flash out like Belisha beacons, which does not impress the black kids who run the show. In there, the NF bonehads are the minority and the black kids give them real hell. They play murder ball with the Skinhead's head as a ball, and the black kids would let Swadey join in. The thought of that cheered me up no end.

Now every now and again they have a Mod night down the Feltham Football Club, and that's where the Sunbury Aces all go in force. Not because it's good. They go because there's nothing else on in the area. I feel like telling them - "You've got scooters – you can go anywhere you like - Soho, Brighton, Paris even. So why the hell would you want to go to the Feltham Football club?"

Especially as Feltham Football Club is a well known magnet for the Dogs of War. There's always trouble at the Feltham Football Club. I reckon the place must have been built over some mining shaft that leads right down to the bowels of hell.

I say all this, but I've never been there. Until this evening that is. I'd had enough of being the kiddy wink hearing about everything and never ever being there. This evening I was going to get down the Football Club and get myself seen with the faces. But I had to be home for 8 'o'clock mind, because Mum needed me back to feed the goldfish – and you can't argue with that.

I needed to make an impression with the Sunbury Aces, so that's why I was giving my paisley scarf its second outing. It's garish, purple and a little bit trippy but hopefully I would stand out in the crowd. I ironed it with ultra-care – I had to look S.H.A.R.P.

A lot of people wonder - how does a Mod know how to dress? Well you just know – it's instinct. You know that flares look daft, but if you stitch your jeans too tight, then that's just silly. It's all about the clothes, but it's not a uniform. Swadey tells me that a proper Mod leads and not follows and as long as a Mod wears it with panache, he can wear whatever he likes. Anything at all - apart from Clarkes Commandos that is. You can only wear those with shame – never panache. Panache – that's a good word isn't it? Panache. Swadey is often using fancy words he's not really sure the meaning of, but I reckon he's bang on with this one.

So I rack up to the Feltham Football club pathetically early. It said on the flyer - doors open at 7pm - and it was half six. Nothing to do but wait outside. Wait outside and try and work out whether I can wear the collar up or down on my boating jacket. Panache or poncey? No collar up looks way too poncey. What about the scarf? I'd only worn it once before, for a trip to the record shop. No one said anything about it then. Will it get the Sunbury Aces seal of approval? My palms were getting sweaty at the very thought of it.

Eventually a bloke not much older than me, modishly dressed in a Harrington and button down shirt, turns up carrying a twelve inch record box and seven inch record box. As he unlocks the door he turns to me. "What you doing here? The kid's disco is Saturday morning."

"I'm not here for the kid's disco. I am here for the Mod night."

"So I see." He says, clocking my purple scarf. Was he admiring it?

Then he opens up the door and I get to see the inside of Feltham Football club for the very first time. It was a palace, twinkling crystal chandeliers, plush expensive furniture. No I'm joking - it's just like the British Legion – battered tables and plastic chairs scattered around a large dancefloor in front of a chipped wooden stage. Just like the place they hold the school discos – just a bit larger.

The bloke with the records walks over to the disco system to the right of the stage. I follow him.

"I can help you set up." I offer eagerly.

"Set up what?"

"The do. The night."

The bloke flicks open the record decks – and his record boxes.

"I'm set up already."

I look at his record boxes. "What you going to play tonight?"

"I thought I'd stick on me Mum's Demis Roussus album."

I'm razor sharp me. I quickly realized he was taken the mick. But was he doing it in a nice way, or a nasty way? I couldn't tell. I pressed on.

"Mind if I look through your records?"

"Yes I do." He snapped. I was bit taken aback by this, I made to move towards the door muttering something like – sorry to bother you. I got halfway across the dance floor when he called me back.

"Go on – have a flick through."

I gratefully returned and rifled through his seven inchers. Some of them I recognized but well over half I didn't. Best not let on.

Then this older fellow shows up wearing a sheepskin coat. Massive bear of a geezer, probably the bouncer.
"Alright Ian" he calls out and he walks over to the bar, turning on the lights, pours himself a drink from the top rack. After doing a few things behind the bar he came over to the decks.
"Going to be busy tonight?"

"It's the Mod night so shouldn't think so." Ian replied.

"We always get trouble at the Mod nights. Remember Long Tall Shorty?" Said the big bloke.

"Hopefully not tonight. I've kept it low key."

Then the sheepskin bloke shoots a look at me – still rifling through the records pretending I was the disc jockey in residence down The Scene.

"Here! You're too young to be here tonight."

"It's alright – he's with me." Said Ian. "He's me apprentice – he's going to take over when I retire." And with that the sheepskin coat bloke walked off.
I remember the Sunbury Aces talking about the Long Tall Shorty gig. They talked about little else for about a month afterwards so I had something to say about it.
"The trouble at that Long Tall Shorty weren't the Mods' fault. It was those horrible herberts waiting outside who wanted to kill anything in a parka."
"True. Very true." Said Ian "But there was fair amount of trouble inside coming from a firm of Mods from Paddington who were starting on the other Mods."
Oh Yes The Paddington Mods. I remember the Aces talking about them and all. It all gets a bit confusing for a kid like me. It's bad enough having

boneheads, rockers, soul patrol, army cadet types, and this new lot the dressers, trying to rip your head off for the clothes you wear. Then you've got to worry about other Mod firms. You're risking your life just by going to see a band. That's the life for a young Mod today.

Two nattily dressed Mod girls - all Mary Quant upped – walk in and go sit in the corner. Their big eyes and long eye lashes, glance over in my direction as they light up their fags. Things are looking up. Then Ian says to me. "Do you want to play some records?"

"Yeah why not?" I flick through the seven inches and I see the familiar label of a Tamla Motown disc. You can't go wrong with *Going to A Go Go* by *Smokey Robinson and the Miracles* – the girls should like this.

I put the record on and look over at the girls, as if to say - I'm open to requests ladies. I line up my next record the instrumental *Grow Your Own* by *The Small Faces*. After that I was going to play *Train Kept A Rolling* – Yardbirds.

I was playing this when the Sunbury Aces walk in. They all give a double take when they saw me behind the decks and bowl over. They must have been mightily impressed that I was DJing.   Dave the Mod tugged at me scarf. "What's going on here? 'I know what's like to be dead?'"

"Leave him alone." Jumped in Swadey – "that is a quality scarf." I blushed with pride. Ian joined us and we were chatting away – having the most marvellous time. I was finally getting somewhere with the Sunbury Aces, when I glanced down at my Timex. Oh gawd! Quarter to eight! Remember the goldfish? I needed to get home and feed those blighters.

I say my hurried good-byes, which was met by a hale of micky-taking - "Is it past your bed time?" "Cinderella!" "See you in a couple of years."

I walked out red-faced. Which obviously clashed horribly with my purple scarf.

On the wall by the bus stop outside the shopping centre, I spot some freshly painted graffiti – "DONT LET FELTHAM BECOME ANOTHER SOUTHALL." I pass through the deserted shopping centre of Feltham, the whistling wind – sending the newspapers swirling around. Now I pull up the collar on my boating jacket and I catch my reflection in Rumbelows shop window. Looking good.

But I am not alone. My heart does a judder. In the distance I spot a collection of shiny bald heads. This happens a lot. But often it's just a couple of old bald men – a false alarm. But my heart wasn't crying wolf this time. I stared hard ahead, there was no mistaking it – green flying jackets, black Crombies, big boots and bald heads.   A proper firm of about twenty Skinheads. They were holding things - bottles, piece of wood. One skin was pouring liquid from a metal carrier into a bottle.

I turned and ran, but I wasn't running away. I was like the kid in the Battle of Britain who spots the Stukkas in the sky and goes back to warn the village.

Breathless I get to the football club and barge past the sheepskin coated doorman. I spot the Aces posing round a table, the only thing that was missing was the cappuccinos. I head straight for Dave and Mod and blurt out what I'd just seen. "NF Boneheads in the shopping centre. Tooled up. They're obviously out to get the Mods here."

A Mod to the side of me said - "Thanks. We'll be ready for them." But Dave stands up and raises his hand. "No we ain't waiting to get ambushed. We've got to nip this in the bud. We go and confront them. Come on." With a wave of a hand he leads the way to the door and all of the Sunbury Aces and a few hangers on – about twenty altogether - follow, leaving the girls behind.

The Mods start marching towards the shopping centre. I caught up with Swadey. He turns to me and says - "You'd better go back and keep the girls company. This ain't for kids."

"I ain't a kid." I said defiantly. "Swade. This is serious. They're tooled up."

"I'm tooled up and all" and he pulls out a cosh from under his jacket. "Those Skinheads will be soreheads by the time I've finished with them."

I give him his due. Dave the Mod looked fearless as he strode ahead and led us into the shopping centre – an inspiring leader. Then he slowed down as we all saw the boneheads in the same place where I saw them before. One of the Skinheads was stood on top of the bench and talking to the others like he was heading the meeting. This Skinhead had mutton chops and a gut. He looked like the Michelin man – you know the big round bloke made of tyres. He wore a crombie – and from this distance I thought I could make out a glimmering metal union jack badge. He stops talking as he sees us approach, and then all the Skinheads turns their head and they face us.

Dave the Mod gets to about ten feet away from them and calls out – "are all those bootles and pieces of wood a present for us?"

"Look lads - it's the Mohair Puffsters. You want some more of what you lot got down the Bus Garage?"

This was going to be my first proper ruck. I was shaking. But wait – the Michelin Man shouts out.

"Hold it. Mods are off season. We don't give a monkeys about you lot. If you want to mince about in parkas and puffy purple scarfs" he points at me "that's fine with us."

Now all the skins were looking at me. I felt a flicker of recognition from one of the younger skins. Some kid in my year at school though he's a good six inches taller than me. Johnny or Mickey I think his name is. I knew he had the Skinhead crop, but I never knew he knocked about with the NF mob.

He gave me a nod – was it a friendly nod? I don't know. I looked away.

The Michelin skin continued – "we're fighting bigger battles."

"Like what?" Shouted back Dave the Mod narrowing his eyes.

"The Battle for Britain."

"What you talking about?"

"There's a parade of four shops down the Mount - and every one of them is a Paki shop. Every single one of them." Said the Michelin Skin – "So we are going to show them a bit of English hospitality. Show them what we think of the Stani takeover of Feltham. Ain't that right lads?"

His skin supporters brayed in support, raising their fists. One raised the bottle full of liquid that could have been petrol.

"You can go back to your mincing Mod disco. We won't be bothering you tonight."

Dave stood still for a sec, then turned his back to the skins and gestured to the Mods to follow him away from them.

Swade grabs Dave by the shoulders and stops him. "Dave – why are we running away?"

"We ain't running away" said Dave – "this ain't our battle."

"They're Skinheads – this will always be our battle."

"We only fight to defend ourselves." And Dave carried on walking with the others following. Swadey stood his ground.

"Call yourself the Sunbury Aces? The Sunbury Arses more like it." He called out. "This exactly how Nazi Germany started." I don't know if that last bit was a joke or not, you can't often tell with Swadey.

By now all the other Mods were in the distance. All but one - me. Swadey turns to me – and smiles – "You're the only true Mod out of all of them."

Easily the best thing anybody has ever said to me – ever. He went on - "We are going to stop them. We are going to fight these boneheads."

"But there's only two of us, what can we do against that lot?"

"A lot. Wait for me by the bus stop."

He ran ahead while I waited at the bus stop staring at the Southall/Feltham graffiti, wondering what the hell Swadey had planned. Minutes later he returned on his dark green Lambretta wearing his Mod target crash helmet.

"Get on."

"Have you got a crash helmet?"

"No I an't got a crash helmet. Get on!"

I comply and holding him around his stomach, we ride slowly around the shopping centre.

Then in the distance we see the twenty Skinheads leave the shopping centre and walk in the direction of the Mount.

They start marching down the Hanworth Road with us following slowly about thirty feet away in the Lambretta on the other side of the road. The Lambretta was whirring loudly like a broken hair-dryer, and I felt a surge of panic race through my stomach. The Skinheads are going to hear us and attack us.

Then Swadey stops the scooter. He pulls out the cosh from inside his jacket and hands it to me.

"I've seen them do this in a film. When those Skinheads cross the dual carriageway I ride in amongst them, and when we get close enough to one of them, you crack one of them in the nut with this."

I was about to jump off his scooter in blind terror when he starts up the scooter and rides off again. No turning back now.

Picking up speed I could see the Skinheads in front of us, getting closer, getting bigger.

Then I see them climb over the barriers over the dual carriageway, there are now in the road in front of us. Even closer now.

Swadey picks up speed and now we are surrounded by them. Some of the Skinheads lurch towards us swinging their legs at us. Swadey rides towards one of the bonehads who seems ready to try and knock us off.

"Now!" Yells Swadey.

FELTHAM MADE ME   362

I aim. I swing. I nearly lose my balance. I hear a THWACK and see the Skinhead's legs buckle as he hits the deck.

The scooter gather speed as I feel a wave of Skinhead anger rise against me. Then when I think Swadey is going to ride us away into the sunset and safety, he only goes and turns back and rides straight at them again.

The on-coming traffic must have stopped because there was nothing in sight on the road now apart from us and the Skinheads.

Forty furious DMs run towards us and then duck out of the way. Then I feel something whistle past my nose, and crash against the barrier. Suddenly it's aflame. It was like something out of Rollerball.

"Swade" I yell "Get us out of here."

Swadey rides away and I jerk my head back to see the running Skinheads and the flames getting smaller in the distance.

Then sudden shock. My teeth crunch together, and I think my eyes are going slide out of their sockets as I feel the scooter slide away from underneath me and I lose grip on Swadey's stomach. The scooter crashes into the barrier with me and Swadey doing a Barry Sheen, skidding along the road like kiddies on a playground slide. I'm on the concrete - scraped and bloody. But I can move. I look up and see the angry mob still coming towards us. My sta prest are ripped and my leg is stinging with pain.

I'm up walking and I look around to see Swadey. He is also on his feet looking dazed, taking off his crash helmet. I turn towards the oncoming Skinheads who must now be able to smell our fresh blood. I try to run – but something pulls me back with a jolt around my neck. It was the bloody scarf! Snagged in the wheel of the scooter. The Skinheads were getting real close. I pull at the scarf- it rips in half.

Swadey picks up the scooter and lifts it over his head, and then with an almighty roar hurls it at the on-coming Skinheads. Three of them go down. But there's plenty more of them right behind. Swadey now swings his crash helmet at them and he shouts back at me.

"Run! Get out here."

I hurdle over the barrier and dodging the cars look back to see Swadey sprinting the other way, putting distance between him and the boneheads.

My sta-prest was now ragged hobo gear, and my boating jacket a write off, but at least half my purple scarf was saveable.

The side street was deserted, but if the Skinheads were to come along – they'd see me immediately under these street lights. I needed to get off the street. Now! So by jumping up on one of those electrical boxes I vaulted over a seven foot fence and I fall into a garden. The lights were on in the house, so I get low and scramble towards the shed and I wedge myself between it and the fence. By grabbing my knees and putting my head down, I made myself as small as possible.

I was thinking about them starving gold fish. I needed to get home – and home before Mum came back from her ballroom dancing, Bingo, darts match or whatever she'd gone out to tonight.

"Ere! What you doing?" I feel hard tap on my shoulder and turn to see an unwelcoming face.

"Sorry I was hiding from some Skinheads. Would you mind if I stay here for a bit?"

"On yer bike! Before I call the police."

Bike – I wish. I had to get out the area as soon as possible. I was back out on the street again. I put what's left of my purple paisley scarf in my pocket and turn my boating blazer inside out. Now is not the time to be looking like a Mod.

I decide it's risky to wait at the bus stop – way too risky, so I walk home along the back lanes staying out the street light glare.

As I walked with my head down I started to worry about Swadey. What had happened to him? I prayed for him to be alright and somewhere safe.

I get home at 10 'o' clock. Mum not home yet and thankfully the goldfish were still alive, I immediately tapped some food into their bowl and went up to my room.

Not soon after that I hear tap on my window. Somebody had thrown something against it. I look out and in the blackness I can see that Swadey is in my back garden. He's all bloody and in ripped up clothes – but at least he's in one piece.

"You alright?" He calls up.

"Yeah. You?"

"Bit shaken and stirred. Listen - if the Old Bill call round tell them nothing. Nothing at all."

"I'll say I was here the whole night, feeding the goldfish."

FELTHAM MADE ME   364

"You don't even need to tell them that. You've got your rights."

"I got to tell them something."

"No seriously clam up. Nothing. Schtum."

"What about your scooter? You should report it stolen so that…."

"No need for that," he interrupted. "It's stolen already. I am a thief remember? It's on fake number plates."

A silence fell upon us, as my mind started racing ahead about what may come out of all this.

"You did well tonight." Said Swadey.

"Did I?"

"You stopped a parade of shops from being wrecked. Those Asian families would have been attacked - and you saved them."

"Maybe if I say that to the police, they'll let us off."

"No, like I said, tell them nothing. Nothing."

"Is he dead?"
    "We can only hope. I hear he's at the hospital. Most likely being operated on by an Asian doctor who's probably saving his life right now. Is that what they call ironic? We should get over there and ambush them. Catch them when they're vulnerable."

Uh! Leave me out of this, I was about to say. But then he said – "but we need to lay low."

"Do you want come inside. Cup of tea?"

Swadey shook his head – "No I gotta go. You're next visitor will probably be the Old Bill and I just needed to brief you - and what is it you've got to do….?"

"Tell them nothing." I said like a top-of-the-class pupil.

"Top Lad. I'm proud of you son."

That had now become the single nicest thing anyone has ever said to me.

"Remember – keep the faith." And with those words he was gone.

I sat in silence and darkness for ages thinking - faith in what? What's Swadey talking about? I could go to Borstal for this – a life sentence in Borstal – and even though Swadey makes Borstal seem like a laugh, I'm certain I won't be allowed to wear the clothes I want inside. And this is all Swadey's fault. He got me into this. Those nice words were just to keep me quiet, so I do as he tells me. I'm no mug. For the first time ever I started to feel anger welling up against Swadey. I hung up my half a purple scarf behind the bedroom door. It could be saved by stitching up the ripped end.

The police came round just after 11 – way past my bedtime. The old dear had got home and let them in, and with a look of shock like I'd never seen on the poor girl before, she led them into my bedroom. There were two of them – one in uniform and the older one was plain clothes - a right shabby suit he must got off the peg from Delamare.

The copper sent my panicked faced mother out of the room and the Spanish inquisition began.

I couldn't tell them nothing. That would have been ridiculous, but I said I was home all night feeding the goldfish.

"Got anybody to back this story up?"

"Yeah – the goldfish."

"I wouldn't try and be funny if I were you son. We know you were there. Do you know how we know? Because one of the Skinheads happens to be in your year at school and told us."

He went on - "Do you know how else we know you were there? Because of that purple scarf. The other half of it was caught in the wheel of the scooter."

And he pointed to my demi-scarf hanging up on my door. I was bang to rights and my purple paisley scarf had grassed me up.

The cooper in the horrible suit then changed his expression. Raising his eye brows, he was now looking all understanding and compassionate.

"Look son. How are old you?"

"14 next month."

"Right so you're 13. We know you didn't instigate this. We know an older lad put you up to it. He's the one we're after."

The copper had me on the racks and he knew it. He pressed on -

"I know it sounds like you're grassing up a mate. But you're not. You're looking out for yourself. You're doing the right thing. And by doing this I can keep you out of Borstal. So who was with you on the scooter?"

I said nothing. Keep the faith.

"We got witnesses to say the older lad shouted Now! Before you swung the cosh. If we get him, it will be a lot easier on you. Give us a name – or it's you we're taking down. Don't be a fool son. Don't ruin your life over this."

Mum, who had obviously got her ear to the door, started screaming.

"Tell them! TELL THEM!"

"Come on son – save yourself." Continued the cooper at Delamare .

Dead silence - until eventually I said "They call him Dave The Mod."

FELTHAM MADE ME   368

Also From Zani Media

The Secret Life of The Novel By Dean Cavanagh

ISBN-10: 1527201538 ISBN-13: 978-1527201538

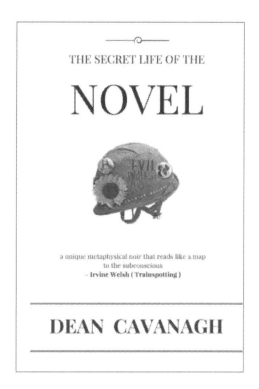

Available on www.zani.co.uk or Amazon

A Crafty Cigarette – Tales of a Teenage Mod
By Matteo Sedazzari
Foreword by John Cooper Clarke

ISBN-10: 1526203561 ISBN-13: 978-1526203564

FELTHAM MADE ME

'I couldn't put it down because I couldn't put it down.'
John Cooper Clarke

'A Great Debut That Deals With The Joys and Pains of Growing Up'
Irvine Welsh

'Crafty Cigarette, all things Mod and a dash of anarchy. Want to remember what it was like to be young and angry? Buy this book. A great read'
Phil Davis (Actor Chalky in Quadrophenia)

'Written in first person narrative, in a style and delivery reminiscent of Hunter S. Thompson.'
Scootering Mag

'It's a good book and an easy read. That's pretty much what most pulp fiction needs to be.'
Mod Culture

'Like a good Paul Weller concert the novel leaves you wanting more. I'll be very interested in reading whatever Matteo Sedazzari writes next.'
Louder Than War

Available on www.zani.co.uk or Amazon

Printed in Great Britain
by Amazon